MILITARY Living's™

Military RV, Camping & Rec Areas

AROUND THE WORLD

By

William "Roy" Crawford, Sr., Ph.D.
President, Military Marketing Services, Inc.
and Military Living Publications

And

L. Ann Crawford
Vice-President, Military Marketing Services, Inc.
and Publisher, Military Living Publications

EDITOR - Rose McLain
COVER DESIGN - Lindsey Tozier-School
VICE PRESIDENT - MARKETING - R.J. Crawford
CHIEF OF STAFF - Nigel Fellers
OFFICE STAFF - Timothy Brown, Eula Mae Brownlee, Irene
Kearney, Lourdes Medina, Emily Peraro, Leon Russ, Donna Russell,
Joel Thomas, MSgt, USA(Ret).

Military Living Publications
P. O. Box 2347
Falls Church, Virginia 22042-0347
TEL: 703-237-0203 - FAX: 703-237-2233

NOTICE

The information in this book has been compiled and edited from information received from the activity/facility listed, its superior headquarters or from other sources which may or may not be so noted. All listed facilities and any or all information about them is subject to change. Please note, however, that many of these RV, camping and recreation areas have been in continuous operation at the same location for over 50 years. This book should be used as a guide to military RV, camping and rec areas with the above understanding. Please forward any corrections or additions to **Military Living Publications, P. O. Box 2347, Falls Church, Virginia 22042-0347.**

This guide is published by **Military Marketing Services, Inc.,** a private firm in no way connected with the U.S. Federal or other governments. The book is copyrighted by William Roy and L. Ann Crawford. Opinions expressed by the publisher and writers are their own and are not to be considered an official expression by any government agency or official.

The information and statements contained in this book have been compiled from sources believed by the publisher to be reliable and to represent the best current opinion on the subject. No warranty, guarantee or representation is made by **Military Marketing Services, Inc.,** as to the absolute correctness or sufficiency of any representation contained in this or other publications and we can assume no responsibility.

Copyright 1994
William Roy Crawford and L. Ann Crawford
First Printing - April 1994
Second Printing - October 1994
Third Printing -June 1995

MILITARY MARKETING SERVICES, INC.
(MILITARY LIVING PUBLICATIONS)

Library of Congress Cataloging-in-Publication Data

Crawford, William Roy, 1932-
    Military Living's military RV camping & rec areas around the world
/ by William "Roy" Crawford and L. Ann Crawford.
        p.   cm.
    On t.p. the registered trademark symbol "TM" is subscript
    following "Military Living's" in the title.
    Includes index.
    ISBN 0914862-50-2 : $8.95
    1. United States--Armed Forces--Facilities--Guidebooks.
2. Recreation areas--United States--States--Guidebooks. 3. Camp
sites, facilities, etc.--United States--States--Guidebooks.
4. Recreation areas--Guidebooks. 5. Camp sites, facilities, etc.-
-Guidebooks. I. Crawford, Ann Caddell. II. Military Living
Publications. III. Title.
UC403.C73   1994
647'.947309--dc20   94-7895
                                                              CIP

ISBN: 0-914862-50-2

INTRODUCTION

You can have a lot of fun with this book. Many military families, both active duty and retired, use their recreational vehicles and camp for fun, but others camp to save money while visiting many famous tourist attractions. Most of these international attractions are referenced in the individual listings of this book. We have provided the information in this book that many military camping families have requested and that we believe will be of the most value to you. In this edition we have retained our easy-to-use block/semi-chart format. Also, we have included full coverage of all the Armed Forces Recreation Centers worldwide. *Military RV, Camping and Rec Areas Around the World* is the first commercial book to focus on RV, camping and recreation areas of all services worldwide to include Army, Navy, Marine Corps, Air Force and Coast Guard. We believe that we have covered most of the active locations. YOU may know of other locations that we did not find. Please tell us about any that we missed so we can research the location to share with you and your fellow military families in the next printing/edition. The publishers of Military Living wish to thank all military recreation and public affairs personnel who so diligently serve the military and their families. **You are real "morale boosters."**

HOW TO USE THIS DIRECTORY

Name of Installation/Facility (AL01R2)
City/Base/APO/FPO, State, ZIP Code

The numbers given under this heading are usually for the installation's main information and/or assistance operator. **Comm:** The commercial telephone service for the installation. Within the U.S. Area Code System, the first three digits are the area code. For foreign country locations, the first two digits are the Country Code. The next two digits are the city code, if used. The next three digits are the area telephone exchange/switch number. The last four digits are the line number. For foreign countries, the exchange number can be either fewer or more digits than in the U.S. system. The last four digits are usually the information or operator assistance number. Again, in foreign countries this number may be fewer or more than four digits. Consult your local directory or operator for specific dialing instructions. **DSN:** The Department of Defense worldwide Defense Switched Network (DSN), "formerly ATVN." **ETS:** The European Telephone System. ETS prefixes for military communities are the same as DSN prefixes. **FTS:** The Federal Telephone System.

Location Identifier: Example (AL01R2). The first two characters (letters) are Country/State abbreviations used in Military Living's books (contents and listings). The next two-character set is a random number (01-99) assigned to a specific location. The fifth character (letter) is an R indicating region and the sixth character (0-9) is the regional location. The location identifiers for listings in this book are keyed to regional maps in Appendix C. The regional maps are designed to provide you with the relative geographic location of each installation/facility worldwide.

Location: The specific driving directions to the installation/facility from local major cities, interstate highways and routes are in this section. Check-in locations and times are given when known. **USMRA:** indicates **Military Living's** *United States Military Road Atlas* coordinates for the installation/facility. For European listings the Hallwag Europe Atlas (**HE:**) is used. **NMI:** The nearest military installation if the recreation area is not located on post/base. **NMC:** The nearest major city. The distance in miles and the direction from the installation/facility to the NMI or NMC is given.

Description of Area: This section provides a description of the RV, camping or recreation area in the listing. Special geographic and topographic features are listed. Other recreational opportunities and military support facilities are noted. Special facilities are included.

Season of Operation: The time frame during which the facility is available for general use is specified in this section.

Eligibility: The category/status of uniformed military and civilian employees who may use the facility is stated in this section. In most cases, eligible family members are also able to use the facilities. Some categories of eligibility are at the discretion of the base/post commander. Therefore, if you have a question about your eligibility, it would be advisable to call the number shown under "Reservations" to determine whether you are authorized to use the facilities.

Reservations: The procedure for establishing reservations, the mailing address, commercial, DSN and FTS contact numbers and special instructions are contained in this section. Please call these numbers for additional information as required. Some areas have complicated priority systems. If the facilities are very limited, priority for space is often given to personnel/families of the sponsoring installation. When writing, it is advisable to include a self-addressed, stamped envelope.

Camp Facilities: This section details any recreational lodging, RV spaces, camping spaces and tent spaces. The number of units is specified along with the hookup facilities available and the fee for each facility used. You should anticipate possible changes in rates/fees and facilities provided.

Support Facilities: Installation facilities available to patrons of the camping/recreation area are listed in this section. In most cases general base support facilities have not been noted. In isolated areas, availability of commercial facilities may be noted.

Activities: General recreational activities available to patrons are listed in this section.

Restrictions: Details of any restrictions, limitations and rules for the use of the facility are in this section. When known, check-out times are given.

Please review Appendix A, General Abbreviations. Also, note the information on Camping on other Federal Property (Appendix B) and Regional Location Maps (Appendix C). **EDITOR'S NOTE**: Because of budget reductions within the Federal Government, both seasons of operation and hours of operation within seasons may be reduced or otherwise changed after the press date of this book.

COVER PHOTOGRAPHS

Front Cover: Waianae Army Recreation Center, Waianae, HI

Back Cover: Hillhaus Lodge, Hill AFB, UT - Top Left
    Villas at "Short Stay", Charleston NS, SC - Middle Left
    Tent Camping, Garmish AFRC, GE - Middle Right
    RV, Blue Angel Navy Recreation Park, FL - Bottom Right

CONTENTS

UNITED STATES

CALIFORNIA (continued)

COLORADO

CONNECTICUT—None

DELAWARE—None

DISTRICT OF COLUMBIA—None

FLORIDA

GEORGIA

HAWAII

IDAHO

ILLINOIS

INDIANA

IOWA—None

KANSAS—None

KENTUCKY

LOUISIANA

MAINE

MARYLAND

MASSACHUSETTS

MICHIGAN

MINNESOTA—None

MISSISSIPPI

MISSOURI

MONTANA

NEBRASKA

NEVADA

NEW HAMPSHIRE

NEW JERSEY

NEW MEXICO

NEW YORK

NORTH CAROLINA

NORTH DAKOTA

OHIO

OKLAHOMA

OREGON—None

PENNSYLVANIA

RHODE ISLAND—None

SOUTH CAROLINA

SOUTH DAKOTA

TENNESSEE

TEXAS

UTAH

VERMONT—None

VIRGINIA

WASHINGTON

WEST VIRGINIA

APPENDICES

* * * * * BASE CLOSURES * * * * *

The 1993 Defense Base Closure and Realignment Commission's Report was accepted by Congress and became Public Law in late 1993.

The 1993 law along with previous directed closures in the Base Closure and Realignment Act, Public Law 100-526, 24 October 1988 and Public Law 101-510, 1 October 1991 have been noted at the beginning of each listing affected with the DoD estimated date of closure. Some bases have already closed and consequently have been deleted from this edition.

It should also be noted that all final closure dates will be established and may change as the DoD completes the final closure plans and funding becomes available to effect the closure. Support facilities on the affected bases will decrease gradually; therefore, it is best to check with each military installation, scheduled for closure, before you go. Some bases scheduled for closure or realignment do not have camping/rec areas and, consequently, are not listed in this book.

When the DoD acts on The 1993 Base Closure Law, the final action on bases which have closed and bases in the process of closing with effective dates as available will be published in upcoming edition, of *Military Living's R & R Space-A Report®* - a worldwide military family travel newsletter.

Lastly, it should be noted that the 1993 Defense Base Closure law and previous Base Closure Laws only apply to domestic United States Bases (CONUS & OCONUS not foreign countries). The Secretary of Defense, acting within his authority, announced on 1 July 1993 and 24 February 1994, the further reduction or realignment of United States Military Sites Overseas (in Foreign countries).

UNITED STATES

ALABAMA

DAUPHIN ISLAND RECREATIONAL COMPLEX (AL07R2)
Mobile Coast Guard Base
Mobile, AL 36615-1390

TELEPHONE NUMBER INFORMATION: Main installation numbers: Comm and FTS: 205-690-2214. Police for rec complex, Comm: 205-961-5523.

LOCATION: Off base. On the Gulf of Mexico approx 40 mi S of Mobile. I-10 to AL-193 (Exit 17, Tillmans Corner/Dauphin Island); S approx 35 mi to Dauphin Island. L at dead end to E end of island. Follow signs to complex. Check in 1600-2200. USMRA: page 36 (B-10). NMI: Mobile CG Base (Brookley), 40 mi N. NMC: Mobile, 40 mi N.

DESCRIPTION OF AREA: Dauphin Island offers a variety of outdoor and sightseeing activities. Explore old Ft Gaines, ancient Indian shell mounds or Audubon bird sanctuary. Limited support facilities available at Mobile CG Base.

SEASON OF OPERATION: Year round.

ELIGIBILITY: Active/Retired/CG Reserve and Auxiliary/CG Civilian Employees.

RESERVATIONS: Required by phone, *followed by application only,* with adv payment. Summer (1 May-30 Sep): up to 60 days in adv for AD CG and CG Reserve on AD within CGD8; up to 45 days, for AD CG and CG Reserve on AD outside CGD8; up to 30 days, all others. Address: Dauphin Island Recreational Complex, PO Box 436, Dauphin Island, AL 36528-0436. **Comm: 205-861-7113**.

CAMP FACILITIES:	NO UNITS	HOOKUPS	FEE*
Cottages, 3 bdrm, furn, kit, CTV, MW**	13		$55-75 wknd/ 70-100 wkly
Camper Spaces	6 Hardstand	W/S/CTV(110/30A)	8.00 dly
Camper/Tent Spaces	100		3.00 dly

*Monthly rate available Oct-Nov.
**All cooking and eating utensils, and all linens (except washcloths and dish cloths) furnished. 3 cottages have ramps for handicapped.

SPT FACILITIES:		
Bath House	Beach/private	Conv Store
Fish Poles/Bait	Food Vending	Grills
Laundry	Picnic Area	Playground
PX/small	Restrooms/hcp	Sewage Dmp Sta
Showers/hcp	Sun Deck	

ALABAMA
DAUPHIN ISLAND RECREATIONAL COMPLEX, continued

ACTIVITIES:		
Bicycling	Boating	Fishing
Golfing Pkg Avail	Rec Equip Avail	Swimming

RESTRICTIONS: No pets allowed. Check out 1400. Summer: 7-day limit for cottages; 14-day limit for camper and tent sites. No firearms allowed.

LAKE MARTIN MAXWELL/GUNTER RECREATION AREA (AL05R2)
Maxwell Air Force Base, AL 36112-5000

TELEPHONE NUMBER INFORMATION: Main installation numbers: Comm: 205-953-1110, DSN: 312-493-1110.

LOCATION: Off base. Located near Dadeville, SE of Birmingham, NE of Montgomery. From I-85 N of Montgomery take exit 32 N on AL-49 to Stillwaters Rd (county road 34) and proceed 2.5 mi to the recreation area. Check in at gate house 1300-1900. USMRA: page 36 (F-5). NMI: Maxwell AFB, 60 mi SW. NMC: Montgomery, 60 mi SW.

DESCRIPTION OF AREA: Located on Lake Martin Reservoir near dam. Excellent fishing; variety of water- and woods-oriented activities. Recreation area includes areas for day picnicking and rough camping. Voted outstanding recreation area of the Air Force. Full range of support facilities available at Maxwell AFB.

SEASON OF OPERATION: Year round.

ELIGIBILITY: Active/Retired/Active Reserve/NG/DoD Civ at Maxwell/Gunter AFB.

RESERVATIONS: Required with payment in full. Address: ITT Office, Bldg 835, Maxwell AFB, AL 36112-5000. **Comm: 205-953-5496, DSN: 312-493-5496.** *(For information,* Comm: 205-825-6251, FAX Comm: 205-825-6251.)

CAMP FACILITIES:	NO UNITS	HOOKUPS	FEE*
Mobile Homes**	12	W/E (110/220/30A)	$30.00 dly
Camper Spaces	50 Gravel	W/E (110/220/30A)	11.00 dly
Tent Spaces	30	None	5.00 dly

*Monthly rates avail 1 Oct-31 Mar.
**2-3 bdrm, ramp, heat, AC; furn exc linens, blankets. TV, radio rental avail.

SPT FACILITIES:			
	Beach	Boat Launch/fee	Boat Rntl
	Boat Storage	Fishing Pier	Gas
	Grills	Laundry	Marina
	Pay Telephone	Picnic Area	Playground
	Restrooms/hcp	Sewage Dmp Sta	Showers/hcp
	Trail		

ALABAMA
LAKE MARTIN MAXWELL/GUNTER RECREATION AREA, continued

ACTIVITIES:	Boating	Fishing/license	Hiking
	Jogging	Sailing	Swimming
	Volleyball	Water Skiing	

RESTRICTIONS: No pets allowed. Check out 1600. 15-day limit. Minimum of 2 nights or weekend 1 May-30 Sep. No open fires. Firearms, fireworks, BB guns, bows and arrows are prohibited. As facility is in an isolated area, check your supplies carefully before arriving. No firearms allowed.

MAXWELL/GUNTER FAM-CAMP (AL11R2)
Maxwell Air Force Base, AL 36112-5000

TELEPHONE NUMBER INFORMATION: Main installation numbers: Comm: 205-953-1110, DSN: 312-493-1110.

LOCATION: On base. Take I-85 S to I-65; exit N to Day St which leads to main gate. Check in at fam-camp office. USMRA: page 36 (E-6). NMC: Montgomery, 1.5 mi SE.

DESCRIPTION OF AREA: Situated in a wooded area on a small lake. Martin Lake and many other freshwater lakes and reservoirs located within 50 mi. Site of Wright Brothers Flying School and historical airplanes which have been retired. Historical city of Montgomery has much to offer in the way of sightseeing. Full range of support facilities available on base.

SEASON OF OPERATION: Year round.

ELIGIBILITY: Active/Retired.

RESERVATIONS: No adv resv. Address: Fam-Camp, Outdoor Recreation, March Rd, Maxwell AFB, AL 36112-5005. Comm: 205-953-5161/5496; FAX: 205-953-6230.

CAMP FACILITIES:	NO UNITS	HOOKUPS	FEE
Camper Spaces	24 Paved	W/S/E(110/220/30A)	$11.00 dly
			60 wk/200 mo
Camper Spaces	Overflow	W/E(110/220)	8.00 dly
Tent Spaces	Open	None	5.00 dly

SPT FACILITIES:	Boat Launch	Chapel	Comm Bldg
	Gas	Golf	Grills
	Laundry	Picnic Area	Rec Center
	Restrooms/hcp	Sewage Dmp Sta	Showers
	Snack Bar	Sports Fields	Stables
	Trails		
	Equipment Rental for All Outdoor Activities		

ACTIVITIES:	Fishing/license	Golfing	Jogging

RESTRICTIONS: No pets allowed. No firearms allowed.

ALABAMA

McCLELLAN RECREATION AREA AND CAMPGROUND (AL09R2)
Fort McClellan, AL 36205-5000

TELEPHONE NUMBER INFORMATION: Main installation numbers: Comm: 205-848-4611, DSN: 312-865-1110

LOCATION: On post. Located 3 mi N of Anniston, off AL-21. Enter Baltzell Gate, to traffic circle; then 20th St to L on 4th Ave. Check in at MWR Central Supply, Bldg 305. USMRA: page 36 (F-3). NMC: Birmingham, 60 mi W.

DESCRIPTION OF AREA: Located in Alabama hills W of Atlanta GA, and E of Birmingham. Campgrounds located 3 mi from main post area on 8-acre lake. Full range of support facilities available on post.

SEASON OF OPERATION: Year round.

ELIGIBILITY: Active/Retired/DoD Civilians at Ft McClellan.

RESERVATIONS: Recommended. Address: MWR, Central Supply Warehouse, Bldg 305, Ft McClellan, AL 36205-5000. **Comm: 205-848-3158/848-3526/820-5459, DSN: 312-865-3158.** Discounts available to holders of Golden Age and Golden Access Passports.

CAMP FACILITIES:	NO UNITS	HOOKUPS	FEE
Camper Spaces	8 Hardstand	W/E (110)	$ 8.00 dly
Camper Spaces	4 Primitive	None	5.00 dly

SPT FACILITIES:			
	Go-Kart Track/	Golf/post	Laundry
	Seasonal	Picnic Area	Restrooms
	Sewage Dmp Sta	Showers	Sports Fields

ACTIVITIES: Fishing/license

RESTRICTIONS: No Firearms allowed.

REDSTONE ARSENAL CAMPGROUND (AL12R2)
Redstone Arsenal, AL 35898-5020

TELEPHONE NUMBER INFORMATION: Main installation numbers: Comm: 205-876-2151, DSN: 312-746-0011. Police for campground, Comm: 205-876-2222.

LOCATION: On post. From US-231 (Memorial Parkway) on S side of Huntsville, turn W on Martin Rd and enter Gate 1. *OR* from I-565 on SW side, take Rideout Rd exit S to Gate 9. Check in at Outdoor Recreation, Bldg 5132, on Sportsman's Rd, 0930-1700 daily. After hours proceed to campground and register the following morning. USMRA: page 36 (E-1). NMC: Huntsville, 6 mi NE.

DESCRIPTION OF AREA: Situated along Tennessee River in northern Alabama. Alabama Space and Rocket Center nearby. Full range of support facilities available on post.

ALABAMA
REDSTONE ARSENAL CAMPGROUND, continued

SEASON OF OPERATION: Year round; no water in winter months.

ELIGIBILITY: Active/Retired/DoD Civilians.

RESERVATIONS: No adv resv. Address: Outdoor Recreation, Bldg 5132, Sportsman's Rd, Redstone Arsenal, AL 35898-5355. Comm: 205-876-4868/6854, DSN: 312-746-4868/6854 (0930-1700 daily).

CAMP FACILITIES:	NO UNITS	HOOKUPS	FEE
Camper/Tent Spaces	23 Hardstand	W/E (110)	$ 5.00 dly
Camper Spaces	Overflow	None	5.00 dly

SPT FACILITIES:			
	Boat Launch	Golf/post	Grills
	Pavilions	Picnic Area	Playground
	Restrooms	Sewage Dmp Sta	Showers
	Softball Field		

ACTIVITIES:			
	Boating	Fishing/license	Hunting/license
	Jogging	Rec Equip Avail	

RESTRICTIONS: Pets allowed on leash. *Campground can accommodate RVs up to 30'; larger vehicles will experience difficulties.*

RUCKER OUTDOOR RECREATION AREA (AL10R2)
Fort Rucker, AL 36362-5000

TELEPHONE NUMBER INFORMATION: Main installation numbers: Comm: 205-255-6181, DSN: 312-558-1110. Police for the recreation area, Comm: 205-255-4175/4176.

LOCATION: On post. From US-231, take AL-249 S to Daleville. After passing through Ft Rucker gates (approx 5 mi), R at first blinking light (Christian Rd) for approx 3 mi and follow signs. USMRA: page 36 (F-3). NMC: Dothan, 25 mi SE.

DESCRIPTION OF AREA: Located in the SE corner of Alabama approx 85 mi S of Montgomery and 90 mi N of the Florida Gulf Coast, the camping area is on the shores of 660-acre Lake Tholocco. Flood damage has been repaired and all lake activities are in full swing. Full range of support facilities available on post.

SEASON OF OPERATION: Year round. Camping area closed Nov-Feb.

ELIGIBILITY: Active/Retired/DoD Civilians.

RESERVATIONS: No adv resv. Address: Community Activities, Outdoor Recreation, Bldg 24201, Lake Tholocco, Ft Rucker, AL 36362-5000. Comm: 205-255-4305, DSN: 312-558-4305, FTS: 533-4305. Discounts available to holders of Golden Age, Golden Access or Golden Eagle Passports.

CAMP FACILITIES:	NO UNITS	HOOKUPS	FEE
Camper Spaces	18 Hardstand	W/E (110)	$ 8.00 dly
Tent Spaces	20 Unimproved	None	8.00 dly

ALABAMA
RUCKER OUTDOOR RECREATION AREA, *continued*

SPT FACILITIES:			
	Archery	Beach	Boat Launch
	Boat Rntl	Camp Equip Rntl	Golf
	Grills	Ice	Laundry
	Marina	Picnic Area	Pistol Range
	Rec Equip Rntl	Restrooms/hcp	Sewage Dmp Sta
	Showers	Skeet Range	Snack Bar
	Stables	Trails	

ACTIVITIES:	Fishing/license	Hunting

RESTRICTIONS: No pets allowed. Toll to enter recreation area during months of May through Sep.

THOMAS MILL CREEK PARK (AL14R2)
Fort Rucker, AL 36362-0789
This facility closed 18 October 1994.

ALASKA

BIRCH LAKE RECREATION AREA (AK01R5)
Eielson Air Force Base, AK 99702-5000

TELEPHONE NUMBER INFORMATION: Main installation numbers: Comm: 907-377-1110, DSN: 317-377-1110. Police for recreation area, Comm: 907-377-5130.

LOCATION: Off base. On SW side of Richardson Highway (AK-2) at mile post 305, 38 mi S of AFB. Turn at Recreation Area sign; 1 mi to entrance. Check in at Boat Shop. USMRA: page 128 (F-4) NMI: Eielson AFB, 35 mi N. NMC: Fairbanks, 64 mi N.

DESCRIPTION OF AREA: Located on Birch Lake which covers 804 acres, is spring fed, and is stocked with rainbow trout and silver salmon. Harding Lake Recrecreation Area approx 10 mi N; Denali National Park, 130 mi SW. Area provides rustic base for enjoying state's unlimited outdoor recreational resources. Spectacular mountain scenery, unsurpassed fishing and hunting in general area. Full range of support facilities at Eielson AFB.

SEASON OF OPERATION: Memorial Day-Labor Day.

ELIGIBILITY: Active/Retired/DoD Civilians.

RESERVATIONS: Accepted. Address: 354 SS/SSRO, 3112 Broadway Ave, Suite 4, Eielson AFB, AK 99702-1870. **Comm: 907-488-6161, DSN: 317-377-4214, FAX Comm: 907-377-2769.** (*For information off-season*, Comm: 907-377-1839.)

CAMP FACILITIES:	NO UNITS	HOOKUPS	FEE
Cabins, Deluxe*	2	E (110)	$35.00 dly
Cabins, Family**	16	E (110)	30.00 dly
Cabins, 2-man***	4	E (110)	15.00 dly
Camper Spaces	40	E (110)	10.00 dly
Tent Spaces	Many	None	6.00 dly

ALASKA
BIRCH LAKE RECREATION AREA, continued

*1 bdrm + sofa bed; stove, refr, table; water for dishes and showers only.
**1- and 2-rm cabins; wood-burning stove, refr, beds, sofa bed; no indoor cooking
or plumbing facilities.
***1-rm with 2 sgl beds and refr; no indoor cooking or plumbing facilities.

SPT FACILITIES:	Beach	Boat Launch	Boat Rntl
	Country Store	Fire Rings	Lodge/hcp
	Picnic Area	Playground	Restrooms/hcp
	Showers		
ACTIVITIES:	Berry Picking	Fishing/license	Hiking
	Wading	Water Skiing	

RESTRICTIONS: Pets allowed on leash. No linens or utensils provided. Check
camper pad size when making reservations. No sewage dump station. No firearms
permitted in site; must be secured in vehicle. Numerous water faucets throughout
the camp supply potable water.

BLACK SPRUCE TRAVEL CAMP (AK16R5)
Fort Richardson, AK 99505-5100

TELEPHONE NUMBER INFORMATION: Main installation numbers: Comm:
907-384-1110, DSN: 317-384-1110. Police for travel camp, Comm: 907-384-0820.

LOCATION: On post. Main gate is on Glenn Highway, 5 mi S of Eagle River.
Camp is located off Loop Road. Patrons may go directly to camp and report to
Skeet Range, Bldg 45-100, the next day. USMRA: page 128 (F-5). NMC:
Anchorage, 8 mi SW.

DESCRIPTION OF AREA: Beautiful mountain scenery. Lakes and rivers
provide excellent fishing. Varied sightseeing and outdoor recreational opportunities. Full range of support facilities available on post.

SEASON OF OPERATION: 1 May-1 Oct.

ELIGIBILITY: Active/Retired/DoD and NAF Civilians.

RESERVATIONS: *No adv resv.* Address: Community Recreation Division, Attn:
APZR-PA-CR, 600 Richardson Dr, #6600, Ft Richardson, AK 99505-6600. Comm:
907-384-1480/428-0001.

CAMP FACILITIES:	NO UNITS	HOOKUPS	FEE
Camper Spaces	22 Gravel	W/S/E (110/30A)	$10.00 dly
Upper Otter Lake Campground			
Camper/Tent Spaces	20	None	5.00 dly
SPT FACILITIES:	Archery	Golf	Grills
	Laundry	Racquetball	Rec Equip Rntl
	Sewage Dmp Sta	Showers	Tennis Courts
ACTIVITIES:	Fishing	Hunting	Snow Skiing

ALASKA
BLACK SPRUCE TRAVEL CAMP, continued

RESTRICTIONS: Pets allowed on leash. 14-day limit. A break of 7 days is required between stays. Hunters must check with Fish & Wildlife as there are many regulations. Firearms must be registered with the military police.

EIELSON FAM-CAMP (AK02R5)
Eielson Air Force Base, AK 99702-5000

TELEPHONE NUMBER INFORMATION: Main installation numbers: Comm: 907-377-1110, DSN: 317-377-1110. Police for fam-camp, Comm: 907-377-5130.

LOCATION: On base. On Richardson Highway (AK-2). Clearly marked. Check in at Bldg 4230, Recreation Issue Annex, 1100-1800 M-F, 1200-1700 Sa-Su. After hours, proceed to fam-camp and register the following day. USMRA: page 128 (F,G-4). NMC: Fairbanks, 26 mi NW.

DESCRIPTION OF AREA: Located in interior of Alaska. Provides base for enjoying state's unlimited outdoor recreational resources. Spectacular mountain scenery; unsurpassed fishing and hunting in general area. Denali National Park approx 130 mi SW. Full range of support facilities available on base.

SEASON OF OPERATION: 1 May-30 Sep.

ELIGIBILITY: Active/Retired/DoD Civilians.

RESERVATIONS: Reservations **accepted only for incoming active duty PCS personnel.** Address: Eielson Fam-Camp, 354 SS/SSRO, 3112 Broadway Ave, Suite 4, Eielson AFB, AK 99702-1870. **Comm: 907-377-1232; DSN: 317-377-1232.** FAX Comm: 907-377-2769. (*For information off-season,* Comm: 907-377-1839.)

CAMP FACILITIES:	NO UNITS	HOOKUPS	FEE
Camper Spaces	24 Paved	W/S/E (110)	$ 7.00 dly

SPT FACILITIES: Sewage Dmp Sta
All other facilities are on the main part of the base, 1.5 mi away.

ACTIVITIES:	Boating	Fishing	Hiking

RESTRICTIONS: Pets allowed on leash. 14-day limit. No firearms permitted in fam-camp; must be secured in vehicle.

ELMENDORF FAM-CAMP (AK12R5)
Elmendorf Air Force Base, AK 99506-5000

TELEPHONE NUMBER INFORMATION: Main installation numbers: Comm: 907-552-1110, DSN: 317-552-1110.

LOCATION: On base. From AK-1 enter base at Muldoon Rd gate. Follow signs. Fam-camp is adjacent to hospital. USMRA: page 131 (B,C,D-1). NMC: Anchorage, adjacent.

ALASKA
ELMENDORF FAM-CAMP, continued

DESCRIPTION OF AREA: Located on the state's southern coast at the head of Cook Inlet in a low-timbered area surrounded by mountains. The camp provides a good base for enjoying spectacular and varied sightseeing and outdoor recreational opportunities. Full range of support facilities available on base.

SEASON OF OPERATION: May-Sep.

ELIGIBILITY: Active/Retired/DoD Civilians.

RESERVATIONS: No adv resv. Address: MWR, 3 SVS/SVRO, 6-920 12th St, Elmendorf AFB, AK 99506-5000. Comm: 907-552-3472, DSN: 317-552-3472, FAX Comm: 907-753-1280. *(For information off season,* Comm: 907-552-4838.)

CAMP FACILITIES:	NO UNITS	HOOKUPS	FEE
Camper Spaces	39 Gravel	W/E (110)	$ 10.00 dly
Tent Spaces	Open	None	

SPT FACILITIES:	Boat Rntl	Camp Equip Rntl	Golf
	Laundry	Picnic Area	Playground
	Rec Equip Rntl	Restrooms	Sewage Dmp Sta
	Showers		

ACTIVITIES:	Fishing	Hiking

RESTRICTIONS: Pets allowed. Boating safety course required prior to renting a boat.

GLASS PARK (AK14R5)
Fort Wainwright, AK 99703-5320

TELEPHONE NUMBER INFORMATION: Main installation numbers: Comm: 907-353-6113/7500, DSN: 317-353-6113/7500.

LOCATION: On post. On eastern side of Fairbanks. Take AK-2 E to main gate. Glass Park is 100 yds inside main gate. Check in with Outdoor Rec Director, Bldg 3452 (Gym I) or Bldg 2062 (Recreation Center), at or soon after arrival. USMRA: page 128 (F-4). NMC: Fairbanks, 3 mi W.

DESCRIPTION OF AREA: Alaska's lakes and rivers abound with many species of fish, and forests teem with many kinds of wildlife. There is plenty of sunshine and great fishing. Both the post and the Fairbanks community offer many and varied activities. Full range of support facilities on post.

SEASON OF OPERATION: Memorial Day-Labor Day.

ELIGIBILITY: Active/Retired/DoD Civilians.

RESERVATIONS: Accepted *for large groups only.* Address: Commander, FWA, ATTN: APVR-FW-PA-CRD/ODR, Ft Wainwright, AK 99703-5320. **Comm: 907-353-2706, DSN: 317-353-2706** (year round). Write or call for Wilderness Adventure in Alaska information.

CAMP FACILITIES: RV/Camper Spaces	NO UNITS Open Area	HOOKUPS None	FEE $ 3.00 dly
SPT FACILITIES:	Arts/Crafts Ctr Gas Marina/N Post Rec Equip Issue	Auto Crafts Golf/9 holes Pavilions Restrooms	Chapel Grills Picnic Area Shoppette
ACTIVITIES:	Boating Hiking	Canoeing Hunting	Fishing Mountain Biking

RESTRICTIONS: Pets allowed on leash. 14-day limit. Sewage dump station available at gas station on post. Firearms not allowed on grounds; must be in vehicle at all times.

RAVENWOOD SKI LODGE (AK13R5)
Eielson Air Force Base, AK 99702-5000

TELEPHONE NUMBER INFORMATION: Main installation numbers: Comm: 907-377-1110, DSN: 317-377-1110. Police for area, Comm: 907-377-5130.

LOCATION: On base. On Richardson Highway (AK-2). Clearly marked. USMRA: page 128 (F,G-4). NMC: Fairbanks, 26 mi NW.

DESCRIPTION OF AREA: Located 4 mi SE of main base. Spectacular mountain scenery. Full range of support facilities available on base.

SEASON OF OPERATION: Depends on snowfall (normally Nov-Mar). Closed M-W.

ELIGIBILITY: Active/Retired/DoD Civilians.

RESERVATIONS: No adv resv. Address: 354 SS/SSRO, 3112 Broadway Ave, Suite 4, Eielson AFB, AK 99702-1870. Comm: 907-377-1328. FAX Comm: 907-377-2769. (*For information off-season*, Comm: 907-377-1839.)

SPT FACILITIES:	Skeet/Trap Rg/ year round Sled Hill Rides	Ski Equip Rntl Ski Lodge/hcp Snack Bar	Ski Lift Ski Trails
ACTIVITIES:	Sledding	Snow Skiing	

RESTRICTIONS: No pets allowed. No firearms permitted in site; must be secured in vehicle.

ALASKA

SEWARD MILITARY RECREATION CAMP (AK06R5)
Fort Richardson, AK 99505-5100

TELEPHONE NUMBER INFORMATION: Main installation numbers: Comm: 907-384-1110, DSN: 317-384-1110.

LOCATION: Off post. Located near Seward off AK-1 on AK-9. Follow signs. Check in at Summer Operations Bldg (South Side) 0600-2300 daily. USMRA: page 128 (F-6) NMI: Fort Richardson, 133 mi N; Elmendorf AFB, 130 mi N. NMC: Anchorage, 110 mi N.

DESCRIPTION OF AREA: The two recreation camps at Seward which had been under separate sponsorship have now been combined and are controlled by Ft Richardson; however, Elmendorf AFB can still accept reservations. The recreation camp is located on Resurrection Bay near Seward. Pine trees throughout picturesque 12-acre site surrounded by mountains on three sides. Superb fishing for salmon, halibut, snapper, ling cod, sea bass and flounder. Nearby streams and lakes also offer outstanding fishing. Abundant wildlife includes: porpoise, whale, puffin, sea otter, and much more. Area is a photographer's dream. Travelers in late Jul to mid-Aug see active salmon spawning areas on drive to Seward. Full range of support facilities at Ft Richardson and Elmendorf AFB.

SEASON OF OPERATION: Memorial Day-Labor Day. 4 cabins: year round.

ELIGIBILITY: Active/Retired/Reserve/DoD, NAF and Contract Civilians.

RESERVATIONS: Resv are accepted starting in May. Call for specific information 0800-1700 local time, M-F. Priority is given to AD in Alaska. Address: ITR Office, PO Box 5-367, Ft Richardson, AK 99505-5100. **Comm: 907-384-1649, 800-770-1858; DSN: 317-384-1649.**

NORTH SIDE FACILITIES

CAMP FACILITIES:	NO UNITS	HOOKUPS	FEE
Cabins, sleep 4	25		$30-35 dly
Camper Spaces	40 Gravel	W/E (110/30A)	10.00 dly
Tent Spaces	7 Open	None	5.00 dly

SPT FACILITIES:			
	Boat Rntl*	Deep Sea Rods	Dining Fac
	Grills	Picnic Area	Playground
	PX Annex	Rec Center	Restrooms
	Sewage Dmp Sta	Showers	Vending Mach

*Boat rental/boat fishing, by drawing. Deep-sea fishing charters/fee.

SOUTH SIDE FACILITIES

CAMP FACILITIES:	NO UNITS	HOOKUPS	FEE**
Mobile Homes*	10	CTV	$40 dly/4 pers**
Motel Units, 1 bdrm	12	CTV	25 dly/2 pers
Camper Spaces	30 Hardstand	E	10.00 dly
Camper Spaces	33 Hardstand	None	7.50 dly
Tent Spaces	12 Improved	None	5.00 dly

ALASKA
SEWARD MILITARY RECREATION CAMP, continued

*2/3 bdrm; furn, including linens, pots, pans; 1 unit for handicapped.
**$50 for 5 or more pers.

SPT FACILITIES:

Boat Launch	BX	Deep-Sea Fishing
Dining Fac	Fish House/Frzr	Fishing Tackle
Food Vending	Ice	Laundry
Nature Trail	Off-Road Veh	Picnic Area
Playground	Rec Room	Restrooms
Sewage Dmp Sta	Showers	Tours

ACTIVITIES:

Basketball	Fishing/license	Hiking
Hunting/license	Volleyball	Tour Boat/fee

RESTRICTIONS: Pets allowed on leash no longer than 6'; will not be left in cabins unattended; are not allowed on boats; owner must clean up after pets. 14-day limit. No open fires are permitted; charcoal grills may be used. No cooking in cabins. The quantity of recreational equipment available for rental is insufficient for the number of patrons who use the area. Patrons must provide own towels and soap.

ARIZONA

APACHE FLATS CAMPGROUND (AZ10R4)
Fort Huachuca, AZ 85613-6000

TELEPHONE NUMBER INFORMATION: Main installation numbers: Comm: 602-538-7111, DSN: 312-879-0111. Police for campground, Comm: 602-533-2181.

LOCATION: On post. Take I-10 to AZ-90; S 25 mi to Sierra Vista and main gate of post. Apache Flats Campground: Check in at campground. Sportsman Center camping area: Check in at Bldg 70914, 1100-1900 W&F, 1100-2100 Th, 1000-1800 Sa-Su. USMRA: page 108 (F,G-9,10). NMC: Tucson, 75 mi NW.

DESCRIPTION OF AREA: Ft Huachuca, located at an altitude of 5,000 feet, is at the base of the Huachuca Mountains. Old mining towns of Bisbee and Tombstone are within short driving distance. Full range of support facilities available on post.

SEASON OF OPERATION: Year round.

ELIGIBILITY: Active/Retired/DoD and NAF Civilians.

RESERVATIONS: Accepted. Address: **Apache Flats Campground:** US Army Garrison, Recreation Division, ATZS-PCR-O, Christy St, Ft Huachuca, AZ 85613-6000. **Comm: 602-538-4786/0821, DSN: 312-879-4786, 0800-1700 M-F;** FAX Comm: 602-533-1349 (Equipment Checkout Center). **Sportsman Center camping:** US Army Garrison, Recreation Division, ATZS-PCR-T, Ft Huachuca, AZ 85613-6000. **Comm: 602-538-8014.**

ARIZONA
APACHE FLATS CAMPGROUND, continued

CAMP FACILITIES:	NO UNITS	HOOKUPS	FEE
Apache Flats Campground			
Camper Spaces	6 Dirt	W/S/E (110)	$ 8.00 dly
Camper Spaces	9 Dirt	W/E (110)	6.00 dly
Tent Spaces	Limited	E (110)	3.00 dly
Sportsman Center			
Camper Spaces	23 Dirt	W/E (110)	5.00 dly
Tent Spaces at	10	None	3.00 dly
Lower Garden Canyon			

SPT FACILITIES:			
	Boat Rntl	Camp Equip Rntl	Chapel
	Gas	Golf	Laundry
	Picnic Area	Playgrounds	Rec Center
	Sewage Dmp Sta	Skeet/Trap Range	Sports Fields
	Stables	Tennis Courts	Walking Trails
ACTIVITIES:	Fishing/license	Hunting/license	Rec Equip Avail

RESTRICTIONS: No zoo animals. Pets must be kept indoors or on leash and controlled. They also *MUST* be registered at Animal Disease Prevention and Control Facility, Bldg 30022. Animals must have valid rabies certificates. Firearms must be registered.

DAVIS-MONTHAN FAM-CAMP (AZ14R4)
Craycraft Road, Davis-Monthan Air Force Base, AZ 85707-3010

TELEPHONE NUMBER INFORMATION: Main installation numbers: Comm: 602-750-3900/4717, DSN: 312-361-1110. Police for fam-camp, Comm: 602-750-4444.

LOCATION: On base. *From E*, exit I-10 at Kolb Rd. N to Escalante Rd; L to Nicaragua, L on Wilmot, R on Quijota Blvd. *From W*, exit I-10N at Alvernon Way. Follow road onto Golf Links Rd.; R on Wilmot Rd.; R on Quijota Blvd. Check in at fam-camp office, Bldg 6013. USMRA: page 108 (F-9). NMC: Tucson, 4 mi NW.

DESCRIPTION OF AREA: Located in a wide desert valley which has beautiful weather year round. Colorado Rockies Spring Training Site. Nearby attractions include Arizona-Sonora Desert Museum, Pima Air Museum, Saguaro National Monument, Old Tucson and Reid Park and Zoo. Full range of support facilities available on base.

SEASON OF OPERATION: Year round.

ELIGIBILITY: Active/Retired/DoD Civilians/TDY Personnel.

RESERVATIONS: No adv resv. Address: Fam-Camp, 355 MWRSS/MWRO, 3775 South Fifth St, Davis Monthan AFB, AZ 85707-5000. Comm: 602-747-9144, DSN: 312-361-1110 (ask for fam-camp).

CAMP FACILITIES:	NO UNITS	HOOKUPS	FEE
Camper Spaces	61 Hardstand	W/S/E (110/30A)	$12.00 dly
Camper Spaces	12 Hardstand	W/S/E (220/50A)	12.00 dly
Overflow	35	None	3.00 dly

25 spaces are paved, 48 are gravel with concrete patios; 12 spaces are 50 Amps, 61 are 30 Amps.

SPT FACILITIES:	Archery	Chapel	Gas
	Golf	Laundry	LP Gas
	Racquetball	Rec Center	Restrooms/hcp
	Sewage Dmp Sta	Showers/hcp	Skeet Range
	Snack Bar	Sports Fields	Tennis Courts

ACTIVITIES: Recreation Equipment Available
Tours Available

RESTRICTIONS: Pets allowed. 7-day limit Jan-May. Check out 1000. Firearms must be declared at Visitor Control upon entry.

FORT TUTHILL RECREATION AREA (AZ11R4)
Luke Air Force Base, AZ 85309-5000

TELEPHONE NUMBER INFORMATION: Main installation numbers: Comm: 602-856-0111, DSN: 312-853-0111. Police for recreation area, call 911 (Coconino County Sheriff).

LOCATION: Off base. Located 4 mi S of Flagstaff. Take I-17 to exit 337 (Airport/Sedona). Take first road to L. Enter park area at Ft Tuthill (adjoins Coconino County fairgrounds). Check in 1300-2200. USMRA: page 108 (E-4). NMI: Luke AFB, Glendale, 138 mi SW. NMC: Flagstaff, 4 mi N.

DESCRIPTION OF AREA: Located at an elevation of 7,000 ' at the base of the San Francisco Peaks. It was created in 1928 as a National Guard summer camp. Tall pines, mild summer temperatures, and skiing in the winter make this an ideal vacation spot. Many opportunities for both sportsperson and tourist within a 30-mile radius. Full range of support facilities at Luke AFB.

SEASON OF OPERATION: Chalets, cabin, yurts and huts: year round. Camping area: May-Oct.

ELIGIBILITY: Active/Retired/Reserve/DoD Civilians.

RESERVATIONS: Required, with deposit. AD at Luke AFB and Gila Bend AFAF may make reservations beginning on the 1st day of the month for the following month; all others call on the 11th for the following month. Reservations may be made 0800-2200 daily. Address: Luke Rec Area, HC 30, Box 5, Flagstaff, AZ 86001-8701. **Comm: 800-552-6268, 520-774-8893; DSN: 312-853-3401.**

ARIZONA
FORT TUTHILL RECREATION AREA, continued

CAMP FACILITIES:	NO UNITS	HOOKUPS	FEE*
Chalets, 2 bdrm, furn	11	W/S/E	$50.00 dly
Cabin, furn	1	W/S/E	35.00 dly
Yurts, furn, no bath/kit**	4	E (110/30A)	20.00 dly
Huts, furn, no bath/kit	8	E (110/30A)	20.00 dly
Camper Spaces	21 Gravel	W/E (110/30A)	12.00 dly
Camper/Tent Spaces	13 Gravel	None	7.00 dly

*Double occupancy; additional fee for extra guests.
**A "yurt" is a cabin/tent structure, 24 feet in diameter with wooden floor, deck and door, 2 windows, and stretched-canvas covering with skylight.

SPT FACILITIES:			
	Arcade	Country Store	Golf/8 mi
	Grills	Handball	Jacuzzi
	Laundry	Lodge	Picnic Area
	Playground	Rec Equip Rntl	Restrooms
	RV Storage	Sewage Dmp Sta	Showers
	Sports Fields	Tennis Courts	TV/VCR
	Mountain bike, cross-country ski, and nature trails.		

ACTIVITIES:			
	Boating	Day Trips	Fishing
	Hiking	Hunting	Mountain Biking
	Movie Night	Sledding	Snow Skiing/XC

RESTRICTIONS: No pets allowed in chalets, cabins, yurts or huts. Pets allowed on leash in camping area. Check out 0800-1100. Firearms are permitted but must remain unloaded and secured in vehicle at all times.

Note: Construction of expanded facilities begins 10/94.

GILA BEND FAM-CAMP (AZ15R4)
Gila Bend Air Force Auxiliary Field, AZ 85337-5000

TELEPHONE NUMBER INFORMATION: Main installation numbers: Comm: 602-683-6200, DSN: 312-853-5200.

LOCATION: On base. 71 mi S of Luke Air Force Base at Auxiliary Field. From I-10 W of Phoenix take Exit 112 (Ajo/Gila Bend); S on AZ-85 through Gila Bend; R at Gila Bend AFAF/Ajo sign approx 4½ mi to AFAF. USMRA: page 108 (C-8). NMC: Phoenix, 63 mi NE.

DESCRIPTION OF AREA: Located between Yuma and Phoenix in area that enjoys pleasant weather year round. Mountain areas and Mexico within easy driving distance. Full range of support facilities available on base.

SEASON OF OPERATION: Year round.

ELIGIBILITY: Active/Retired/DoD and NAF Civilians.

RESERVATIONS: *Accepted for AD and DoD Civilians on official orders only.* Address: Billeting Office, 56 SPTS, Gila Bend AFAF, AZ 85337-5000. **Comm: 602-683-6238/6211, DSN: 853-5275/5211.**

ARIZONA
GILA BEND FAM-CAMP, continued

CAMP FACILITIES:	NO UNITS	HOOKUPS	FEE
Camper Spaces	31 Gravel	W/S/TV/E(30A)	$ 8 dly/95 biwkly
Dry Camp Area		None	3.00 dly

SPT FACILITIES:	Golf Driv Range	Picnic Area	Restrooms
	Sewage Dmp Sta	Sports Fields	Tennis Courts

ACTIVITIES:	Fishing	Jogging

RESTRICTIONS: Pets allowed on leash. Animals must have rabies shots. 14-day limit. Host and hostess are present for check-in and information (Oct-May) in site 8 area; contact Recreation Officer during remainder of the year.

MARTINEZ LAKE RECREATION AREA (AZ12R4)
Yuma Marine Corps Air Station, AZ 85369-5000

TELEPHONE NUMBER INFORMATION: Main installation numbers: Comm: 602-341-2011, DSN: 312-951-2011.

LOCATION: Off base. Located on Colorado River 38 mi N of Yuma. N on US-95; L on Imperial Wildlife Refuge access road; travel approx 10 mi. R at sign for USMC Rec Area; follow road approx 2 mi. USMRA: page 108 (A-7). NMI: US Army Yuma Proving Ground, 15 mi N. NMC: Yuma, 38 mi S.

DESCRIPTION OF AREA: Located on land administered by the US Fish and Wildlife Service. Area provides rustic semi-private fishing camp. Campground is barren desert peninsula extending into river. Full range of support facilities available at Yuma US Army Proving Ground.

SEASON OF OPERATION: Year round.

ELIGIBILITY: Active/Retired.

RESERVATIONS: Accepted. Address: MWR, Bldg 633, MCAS, Yuma, AZ 85369-5000; **Comm: 602-341-2278, DSN: 312-951-2007.** *Recreation Area*: Martinez Lake Rec Area, PO Box 72202, Martinez Lake, AZ 85364; Comm: 602-783-3422.

CAMP FACILITIES:	NO UNITS	HOOKUPS	FEE
Cabins, A/C, furn,	5		$20.00 dly
except dishes & linens			
Mobile Homes	4		25.00 dly
Camper Spaces	17 Hardstand	W/E (110)	7.00 dly
Camper/Tent Spaces	3 Primitive	None	4.00 dly

SPT FACILITIES:	Boat Rntl	Grills	Picnic Area
	Playground	Restrooms	Showers
	Swimming Area		

ARIZONA
MARTINEZ LAKE RECREATION AREA, continued

ACTIVITIES:　　　Fishing　　　Horseshoes　　　Swimming

RESTRICTIONS: No children under 16, no smoking, and no pets allowed in mobile homes. Pets allowed on leash in other areas. 14-day limit for cabins and some campsites. No weapons allowed.

YUMA PROVING GROUND TRAVEL CAMP (AZ21R4)
Yuma Army Proving Ground, AZ 85365-9102

TELEPHONE NUMBER INFORMATION: Main installation numbers: Comm: 602-328-2151, DSN: 312-899-2151.

LOCATION: On post. From I-8 at Yuma take US-95. *OR* from I-10 take US-95 S. Exit US-95 at Yuma Proving Ground (YPG) main gate on 3rd St. Check in at Recreation Center, Bldg 530, 0900-1630 M-F. USMRA: page 108 (A,B-7). NMC: Yuma, 27 mi S.

DESCRIPTION OF AREA: Located near the Colorado River in a mountainous area near California and Mexico in one of the driest parts of the US. The Colorado River has numerous irrigation canals and hundreds of small lakes with excellent boating, fishing, swimming and water skiing opportunities. Full range of support facilities available on post.

SEASON OF OPERATION: Year round.

ELIGIBILITY: Active/Retired/YPG DOD Civilians and Contractors.

RESERVATIONS: Accepted 30 days in adv. Address: Commander, USAYPG, Attn: STEYP-CA-CRD, Yuma, AZ 85365-9102. **Comm: 602-328-2586/4586, DSN: 312-899-2586/4586.** Discounts available to holders of Golden Age Passports.

CAMP FACILITIES:	NO UNITS	HOOKUPS	FEE
Camper Spaces	6	W/S/E (110/30A)	$ 8.00 dly

SPT FACILITIES:	Chapel*	Golf*	Laundry*
	Restrooms*	Showers*	

*On post

There is a Marina with boat rental on the Colorado River.

ACTIVITIES:　　　Boating　　　Fishing　　　Hunting*

*Deer, big horn, quail and dove; call for information.

RESTRICTIONS: Pets allowed on leash; owner must clean up after pet. 3 spaces have a 14-day limit.

ARKANSAS

CHAFFEE TRAILER PARK (AR06R2)
Fort Chaffee, AR 72905-5000

TELEPHONE NUMBER INFORMATION: Main installation numbers: Comm: 501-484-2141, DSN: 312-962-2111.

LOCATION: On post. From I-40 N of Fort Smith exit to I-540 W (traveling S); then take AR-22 (Rogers Ave) E through Barling to Fort Chaffee. Check in at Billeting Office, Bldg 1337 (see hours below). USMRA: page 76 (A,B-4,5). NMC: Fort Smith, 6 mi NW.

DESCRIPTION OF AREA: Situated in a flat, wooded area near the Arkansas/Oklahoma state line. Limited support facilities available on post.

SEASON OF OPERATION: Year round.

ELIGIBILITY: Active/Retired/Reserve/NG/Federal Employees.

RESERVATIONS: No adv resv. Address: Billeting Office, Bldg 1377, Fort Chaffee, AR 72905-5000. Comm: 501-484-2252, DSN: 312-962-2252.

CAMP FACILITIES:	NO UNITS	HOOKUPS	FEE
Camper Spaces	39 Gravel	W/S/E(110/220)	$ 4.00 dly
SPT FACILITIES:	Port-a-Potties	Swimming Pool	
ACTIVITIES:	Fishing	Swimming	

RESTRICTIONS: Pets allowed on leash. Space is extremely limited during annual training in May through August. *Camper spaces cannot accommodate mobile homes.* Check in and check out 0730-1600 M-F; 0930-1600 Sa, Su. Office closed on hol. No firearms allowed.

LITTLE ROCK FAM-CAMP (AR05R2)
Little Rock Air Force Base, AR 72099-5000

TELEPHONE NUMBER INFORMATION: Main installation numbers: Comm: 501-988-3131, DSN: 312-731-1110. Police for fam-camp, Comm: 501-988-3221.

LOCATION: On base. Located 10 mi NE of Little Rock off US-67/167 at Jacksonville. AFB exit to main gate. Take Vandenberg Dr to Arnold Dr, L to Arkansas Dr, R to fam-camp on L. Check in at fam-camp. USMRA: page 76 (D-5). NMC: Little Rock, 10 mi SW.

DESCRIPTION OF AREA: Located in central region of state in open terrain near lakes and wooded area. Full range of support facilities available on base.

SEASON OF OPERATION: Year round.

ARKANSAS
LITTLE ROCK FAM-CAMP, continued

ELIGIBILITY: Active/Retired/DoD Civilians.

RESERVATIONS: No adv resv. Address: Recreation Services, 314 SVS/SVRO, 3510 Leadership Circle, Little Rock AFB, AR 72099-5000. Comm: 501-988-3365, FAX : 501-988-6164; DSN: 312-731-3365, FAX: 312-731-6164.

CAMP FACILITIES:	NO UNITS	HOOKUPS	FEE
Camper Spaces	10 Hardstand	W/E (110/220)	$ 8.00 dly
Camper Spaces*	14 Gravel	W/E (110/220)	8.00 dly
Tent Spaces	Wilderness	None	3.00 dly

*Scheduled for completion 2 Jul 94

SPT FACILITIES:	Boat Rntl/	Camp Equip Rntl	Chapel
	sumr wknds	Gas	Golf
	Grills	Laundry*	Picnic Area
	Playground	Racquetball	Rec Center
	Restrooms*	Sewage Dmp Sta	Shoppette
	Sports Fields	Tennis Courts	Trailer Rntl

ACTIVITIES:	Fishing/license	Hunting/license	Jogging
	Rec Equip Avail		

RESTRICTIONS: Pets allowed on leash. 7-day limit. Check out 1400. No firearms allowed.

CALIFORNIA

ADMIRAL BAKER FIELD CAMPGROUND (CA64R4)
San Diego Naval Station, CA 92136-5000

TELEPHONE NUMBER INFORMATION: Main installation numbers: Comm: 619-556-1011, DSN: 312-526-1011. Police for campground, Comm: 619-556-5555.

LOCATION: Off base. From I-15 approx 1/2 mi N of intersection with I-8, go E on Friar's Rd, then L on Santo Rd and an immediate R onto Admiral Baker Rd. USMRA: page 118 (D-4). NMI: San Diego NS, 11 mi SW. NMC: San Diego, 4 mi SW.

DESCRIPTION OF AREA: Campground is located in the midst of 44-acre picnic area and caters to families. Golf Crest RV Park is located N of campground, adjacent to the golf course and caters primarily to golfers. Full range of support facilities at San Diego Naval Station.

SEASON OF OPERATION: Year round.

ELIGIBILITY: Active/Retired.

CALIFORNIA
ADMIRAL BAKER FIELD CAMPGROUND, continued

RESERVATIONS: Recommended. Up to 60 days in adv for AD; 30 days for Ret. Address: Mission Gorge RV Park, c/o Navy Golf Course, Friar's Road and Santo Road, Naval Station San Diego, CA 92120-5000. **Comm: C-619-556-5525, FAX: 619-556-6459.**

CAMP FACILITIES:	NO UNITS	HOOKUPS	FEE
Camper Spaces	27 Dirt	W/E (110/220)	$12.00 dly
Camper Spaces	12 Overflow	None	10.00 dly

RV Spaces at Golf Crest

	14 Gravel	W/E	10.00 dly

SPT FACILITIES:	Golf	Grills	Picnic Area
	Playground	Sewage Dmp Sta	Showers/at pool
	Sports Fields	Swimming Pool	Tennis Courts
ACTIVITIES:	Basketball	Rec Equip Avail	Swimming

RESTRICTIONS: Pets allowed on leash in campground area only. Must keep noise down and clean up after pet. No tent camping.

ALAMEDA MARINA RV PARK (CA69R4)
199 Coral Sea Dr, Alameda Naval Air Station, CA 94501-5000
(Alameda NAS is mandated to close under the 1993 Base Closure Law.
A closure date has not been announced.)

TELEPHONE NUMBER INFORMATION: Main installation numbers: Comm: 510-263-0111, DSN: 312-993-0111. Police for RV park, Comm: 510-263-3767.

LOCATION: On base. From the North on I-88 (Nimitz Highway), take Broadway/Alameda exit; OR from the South on I-880, take Broadway exit. Directions to NAS clearly marked. Check in at Fleet Recreation Center, Bldg 542, next to RV park 1100-2300. USMRA: page 119 (D-5). NMC: Oakland, 2 mi NE.

DESCRIPTION OF AREA: This RV park is located along the San Francisco Bay and offers beautiful views of the bay area. Only a 30-minute drive to San Francisco and other varied attractions. Civilian golf course available off base. Exchange, commissary and recreational facilities are nearby. Full range of support facilities on base.

SEASON OF OPERATION: Year round.

ELIGIBILITY: Active/Retired/Reserve/NG/DoD Civilians.

RESERVATIONS: Accepted. Address: MWR, 199 Coral Sea Dr, Naval Air Station, Alameda, CA 94501-5000. **Comm: 510-263-3166, FAX: 510-263-3152, DSN: 312-993-3166.**

CALIFORNIA
ALAMEDA MARINA RV PARK, continued

CAMP FACILITIES:	NO UNITS	HOOKUPS	FEE
Camper Spaces, pull thru	24 Gravel	W/E (110/20&30A)	$12.00 dly*
Camper Spaces	Overflow	None	$5.00 dly

*Weekly and off-season (Nov-Mar) rates available.

SPT FACILITIES:	Auto Hobby Shop	Boat Rntl	Camp Equip Rntl
	Gas	Grills	Laundry
	Marina	Pavilion	Picnic Area
	Rec Equip Rntl	Restrooms*	Sewage Dmp Sta
	Showers*	Snack Bar*	

*Located in Fleet Recreation Center and gymnasium.

ACTIVITIES:	Boating	Fishing/license	Sightseeing

RESTRICTIONS: Pets allowed on leash; owner must clean up after pet. No washing of vehicles. No hanging of laundry. RV servicing available at Navy Exchange garage adjacent to RV parks. Check out 1400. Register firearms with Security upon arrival.

BEALE FAM-CAMP (CA60R4)
Beale Air Force Base, CA 95903-5000

TELEPHONE NUMBER INFORMATION: Main installation numbers: Comm: 916-634-3000, DSN: 312-368-3000. Police for fam-camp, Comm: 916-634-2000/911.

LOCATION: On base. Take US-70 S from Marysville for approx 1 mi to Beale AFB exit. Follow signs to main gate, approx 10 mi. Well marked. Check in at Billeting, Bldg 24112. USMRA: page 110 (D-6). NMC: Sacramento, 40 mi SW.

DESCRIPTION OF AREA: Located in northern California in the midst of a variety of interesting recreational opportunities. 2-hour drive to Reno. Full range of support facilities on base.

SEASON OF OPERATION: Year round.

ELIGIBILITY: Active/Retired/DoD Civilians.

RESERVATIONS: No adv resv. Address: Recreation Services, 9 SPTG/MWRO, 6000 C St., Suite 200 Beale AFB, CA 95903-5000. Comm: 916-634-3382, DSN: 312-368-3382.

CAMP FACILITIES:	NO UNITS	HOOKUPS	FEE
Camper Spaces (self-contained veh only)	44 Paved	W/S/E (110/30A) (220/50A)	$ 9.00 dly*

*Weekly and monthly rates available

SPT FACILITIES:	Boat Rntl	Camp Equip Rntl	Chapel
	Game Farm	Gas	Golf
	Laundry	Off-Road Veh	Pay Telephones
	Rec Center	Sewage Dmp Sta	Skeet Range
	Snack Bar	Trails	

CALIFORNIA
BEALE FAM-CAMP, continued

ACTIVITIES: Fishing   Hunting/license   Rec Equip Avail
                   Snow Skiing   Whitewater Rafting

RESTRICTIONS: Pets allowed on leash. Policy on firearms is in accordance with Air Force Regulations and CA state laws. No tents allowed.

BIG BEAR RECREATION FACILITY (CA05R4)
El Toro Marine Corps Air Station, CA 92709-5000
(El Toro MCAS is mandated to close under the 1993 Base Closure Law. A closure date has not been announced.)

TELEPHONE NUMBER INFORMATION: Main installation numbers: Comm: 714-726-3011, DSN: 312-997-3011.

LOCATION: Off base; located in Big Bear Lake. From I-10 at Redlands, take CA-30 N a short distance to CA-38. E on CA-38; L on Big Bear Blvd (CA-18); L on Moon Ridge Blvd, then R on Elm. (If you look carefully, you'll see a small sign for Big Bear Rec Area.) R on Switzerland and then an immediate L. *NOTE: Don't be tempted to take a shortcut through Snow Summit Ski Area as many people have been stuck in snow and mud on the forestry service road over which you must travel.* USMRA: page 111 (G-13). NMI: March AFB, 65 mi SW. NMC: San Bernardino, 50 mi SW.

DESCRIPTION OF AREA: Centrally located 7,000 feet above sea level between Snow Summit and Bear Mountain ski resorts in the San Bernardino National Forest. Area offers excellent fishing, boating, hiking and skiing. Full range of support facilities available at March AFB.

SEASON OF OPERATION: Cabins: Year round; RV campsites: May-Oct.

ELIGIBILITY: Active/Retired/DoD Civilians.

RESERVATIONS: Required. *Address for chalet resv*: ITT, Bldg 75, MCAS El Toro, Santa Ana, CA 92709-5007; **Comm: 714-726-2626/3725, DSN: 312-997-2626/2572.** *For Rec Facility general info and campsite resv*: Big Bear Recreation Facility, PO Box 1664, Big Bear Lake, CA 92315-1664; **Comm: 909-866-3965, FAX Comm: 909-866-4069.**

CAMP FACILITIES:	NO UNITS	HOOKUPS	FEE
Chalets, slp 6-8*	8		$45-65 dly**
Camper/Tent Spaces	5 Paved	W/E (110)	12 dly

*Some equipped for handicapped. 1 bdrm w/queen bed, sofa bed in living rm, 2 dbl beds in loft; fireplace, color TV, refr, MW, gas range, grill, picnic table, cooking and eating utensils; bring personal bath items, dish towels, radio, VCR. AD at MCAS El Toro and Tustin have priority.
**Depending on season, day of week, length of stay and status of sponsor.

CALIFORNIA
BIG BEAR RECREATION FACILITY, continued

SPT FACILITIES:	Bicycle Rntl Group Fire Pit with BBQ Showers	Boat Rntl Picnic Area Rec Equip Rntl Snow Play Area	Grills Playground Restrooms
ACTIVITIES:	Boating Horseshoes Water Skiing	Fishing Snow Skiing	Hiking Volleyball

RESTRICTIONS: No pets allowed. *No wood may be burned in cabin fireplace; USE PRESSED LOGS ONLY.* No firearms (including air-powered and bow weapons) allowed. No campfires. No fireworks. Maximum of 8 occupants per site. Quiet hours 2200-0800.

CAMP SAN LUIS OBISPO RV PARK (CA82R4)
San Luis Obispo, CA 93403-8104

TELEPHONE NUMBER INFORMATION: Main installation numbers: Comm: 805-549-3800, FTS: 629-3800.

LOCATION: On post. From US-101 at San Luis Obispo, take CA-1 W. USMRA: page 111 (C-11). NMC: San Luis Obispo, 5 mi SE.

DESCRIPTION OF AREA: Located on California Central Coast in an area offering a variety of entertainment, sports, sightseeing and tourist activities, including Mission San Luis Obispo, Hearst Castle and Morro Rock. Limited support facilities available on post; full range of facilities available at Vandenberg AFB, 60 mi S.

SEASON OF OPERATION: Year round.

ELIGIBILITY: Active/Retired/NG/Federal and State Employees.

RESERVATIONS: Accepted. Address: Billeting Office, Camp San Luis Obispo, PO Box 8104, San Luis Obispo, CA 93403-8104. **Comm: 805-549-3800, FTS: 630-9800.**

CAMP FACILITIES:	NO UNITS	HOOKUPS	FEE
Camper Spaces	4 Hardstand	W/S/E (110/30A)	$ 8.00 dly
Camper Spaces	8 Hardstand	W/E	7.00 dly
Tent Spaces	Primitive	None	4.00 dly

SPT FACILITIES:	Chapel/sumr Laundry PX Showers	Clubs Picnic Area Restrooms	Grills Playground Sewage Dmp Sta
ACTIVITIES:	Fishing	Jogging	Sightseeing

RESTRICTIONS: No pets allowed. No firearms allowed.

CALIFORNIA

CASTLE FAM-CAMP (CA72R4)
Castle Air Force Base, CA 95342-5000
(This base is scheduled to close 30 September 1995 under the 1991 Base Closure Law.)

TELEPHONE NUMBER INFORMATION: Main installation numbers: Comm: 209-726-2011, DSN: 312-347-1110.

LOCATION: On base. From CA-99, exit at Buhach Rd/Castle AFB (Atwater from N or Merced from S). Check in at Billeting, Bldg 1108, 24 hrs dly. USMRA: page 110 (D-8). NMC: Merced, 7 mi S.

DESCRIPTION OF AREA: Centrally located in San Joaquin Valley, Castle AFB is a max of 2 hours from some of the world's most picturesque sites and cities: Yosemite National Park, San Francisco, Sequoia and Kings Canyon National Parks. The base is less than an hour away from the foothills of the Sierra Nevada. Full range of support facilities on base.

SEASON OF OPERATION: Year round.

ELIGIBILITY: Active/Retired/NG on AD/DOD Civilians.

RESERVATIONS: Reservations accepted with prepayment. Address: MWR, 93 SPTG/MWRO, Castle AFB, CA 95342-5000. **Comm: 209-726-2715, DSN: 312-347-2531.**

CAMP FACILITIES:	NO UNITS	HOOKUPS	FEE
Camper Spaces	4 Hardstand	W/S/E (110)	$ 7.50 dly
Camper Spaces	36 Hardstand	None	5.00 dly

SPT FACILITIES:	Boat Rntl	Camp Equip Rntl	Chapel
	Gas	Laundry	Picnic Area
	Playground	Sewage Dmp Sta	Sports Equip Rntl

ACTIVITIES:	Boating	Fishing	Snow Skiing
	Windsurfing		

RESTRICTIONS: Pets allowed. No firearms allowed.

CHANNEL ISLANDS HARBOR FAMILY RECREATIONAL FACILITY (CA88R4)
Channel Islands Coast Guard Station
4201 Victoria Avenue, Oxnard, CA 93035-5000

TELEPHONE NUMBER INFORMATION: Main installation numbers: Comm: 805-985-9822.

LOCATION: On base. West of Los Angeles. From US-101 at Oxnard take Victoria Ave exit S past Channel Islands Blvd to CG Station on R. Check in with OOD, CG Station 0800-1630. USMRA: Page 111 (D-13). NMI: Port Hueneme Naval Construction Battalion Center, adjacent. NMC: Los Angeles, 60 mi SE.

CALIFORNIA
CHANNEL ISLANDS HARBOR FAMILY REC FACILITY, continued

DESCRIPTION OF AREA: Located near the southern coast of California at Channel Islands Harbor. Minutes away from water sports, charter boat fishing, shopping and bicycle touring and within easy driving distance of world-famous tourist attractions in the Los Angeles area. Full range of support facilities available at Port Hueneme Naval Construction Battalion Center.

SEASON OF OPERATION: Year round.

ELIGIBILITY: Active/Retired/CG Reserve/Federal Civilians.

RESERVATIONS: Required, **by application only.** Resv should be made no more than 50 days in adv. Address: Commanding Officer, US Coast Guard Station, Channel Islands Harbor, 4201 Victoria Ave, Oxnard, CA 93035-8399. **Comm: 805-985-9822, FAX Comm: 805-984-1842.**

CAMP FACILITIES:	NO UNITS	HOOKUPS	FEE
Camper Spaces	5 Gravel	W/E (110)	$ 5.00 dly
SPT FACILITIES:	Grills	Pavilion	Picnic Area
	Playground	Sewage Dmp Sta	Tennis
ACTIVITIES:	Bicycling	Boating	Fishing
	Hiking	Horseshoes	Surfing
	Swimming	Touring	Volleyball

RESTRICTIONS: Pets allowed on leash; owner must clean up after pet daily. 12-day limit, to include only 1 weekend. No open fires. Firearms must be secured in trunk.

CLUB DEL COTTAGES (CAMP DEL MAR BEACH) (CA03R4)
Marine Corps Base, Camp Pendleton, CA 92055-5001

TELEPHONE NUMBER INFORMATION: Main installation numbers: Comm: 619-725-4111, DSN: 312-365-4111.

LOCATION: On base. Exit I-5 at Oceanside. Check in 1400-1630. USMRA: page 111 (F-15). NMC: San Diego, 50 mi S.

DESCRIPTION OF AREA: Located in southern California approx 90 mi S of Los Angeles. Campsites situated on 26 miles of Pacific Ocean shoreline. Full range of support facilities available on base.

SEASON OF OPERATION: Year round (some restrictions).

ELIGIBILITY: Active/Retired/Reserve.

CALIFORNIA
CLUB DEL COTTAGES (CAMP DEL MAR BEACH), continued

RESERVATIONS: *Accepted by phone or in person,* with payment in full due 4 weeks in adv of resv: up to 12 weeks in adv for AD at Camp Pendleton; up to 10 weeks in adv for other AD; up to 8 weeks in adv for Ret and Reserve. **Comm: 619-725- 2463 (0800-1630).** Address: AC/S MWR, BOX 555020, Camp Pendleton, CA 92055-5020, ATTN: Club Del Campsites. *This office is not equipped to handle written inquiries.*

CAMP FACILITIES:	NO UNITS	HOOKUPS	FEE*
Cottages, 1 bdrm*	48		$30.00 dly
Mobile Home, 4 bdrm**	1		60.00 dly
Mobile Home, 2 bdrm***	14		30.00 dly
Camper Spaces	18 Paved	W/E (110/30A)	12.00 dly
Camper Spaces	87 Hardpack	W/E (110/30A)	12.00 dly
Camper Spaces	19 Beach	W/E (110/30A)	12.00 dly

*Winter rates available; security deposit required. Cottages and mobile homes have fully equipped kitchens; bring bed linens, blankets, pillows, towels, detergent, radio, firewood for use in designated fire rings on the beach.
**Double wide, 2 baths, sleeps 16.
***2 sets of bunk beds and double bed, sleep 6, MW, TV.

SPT FACILITIES:			
	Bicycle Route	Boat Rntl &	Cabanas
	Chapel	Supply	Charter Fishing
	Fire Rings	Golf	Marina
	Picnic Area	Racquetball	Sewage Dmp Sta
	Snow Ski/nearby	Tennis Courts	

ACTIVITIES:			
	Fishing	Jogging	Rec Equip Avail
	Swimming		

RESTRICTIONS: No pets. No bottles or glass containers on beach. Late arrival should be pre-arranged; key may be picked up from Night Host at Campsite 53. No firearms allowed.

EDWARDS FAM-CAMP (CA62R4)
115 Methusa Avenue
Edwards Air Force Base, CA 93524-5000

TELEPHONE NUMBER INFORMATION: Main installation numbers: Comm: 805-277-1110, DSN: 312-527-0111. Police for fam-camp, Comm: 805-277-3340.

LOCATION: On base. Off CA-14, 18 mi E of Rosamond and 30 mi NE of Lancaster. Off CA-58, 10 mi SW of Boron and 40 mi NW of Barstow (Jct I-15 & I-40). Check in at Billeting Office, Bldg 5602. USMRA: page 111 (F-12). NMC: Los Angeles, 90 mi SW.

DESCRIPTION OF AREA: Located in Mojave-Lancaster-Barstow section of California's hilly desert region NE of Los Angeles metropolitan area. Convenient base for visiting Lake Arrowhead and other points of interest in the San Bernardino-Pasadena-Los Angeles complex. Full range of support facilities available on base.

CALIFORNIA
EDWARDS FAM-CAMP, continued

SEASON OF OPERATION: Year round.

ELIGIBILITY: Active/Retired/DoD Civilians.

RESERVATIONS: No adv resv. Address: Fam-Camp, 115 Methusa Ave, Bldg 2420, Edwards AFB, CA 93524-5000. Comm: 805-277-3394/3586/3546, DSN: 312-527-3394.

CAMP FACILITIES:	NO UNITS	HOOKUPS	FEE
Camper Spaces	26 Hardstand	W/S/E (30A)	$10.00 dly
Camper Spaces	9	None	5.00 dly

SPT FACILITIES:			
	Chapel	Gas	Golf
	Racquetball	Sports Fields	Trails

ACTIVITIES: Recreation Equipment Available

RESTRICTIONS: Pets allowed. No open fires. No feeding of wild animals. No firearms allowed.

EL CENTRO NAF CAMPGROUND (CA76R4)
El Centro Naval Air Facility, CA 92243-5001

TELEPHONE NUMBER INFORMATION: Main installation numbers: Comm: 619-339-2699, DSN: 312-958-8699. Police for campground, Comm: 619-339-2524

LOCATION: On base. From I-8 at Seeley, take Drew Road exit N to NAF. Clearly marked. Check in at Rec Center, Bldg 364, next to Base Chapel. USMRA: page 111 (H-15,16). NMC: Yuma AZ, 60 mi E.

DESCRIPTION OF AREA: Located in the Imperial Valley of southern CA. Climate is most delightful during winter and early spring with daytime temperatures between 75° and 110°. There is little rainfall except for brief downpours during the summer. Full range of support facilities available on base.

SEASON OF OPERATION: Year round.

ELIGIBILITY: Active/Retired/DoD Civilians.

RESERVATIONS: No adv resv. Address: MWR, Code 60, Bldg 318, 1635 Third St, Naval Air Facility, El Centro, CA 92243-5001. Comm: 619-339-2489, DSN: 312-958-8489.

CAMP FACILITIES:	NO UNITS	HOOKUPS	FEE*
Camper Spaces,	53 Hardstand	W/S/E (110)	$9-12 dly
35' max	12 Gravel		183-225 monthly
Dry Camp	Unlimited	None	3 dly

*Weekly, monthly and off-season (1 May-30 Oct) rates avail.

CALIFORNIA
EL CENTRO NAF CAMPGROUND, continued

SPT FACILITIES:	Boat Rntl	Chapel	Driving Range
	Gas/LP	Golf*	Grills
	Laundry/nearby	Movies	Picnic Area
	Racquet Sports	Restrooms	Sewage Dmp Sta
	Showers	Sports Field	Trailer Rntl

*9-hole short course in El Centro.

| ACTIVITIES: | Fishing | Hunting (Dove/Sep) | Rec Equip Avail |
| | Swimming | | |

RESTRICTIONS: Pets allowed; must be confined at all times (leash, cage, inside RV, etc). Pets *will not* be allowed on the running track or football field. Firearms must be checked at Security.

EL TORO CAMPGROUNDS (CA81R4)
El Toro Marine Corps Air Station, CA 92709-5000
(El Toro MCAS is mandated to close under the 1993 Base Closure Law. A closure date has not been announced.)

TELEPHONE NUMBER INFORMATION: Main installation numbers: Comm: 714-726-3011, DSN: 312-997-3100. Police for campgrounds, Comm: 714-726-6767/3525.

LOCATION: On base. Take I-5 to Sand Canyon Rd exit; E to Trabuco Rd, then R to main gate. USMRA: page 117 (H-7,8). NMC: Anaheim, 15 mi NW.

DESCRIPTION OF AREA: The campsites are located near the picnic grounds. **The Lodge** offers a limited number of transient rooms. However, when they are filled the staff will be happy to contact local commercial facilities and obtain accommodations at greatly discounted rates. The area surrounding the MCAS offers many attractions for residents and visitors alike, among them are Disneyland, Anaheim Stadium, Marineland, Crystal Cathedral, mountains, beaches and boating. All are easy to reach. Full range of support facilities available on base.

SEASON OF OPERATION: Year round.

ELIGIBILITY: Active/Retired.

RESERVATIONS: Required. Address: ITT Office, MWR/MCAS, El Toro, PO Box 94008, Santa Anna, CA 92709-4008. **Comm: 714-726-2572/2626, DSN: 312-997-2626.**

CAMP FACILITIES:	NO UNITS	HOOKUPS	FEE
Camper Spaces	4	W/S/E (110/20A)	$12.00 dly
Camper Spaces	11	None	6.00 dly

SPT FACILITIES:	Golf	Grills	Jogging Track
	Playground	Restroom	Showers/gym
	Sports Field	Tennis Courts	

CALIFORNIA
EL TORO CAMPGROUNDS, continued

ACTIVITIES: Sightseeing   Softball

RESTRICTIONS: Pets allowed on leash. 7-day limit. No firearms allowed, all firearms on base must be stored at the armory.

FHL PRIMITIVE CAMPGROUND (CA78R4)
Fort Hunter Liggett, Jolon, CA 93928-5000

TELEPHONE NUMBER INFORMATION: Main installation numbers: Comm: 408-385-5911, DSN: 312-359-2677. Police for campground, Comm: 408-385-2513/2526.

LOCATION: On post. Off US-101. *From S at Bradley* take Route G18 (Fort Hunter Liggett/Jolon Rd) W 20 mi to Jolon; L on Mission Rd into post. *From N at King City* take Route G14 (Fort Hunter Liggett/Jolon Rd) W 20 mi to Jolon; R on Mission Rd. Immediately after Military Police booth, L on Alamo Rd 1/2 mi, and R at fork. Register at Outdoor Rec, Bldg T-630 on L. USMRA: page 111 (C-10). NMC: San Luis Obispo, 75 mi S.

DESCRIPTION OF AREA: Located approx 5 mi from post headquarters in a primitive area abounding in wildlife, including protected species. Observe tule elk, bald eagles, kit fox, pumas, bobcats, and more. Excellent opportunities for hunting and fishing. Visit Mission San Antonio. Limited support facilities available on post; full range of facilities available at Ft Ord, 85 mi N.

SEASON OF OPERATION: Year round; 1200 Fri-1200 Mon + some hol.

ELIGIBILITY: Open to public.

RESERVATIONS: No adv resv. Address: Outdoor Recreation, Ft Hunter Liggett, PO Box 896, Jolon, CA 93928-5000. For current information call Comm: 408-385-1205.

CAMP FACILITIES:	NO UNITS	HOOKUPS	FEE
Camper/Tent Spaces	18 Graded	Central W	$ 5.00 dly
	Overflow*	None	3.00 dly

*Open during peak periods

SPT FACILITIES:			
	Archery	Conv Store/1 mi	Gas/1 mi
	Grills	Laundry/1 mi	Restrooms
	Outdoor Eq Rntl	Tables	

ACTIVITIES:		
	Fishing/license	Hunting/license

RESTRICTIONS: Pets allowed on leash; $1 fee daily. Checkout 1200. Horses not allowed for hunting. Quiet hours 2200-0600. Open fires prohibited except in containers or site grills. Call Comm: 408-385-1205 for specific information on hunting and fishing. No discharging of firearms allowed in or around camp area. No sidearms with less than 6" barrel. All rifles must be center fire.

FIDDLERS COVE RV PARK (CA87R4)
Coronado Naval Amphibious Base, San Diego, CA 92155-5000

TELEPHONE NUMBER INFORMATION: Main installation numbers: Comm: 619-437-2011, DSN: 312-577-2011. Police for RV park, Comm: 619-437-3432.

LOCATION: Off base. *From N on I-5 in San Diego,* take Coronado Bridge exit; cross bridge and go S (L) on CA-75 (Orange Ave). *From S on I-5,* exit to Palm Ave W, which later becomes CA-75. RV Park is next to Naval Amphibious Base Marina (Navy Yacht Club) and Aquatic Sports Center. Check in 0800. USMRA: page 118 (D-8). NMI: Coronado Naval Amphibious Base, 1.5 mi N. NMC: San Diego, 6.5 mi NE.

DESCRIPTION OF AREA: Situated on E side of Silver Strand facing San Diego Bay and within 1/2 mi of the Pacific Ocean and state beach. Popular activities include tours of historic sites, shopping in Tijuana, and attractions in San Diego. Full range of support facilities available on base.

SEASON OF OPERATION: Year round.

ELIGIBILITY: Active/Retired/DOD Civilians.

RESERVATIONS: Accepted up to 90 days in advance with $25 deposit: VISA and MasterCard accepted. Address: NAB Aquatic Sports Center/RV Park, 3205 Hwy 75, Naval Amphibious Base Coronado, San Diego, CA 92155-5000. **Comm: 619-435-8788/4700.**

CAMP FACILITIES:	NO UNITS	HOOKUPS	FEE
Camper Spaces	48 Hardstand	Fresh W/E(110)	$14.00 dly

Special rates for groups of 7 or more RVs.

SPT FACILITIES:	Beach	Boat Slip Rntl	Boat Landing
	Boat Rntl	Charter Fishing	Fire Rings
	Laundry	Marina	Patio/covered
	Picnic Area	Restrooms	Sewage Dmp Sta
	Shoppette	Showers	Snack Bar
ACTIVITIES:	Bicycling	Boating	Fishing
	Jogging	Sailing	

RESTRICTIONS: Pets allowed on leash in campground; owner must keep noise down and clean up after pet. No tent camping. No open fires except in designated areas.

LAKE O'NEILL RECREATION PARK (CA65R4)
Marine Corps Base, Camp Pendleton, CA 92055-5001

TELEPHONE NUMBER INFORMATION: Main installation numbers: Comm: 619-725-4111, DSN: 312-365-4111, FTS: 725-4111. Police for recreation park, Comm: 619-725-3888/911.

CALIFORNIA
LAKE O'NEILL RECREATION PARK, continued

LOCATION: On base. Exit I-5 at Oceanside Harbor/Camp Pendleton. Enter main gate; NE on Vandegrift Blvd approx 8½ mi. L at Santa Margarita Road; R at entrance to campground. USMRA: page 111 (F-15). NMC: Oceanside, 10 mi SW.

DESCRIPTION OF AREA: 12-square-mile facility on northern side of Lake O'Neill. Southern side offers a large variety of recreational activities. Full range of support facilities available on base.

SEASON OF OPERATION: Year round.

ELIGIBILITY: Active/Retired/Active Reserve.

RESERVATIONS: Accepted, *in person or by telephone*: up to 5 wks in adv for AD at Camp Pendleton; up to 4 wks in adv for other AD; up to 3 wks in adv for Ret and Active Reserve. Payment required 1 wk in adv. *Reservations by mail not accepted.* Address: AC/S MWR, Attn: Rec Div, Lake O'Neill, Box 555020, Camp Pendleton, CA 92055-5020. **Comm: 619-725-4241, DSN: 312-365-4241, FTS: 725-4241.**

CAMP FACILITIES:	NO UNITS	HOOKUPS	FEE
Camper Spaces	40 Paved	W/E (110/220)	$12.00 dly
Camper Spaces	20 Gravel	W	10.00 dly
Camper/Tent Spaces	100 Dirt	None	6-8 dly

SPT FACILITIES:			
	Boat Rntl	Grills	LP Gas
	Mini Golf	Picnic Area	Restrooms
	Sewage Dmp Sta	Showers	Sports Fields

ACTIVITIES:			
	Fishing	Horseshoes	Softball
	Volleyball		

RESTRICTIONS: Pets allowed on leash. Swimming in lake is prohibited.

LAKE TAHOE CG RECREATION FACILITIES
(CA24R4)
2500 Lake Forest Road,
Lake Tahoe Coast Guard Station, Tahoe City, CA 96145-5000

TELEPHONE NUMBER INFORMATION: Main installation numbers: Comm: 916-583-7438 (0700-1500 M-F). Police for recreation facilities, Comm: 911.

LOCATION: On base. Take I-80 to CA-89 (N Lake Blvd); S through Tahoe City; N on CA-28 to Lake Forest Blvd; R to USCG Station Lake Tahoe (marked). Check in 1600-2000 with caretaker (Comm: 916-583-4439). USMRA: page 110 (E-6). NMI: McClellan AFB, Sacramento CA, 80 mi SW. NMC: Reno NV, 45 mi NE.

CALIFORNIA
LAKE TAHOE CG RECREATION FACILITIES, *continued*

DESCRIPTION OF AREA: Located at Coast Guard Station Lake Tahoe on NW shore of the beautiful lake which is on the California/Nevada border in the heart of the Sierra Nevada Mountains at 6,225 feet above sea level. Much to do and see in nearby cities of Reno and Carson City. Many recreational activities available on Lake Tahoe and surrounding Sierra Nevada mountains. Full range of support facilities available at McClellan AFB.

SEASON OF OPERATION: Year round.

ELIGIBILITY: Active/Retired/Reserve/CG NAF and other Federal Civilians.

RESERVATIONS: Required, *by written application only*, with payment in full, up to 10 weeks in adv. Address: A-Frame Coordinator, Coast Guard Station Lake Tahoe, 2500 Lake Forest Road, PO Box 882, Tahoe City, CA 96145-0882. Comm: 916-583-7438 (Leave name, phone, and address.)

LODGING: 2 A-Frame cottages, each with 2 apartments, heat, fully furn, PB, kit, color CTV, microwave ovens. Only 1 apartment will be rented to any applicant.

2-bdrm Apt, sleeps 9	$30-45 dly min
1-bdrm Apt, sleeps 7	15-30 dly min

Rates shown are *minimum* rates and vary according to rank of sponsor and number of persons.

SUPPORT FACILITIES: Boat launching ramp. There are no other military support facilities available but nearby businesses offer marina, boat rental and boat launch facilities.

ACTIVITIES:

Boating	Fishing	Hiking
Picnicking	Playground	Sailing
Skiing/DH&XC	Swimming	Water Skiing

RESTRICTIONS: No pets allowed. 12-day limit, to include only 1 weekend. Check out 1100. This unit is an operational Search and Rescue and Law Enforcement Unit. Check-ins are handled by duty personnel on a not-to-interfere basis. Persons residing in the cabins are not allowed to loiter in the area of the main station building.

LAKE TAHOE OAKLAND CONDOMINIUM
(CA49R4)
Oakland Army Base, CA 94626-5000

TELEPHONE NUMBER INFORMATION: Main installation numbers: Comm: 510-466-9111, DSN: 312-859-9111.

LOCATION: Off post. Located at Lake Tahoe. Specific directions may be obtained from Jacobs Hall Guest House at the address shown below. USMRA: page 110 (E-6). NMI: McClellan AFB, Sacramento CA, 110 mi SW. NMC: Carson City NV, 30 mi SE.

CALIFORNIA
LAKE TAHOE OAKLAND CONDOMINIUM, continued

DESCRIPTION OF AREA: The Oakland Army Base has leased 1 condominium on the S shore of Lake Tahoe for year-round enjoyment. It is conveniently located for taking advantage of a wide range of mountain- and water-oriented recreational activities. Casinos are located within a few miles. Full range of support facilities available at McClellan AFB.

SEASON OF OPERATION: Year round.

ELIGIBILITY: Active/Retired/Reserve/US Government Civilian Employees.

RESERVATIONS: Accepted up to 6 mo in adv with payment/deposit. VISA, MasterCard, Diners Club and DISCOVER credit cards accepted. Address: Jacobs Hall Guest Facility, Bldg 650, Oakland Army Base, CA 94626-5000. **Comm: 510-444-8107, DSN: 312-859-3113.**

LODGING: 1 3-bdrm, 2 PB, fireplace, 2 decks, 2-level unit; furn, including dishes, kitchen utensils, dishwasher, VCR, CTV, MW, coffeepot, toaster and vacuum cleaner. Private beach, indoor/outdoor swimming pool. Bring bed linens, towels and wash cloths. Unit sleeps 10 persons.

FEE: $65.00 dly, Su through Th
90.00 dly, F, Sa and any night preceding hol

SPT FACILITIES:	Basketball Court	Boat Dock	Playground/nearby
	Swimming Pool	Tennis Courts	

ACTIVITIES:	Bicycling	Hiking	Skiing
	Swimming	Tennis	

RESTRICTIONS: No pets allowed. $50 refundable key/cleaning deposit.

MIRAMAR RV PARK (CA07R4)
45249 Miramar Way, Miramar Naval Air Station, CA 92145-5000

TELEPHONE NUMBER INFORMATION: Main installation numbers: Comm: 619-537-1011, DSN: 312-577-1011. Police for RV park, Comm: 619-537-4059.

LOCATION: On base. 14 mi N of San Diego, 1 mi W of I-15. Take Miramar Way exit. Check in Bldg-11 on Kochab Rd. USMRA: Page 118 (C,D,E-2,3). NMC: San Diego, 14 mi S.

DESCRIPTION OF AREA: Beautiful area with many activities available and many special events. Sea World, zoo, museums and historical parks are all nearby. Full range of support facilities available on base.

SEASON OF OPERATION: Year round.

ELIGIBILITY: Active/Retired/DoD Civilians at NAS Miramar.

RESERVATIONS: Accepted up to 4 months in adv, in person or by mail with $12 dep; *no phone resv.* Address: MWR, 45249 Miramar Way, Camp Gear Issue, Naval Air Station Miramar, San Diego, CA 92145-5005. **Comm: 619537-4149.**

CALIFORNIA
MIRAMAR RV PARK, continued

CAMP FACILITIES:	NO UNITS	HOOKUPS	FEE
Camper Spaces	36 Hardstand	W/S/E (30&50A)	$12.00 dly
Camper Space	12 Hardstand	W/E (110)	10.00 dly
Camper Spaces	Overflow	None	5.00 dly

SPT FACILITIES:	Gas	Golf	Grills
	Jet Mart	Laundry	Picnic Area
	Playground	Propane	Racquetball
	Restrooms/hcp	RV Rntl	Sewage Dmp Sta
	Showers	Tennis Courts	

ACTIVITIES:	Boating	Fishing	Jogging
	Rec Equip Avail	Scuba Diving	Softball
	Swimming	Water Skiing	

RESTRICTIONS: One pet allowed per rental space; must be on leash at all times; spaces must be cleaned daily. 30-day limit. No firearms allowed on base.

PETALUMA LAKE AREA CAMPSITES (CA66R4)
Coast Guard Training Center, Petaluma, CA 94952-5000

TELEPHONE NUMBER INFORMATION: Main installation numbers: Comm: 707-765-7211/7215.

LOCATION: On base. Exit US-101 in Petaluma at Washington St (becomes Bodega Ave); 11 mi W to CG Training Center. Follow CG signs and turn L on Tomales Rd. Check in at gymnasium, 0830-2100. USMRA: page 110 (B-6,7). NMC: San Francisco, 50 mi S.

DESCRIPTION OF AREA: Located in beautiful Sonoma County. Campsites are near a small lake in a quiet, rustic atmosphere. Full range of support facilities on base.

SEASON OF OPERATION: Year round.

ELIGIBILITY: Active/Retired/DoT Civilians.

RESERVATIONS: Required, *by application only*, at least 30 days in adv. Address: Athletic Dept, 599 Tomales Rd., Coast Guard Training Center, Petaluma, CA 94952-5000. Comm: 707-765-7348.

CAMP FACILITIES:	NO UNITS	HOOKUPS	FEE
Camper Space/Lake Area	6 Dirt	None	$ 7.00 dly
Camper Space/Garden	2	None	7.00 dly
Tent Space/Lake Area	25 Grass	None	3.00 dly

SPT FACILITIES:	Camp Equip Rntl	Deli	Gas
	Grills	Mini Mart	Nature Trails
	Picnic Area	Playground	Racquetball
	Restrooms	Sewage Dmp Sta	Swim Pool/sumr
		(1/2 mi)	

CALIFORNIA
PETALUMA LAKE AREA CAMPSITES, continued

ACTIVITIES:

Basketball	Fishing	Horseshoes
Jogging	Rec Equip Avail	Softball

RESTRICTIONS: Pets allowed on leash; owner must clean up after pets daily. No open fires. 2-week limit. Water hookups are available on a temporary basis.

POINT MUGU RECREATION FACILITIES (CA11R4)
Point Mugu Naval Air Weapons Station
Point Mugu, CA 93042-5001

TELEPHONE NUMBER INFORMATION: Main installation numbers: Comm: 805-989-1110, DSN: 312-351-1110. Police for rec area, Comm: 805-989-7950.

LOCATION: On base. 8 mi S of Oxnard and 40 mi N of Santa Monica on Pacific Coastal Highway (PCH), CA-1. Enter Main Gate on Mugu Rd; L on Laguna Rd. Check in at Beach Motel. USMRA: page 111 (D,E-13). NMC: Los Angeles, 50 mi SE.

DESCRIPTION OF AREA: Located along Pacific Ocean N of picturesque Point Mugu State Park and within easy driving distance of world-famous tourist attractions such as Magic Mountain Amusement Park, Disneyland, and Knott's Berry Farm. Full range of support facilities available on base.

SEASON OF OPERATION: Year round.

ELIGIBILITY: Active/Retired/DoD Civilians.

RESERVATIONS: *Accepted for cabins and motel only*, with payment in full, up to 30 days in adv (Point Mugu AD: up to 90 days). Address: MWR Dept (Code P703), Naval Air Weapons Station, 521 9th St, Point Mugu, CA 93042-5001. **Comm: 805-989-8407, DSN: 312-351-8407.**

CAMP FACILITIES:	NO UNITS	HOOKUPS	FEE
Cabins, slp up to 5	5		$30-40 dly*
Cabin, single	1		25-35 dly*
Motel Rooms, suites	2		50-60 dly**
Motel Rooms, kit	12		33-40 dly**
Motel Rooms, Refr, MW	10		33-40 dly**
Camper Spaces	51 Paved	W/S/E (110)	15-17 dly***
Camper Spaces	5 Paved	E (110)	10-12 dly***
Camper Spaces	6	None	8-10 dly***
Tent Spaces	10 On Beach		6-8 dly

*2 rms, kit, grill, CTV, fenced-in porch.
**CTV, fully furn kit; equipped for handicapped.
***CTV, phone hookups available; monthly rates available.

SPT FACILITIES:

Beach	Camp Equip Rntl	Chapel
Gas	Golf	Laundry
Picnic Area	Restrooms/hcp	Sewage Dmp Sta
Showers/hcp	Skeet Range	Sports Fields
Tennis Courts	VCR Rntl	

CALIFORNIA
POINT MUGU RECREATION FACILITIES, continued

ACTIVITIES:	Bicycling	Fishing/license	Hunting/license
	Jogging	Swimming	

RESTRICTIONS: Pets on leash allowed in camping and cabin areas; additional fee charged in cabins. No pets allowed in motel. 7-day limit for cabins and motel; 1 month for campsites. Fires allowed in fire rings only; all others must be approved by NAWS fire department. No firearms allowed unless approved by NAWS Security Dept.

SAN ONOFRE RECREATION BEACH (CA31R4)
Marine Corps Base, Camp Pendleton, CA 92055-5001

TELEPHONE NUMBER INFORMATION: Main installation numbers: Comm: 619-725-4111, DSN: 312-365-4111, FTS: 725-4111. Police, Comm: 911.

LOCATION: On base. Exit I-5 on Basilone Rd 3 mi S of San Clemente. E to San Onofre Military Gate; 1.6 mi from gate turn R; road will take you to beach. USMRA: page 111 (F-15). NMI: Camp Pendleton, 17 mi SE. NMC: Oceanside, 15 mi SE.

DESCRIPTION OF AREA: Located on the oceanfront along one of California's most beautiful beaches. Large variety of recreational activities. Full range of support facilities on base.

SEASON OF OPERATION: Year round.

ELIGIBILITY: Active/Retired/Active Reserve/DoD Civilians.

RESERVATIONS: Accepted up to 5 wks in adv for AD at Camp Pendleton; up to 4 wks in adv for AD stationed elsewhere; up to 3 wks for Ret and Active Reserve; and 2 wks for DoD and MWR employees. Payment req 1 wk in adv. *Reservations by mail not accepted.* Address: Recreation Services, Marine Corps Base, Camp Pendleton, CA 92055-5018, ATTN: San Onofre Beach. **Comm: 619-725-7935, DSN: 312-365-7935, FTS: 725-7935.**

CAMP FACILITIES:	NO UNITS	HOOKUPS	FEE
Mobile Homes/Cottages*	36		$30.00 dly*
Camper Spaces	80 Hardstand	W/E (110)	12.00 dly
Camper/Tent Spaces	42 Sand	W	10.00 dly
Camper Spaces	26 Paved/Sand	None	8.00 dly

*1-3 bdrm, furn exc linens and towels; TV, radio, toaster, cooking utensils, coffeepot provided.

SPT FACILITIES:	Beach	Beach Club	Bicycle Route*
	Conv Store	Gas	Golf
	Laundry	Mini Exchange	Picnic Area
	Playground	Restrooms	Sewage Dmp Sta
	Showers/hcp	Snack Bar	Sports Fields

CALIFORNIA
SAN ONOFRE RECREATION BEACH, continued

*Along coastline. Groups of 10 or more must get written permission to use route. Write JPAO, MCB, Camp Pendleton, CA 92055-5018 at least 45 days in adv.

ACTIVITIES: Fishing   Surfing   Swimming

A wide variety of camping, fishing, boating and water skiing equipment is available for rent to active duty and retired military.

RESTRICTIONS: Pets on leash allowed on facility but not on beach. Swimming allowed only when lifeguards are on duty. No firearms allowed.

SHARPE TRAVEL CAMP (CA63R4)
Stockton Defense Distribution Region West (Sharpe Site)
Stockton, CA 95296-0002

TELEPHONE NUMBER INFORMATION: Main installation numbers: Comm: 209-982-2000, DSN: 312-462-2000.

LOCATION: On post: *located in Lathrop*. From I-5 S of Stockton, E on Roth Rd. OR from CA-99, W on French Camp Rd, S on Airport Way, W on Roth Rd. USMRA: Page 110 (C,D-7). NMC: Stockton, 7 mi N.

DESCRIPTION OF AREA: Located in the Delta Country (known for its 1000 mi of waterways). Oakwood Lake Resort within minutes. Easy drive to San Francisco, Lake Tahoe, Yosemite National Park, Great American Park and Sacramento. Limited support facilities available on site.

SEASON OF OPERATION: Year round.

ELIGIBILITY: Active/Retired.

RESERVATIONS: No adv resv. Address: Community Recreation Office, Bldg S-10, DDRW, PO Box 960001, Stockton, CA 95296-0280. Comm: 209-982-2232, DSN: 312-462-2232. Discount available to holders of Golden Age, Golden Access and Golden Eagle Passports.

CAMP FACILITIES:	NO UNITS	HOOKUPS	FEE
Camper Spaces	12 Gravel	W/S/E (110)	$ 10.00 dly

SPT FACILITIES:	Consol Club	Fitness Center	Grills
	Laundry	Picnic Area	Playground
	PX	Racquetball	Restrooms/hcp
	Showers/hcp	Sports Fields	Swim Pool/sumr
	Tennis Courts		

ACTIVITIES: Recreation Equipment Available

RESTRICTIONS: Pets allowed on leash. No open fires. Firearms must be checked in to Security.

CALIFORNIA

SOUTH LAKE TAHOE RECREATION HOUSING (CA17R4)
Presidio of Monterey, CA 93944-5000

TELEPHONE NUMBER INFORMATION: Main installation numbers: Comm: 408-242-2211, DSN: 312-929-1110.

LOCATION: Off post. Located at Lake Tahoe; specific directions will be furnished when resv is made. *Obtain keys in Lake Tahoe by making arrangements with Equipment Center, Bldg 228, Presidio of Monterey: From US-101 100 mi S of San Francisco, take CA-156 W 10 mi follow signs to Presidio of Monterey.* USMRA: page 110 (E-6). NMI: McClellan AFB, Sacramento CA, 110 mi SW. NMC: Carson City NV, 30 mi SE.

DESCRIPTION OF AREA: Leased lodging facilities on the S shore of Lake Tahoe for year-round enjoyment. Located in Heavenly Resort Valley. Conveniently located for taking advantage of a wide range of mountain- and water-oriented recreational activities. Casinos located within a few miles. Full range of support facilities available at McClellan AFB.

SEASON OF OPERATION: Year round.

ELIGIBILITY: Active/Retired/Reserve/US Government Civilian Employees.

RESERVATIONS: Required, with $50 non-refundable dep, up to 6 mo in advance. Full payment req 30 days before departure. Resv for hol accepted only for a complete hol period—exact days/dates set by Outdoor Rec based on an annual calendar. Payment in full req for "holiday" resv. Checks, VISA, MasterCard accepted. Address: Outdoor Recreation Equipment Center, Bldg 228, Lewis Hall, Presidio of Monterey, CA 93944-5000. **Comm: 408-242-5506/6132, DSN: 312-878-5506/6132, 1030-1400 and 1500-1800, Mon-Fri.**

LODGING: Min stay 2 nights. Rates vary depending on day of week, length of stay, and hol. Wkly rates apply for 7 consecutive days. All kit completely furn. Patrons must provide sheets, towels, all toilet items, paper towels, bathroom tissue and firewood. Ski vacation packages available.

1 A-Frame Chalet, slp 10: modern unit located in middle of city off Pioneer Trail in a rural subdivision. 3 bdrm, 2 PB, wood-burning stove, kit, entertainment system, color CTV, MW, DW, W/D.   **FEE:** $75-100 dly/$500 wkly

1 Gardner Cabin, slp 8: rustic cabin, located at edge of town off CA-89 in rural subdivision. 3 bdrm, PB, color CTV, kit, W/D, MW, fireplace, dining area.   **FEE:** $70-95 dly/475 wkly.

2 Ski Run Condominiums, slp 2-6: located next to Heavenly Valley Ski Resort. modern units, 2 BR, living area with fireplace, full kitchen, 2 PB, color CTV, MW, DW, W/D.   **FEE:** $65-80 dly//$400 wkly.

Motel Lodgings (subcontracted units in local motels): 2 dbl beds, CTV, PB, 2 blocks from casinos.   **FEE:** $45-70 dly (double occupancy)

CALIFORNIA
SOUTH LAKE TAHOE RECREATION HOUSING, continued

RESTRICTIONS: No pets allowed. No parties may be held on the premises. No car washing. Check in 1400. Check out 1100; $10 check-out fee. $50 refundable key/cleaning deposit.

TRAVIS FAM-CAMP (CA68R4)
Travis Air Force Base, CA 94535-5000

TELEPHONE NUMBER INFORMATION: Main installation numbers: Comm: 707-424-1110/5000, DSN: 312-837-1110.

LOCATION: On base. From I-80 at Fairfield take Travis Airbase Parkway exit E to main gate. Camp is adjacent to main gate. Check in at fam-camp office 0830-1030 or 1530-1700 (1630-1800 DST) M-Sa. (On Su and hol follow instructions for entering camp posted on office window.) USMRA: page 110 (C-7). NMC: San Francisco, 45 mi SW.

DESCRIPTION OF AREA: Located in state's famed valley region near Sacramento. Major water sports centers of San Pablo Bay and Lake Berryessa are nearby. Full range of support facilities available on base.

SEASON OF OPERATION: Year round.

ELIGIBILITY: Active/Retired/DoD Civilians.

RESERVATIONS: No adv resv; no one turned away. Address: 60 MWRS/MWRO, Attention Fam-Camp Manager, 561 Travis Ave, Travis AFB, CA 94535-5000. Comm: 707-424-3583, DSN: 312-837-3583.

CAMP FACILITIES:	NO UNITS	HOOKUPS	FEE
Camper Spaces	22 Gravel	W/S/CTV/E (110)	$ 9.00 dly
	24 Gravel	W/CTV/E (110)	7.00 dly
Camper/Tent Spaces	8 Dirt	None	3.00 dly
SPT FACILITIES:	Grills	Laundry/nearby	Picnic Area
	Restrooms	Sewage Dmp Sta	Showers
ACTIVITIES:	Fishing/license	Rec Equip Avail	Sightseeing

RESTRICTIONS: Pets allowed on leash; must not annoy others; owner must clean up after pet immediately. No campfires. No firearms allowed. Check out 1000. Quiet hours 2300-0800.

VANDENBERG FAM-CAMP (CA67R4)
Vandenberg Air Force Base, CA 93437-5000

TELEPHONE NUMBER INFORMATION: Main installation numbers: Comm: 805-734-8232, DSN: 312-276-1110. Police for fam-camp, Comm: 805-734-8232-EX-6-3911.

LOCATION: On base. Located between Lompoc and Santa Maria. From US-101, W on CA-1 to AFB. Check in at fam-camp office, Bldg 5002, during duty hours. USMRA: page 111 (C-12). NMC: Lompoc, 6 mi S.

DESCRIPTION OF AREA: Space and missile center. Installation covers over 98,000 acres. Fam-camp is situated about 3 mi from main base and provides unlimited sightseeing and recreational opportunities in nearby areas. Full range of support facilities available on base.

SEASON OF OPERATION: Year round.

ELIGIBILITY: Active/Retired/DoD Civilians.

RESERVATIONS: No adv resv. Address: Fam-Camp, 4392 ASW/MWRO, PO Box 5938, Vandenberg AFB, CA 93437-5000. Comm: 805-734-8232-EX-6-8579, DSN: 312-276-8579, FAX Comm: 805-276-0410.

CAMP FACILITIES:	NO UNITS	HOOKUPS	FEE
Camper Spaces	20 Hardstand	W/S/E (110/30A)	$10.00 dly
Camper Spaces	30 Hardstand	W/E (110/30A)	8.00 dly
Camper Spaces	19 Gravel	None	4.00 dly
Tent Spaces, fenced	15 Grass	None	4.00 dly

SPT FACILITIES:			
	Camp Equip Rntl	Game Room	Gas
	Golf	Grills	Laundry
	Lounge/hcp	Picnic Area	Playground
	Racquetball	Restrooms/hcp	RV Parts Store
	Sewage Dmp Sta	Showers/hcp	Skeet Range
	Snack Bar	Sports Fields	Tennis Courts
	Trails	Vending Machines	

ACTIVITIES:			
	Hunting/license	Rec Equip Avail	Surf Fishing

RESTRICTIONS: Pets allowed; must comply with local license and leash laws. No swimming. To check in after duty hours, use the fee collection box located in front of fam-camp office and see office personnel the following day. Firearms permitted during hunting season.

COLORADO

DILLON RECREATION AREA (CO08R3)
Fitzsimons Army Medical Center, Aurora, CO 80045-0501

TELEPHONE NUMBER INFORMATION: Main installation numbers: Comm: 303-361-8241, DSN: 312-943-1101.

LOCATION: Off post. From I-70 at Dillon take US-6 S to Swan Mountain Rd (County Rd 1); W to Dillon Recreation Area. USMRA: page 109 (E-3). NMI: Fitzsimons Army Medical Center, 80 mi E. NMC: Denver, 80 mi E.

COLORADO
DILLON RECREATION AREA, continued

DESCRIPTION OF AREA: Located on Dillon Reservoir on 69 acres of wooded campground. Boating and fishing available within 1 mi of area. Full range of support facilities available at Fitzsimons Army Medical Center.

SEASON OF OPERATION: Memorial Day Weekend-Labor Day Weekend.

ELIGIBILITY: Active/Retired/Civilians.

RESERVATIONS: Resv recommended. Address: Outdoor Recreation, Attn: Recreation Area, Bldg T-23, Fitzsimons Army Medical Center, Aurora, CO 80045-5001. **Comm: 303-361-8956, DSN: 312-943-8956, FAX Comm: 303-340-1145.**

CAMP FACILITIES:	NO UNITS	HOOKUPS	FEE
Camper/Tent Spaces*	30 Gravel	E (110)	$10-14 dly
Camper/Tent Spaces	3 Gravel	None	7-8 dly

*14 have water available.

SPT FACILITIES:	Conv Store/small	Fire Rings	Grills
	Outhouses	Picnic Area	Well Water

ACTIVITIES:	Canoeing	Fishing/license	Volleyball

RESTRICTIONS: Pets allowed on leash. Quiet hours 2200. No firearms allowed.

FARISH RECREATION AREA (CO01R3)
United States Air Force Academy, Colorado Springs, CO 80840-5000

TELEPHONE NUMBER INFORMATION: Main installation numbers: Comm: 719-472-1818, DSN: 312-259-3110.

LOCATION: Off base. From I-25 at Colorado Springs, take US-24 W to Woodland Park; N (near McDonalds) on Rampart Range Rd approx 6 mi. Follow the Farish signs. (Call manager at 719-687-9098 for additional information.) USMRA: page 109 (F-4). NMI: US Air Force Academy, 40 mi E; Peterson AFB and Fort Carson, 40 mi SE. NMC: Colorado Springs, 30 mi SE.

DESCRIPTION OF AREA: Located on 655 acres of magnificent woodland at an altitude of 9,150 feet in the Rocky Mountains. Surrounded by Pike National Forest 15 mi N of Pikes Peak. Abundant wildlife and 3 fishing lakes. Enjoy a mountain getaway with a real backwoods feeling within driving distance of area attractions. Wide range of support facilities available at the US Air Force Academy, Peterson AFB and Fort Carson.

SEASON OF OPERATION: Year round for lodge and cottage and for day use; limited campsites available during the winter. Call for conditions during winter months.

ELIGIBILITY: Active/Retired/Reserve/DoD Civilians and Retired/NAF Civilians.

RESERVATIONS: Adv resv req. Accepted up to 90 days in adv; Academy AD and their family members and guests have first priority.

Address: Outdoor Recreation Center, PO Box 217, USAF Academy, CO 80840-0217. **Comm: 719-472-4356, DSN: 312-259-4356.** (*Recreation Area*: Comm: 719-687-9098, M-F 0800-1630).

CAMP FACILITIES:	NO UNITS	HOOKUPS*	FEE
Cottage, 2 bdrm slps 8*	1		$ 65.00 dly
Sleeping Lodge*	4 Rooms		36-65 dly
Entire Lodge, slps 17			157.00 dly
Camper Cabins**	4		20.00 dly
Yurt**	1		20.00 dly
Scamp Travel Trailers	3 In Place	E (110/220)	20.00 dly
Camper Spaces	15 Gravel	E (110/220/30A)	9.00 dly
Camper Space w/pavilion	1 Gravel	E (110/220/30A)	15.00 dly
Camper/Tent Spaces	15 Gravel	None	7.50 dly
Tent Spaces	Primitive	None	7.50 dly

*Basic linens, towels and cooking utensils provided. Lodge has PB in Room 1, SB with others; kit fac avail. No maid service.
**Guests should provide own bedding.

SPT FACILITIES: Chapel/outdoor Grills Grocery/small
Mountn Bike Rntl Pavilions/fee Picnic Area
Playground Port-a-Potties Rec Equip Avail
Stables* Trails

*Call for information on boarding horses.

ACTIVITIES: Hiking Horseback Riding Horseshoes
Ice Fishing Ice Skating Sledding
Snow Skiing/XC Tubing Volleyball
Outdoor Adventure Program

RESTRICTIONS: No pets allowed in lodge or cottage; allowed on leash in camping area; owner must clean up after pet. No sewage dump station. Fishing is restricted to Government military and civilian employees, retirees, guests, and family members; special USAF Academy permits are available for overnight guests. Check in 1400, check out 1200 for lodge and cottage; check in and out 1200 for camping area. Questions may be addressed to Farish Management, Comm: 719-687-9098. Due to rough roads and high altitude, patrons with campers over 26 ' are advised not to try to reach the facility. All visitors are advised to call for road and weather conditions before making the trip especially in winter, fall and spring. Gate fee. No firearms allowed.

PEREGRINE PINES FAM-CAMP (CO04R3)
United States Air Force Academy, Colorado Springs, CO 80840-5000

TELEPHONE NUMBER INFORMATION: Main installation numbers: Comm: 719-472-1818, DSN: 312-258-3110.

COLORADO
PEREGRINE PINES FAM-CAMP, *continued*

LOCATION: On base. From I-25 N of Colorado Springs, take Air Force Academy exit. Fam-camp is on Stadium Blvd approx 1 block N of Falcon Football Stadium. Follow fam-camp signs to entrance. Check in with fam-camp host or at Outdoor Recreation Center in Community Center, Bldg 4560. USMRA: page 115 (A,B-1,2). NMC: Colorado Springs, 5 mi S.

DESCRIPTION OF AREA: The fam-camp is at an elevation of 7,000 feet, nestled in a peaceful, wooded area where wildlife roams free. Enjoy the feeling of seclusion, the varied attractions in the Colorado Springs area, and many activities available through the Outdoor Recreation Center. The Academy has a visitors center (with cafeteria) on Academy Drive. Full range of support facilities available on base.

SEASON OF OPERATION: Year round, weather permitting.

ELIGIBILITY: Active/Retired/Reserve/Families of Cadets/DoD Civilians and Retired/NAF Civilians.

RESERVATIONS: Recommended. Accepted up to 90 days in adv; Academy AD and their family members and guests have first priority. Address: Outdoor Recreation Center, PO Box 217, USAF Academy, CO 80840-0217. **Comm: 719-472-4356/4980, DSN: 312-259-4356, FAX Comm: 719-472-4356.**

CAMP FACILITIES:	NO UNITS	HOOKUPS	FEE
Camper Spaces*	38 Gravel	W/S/E (110/220)	$12.00 dly
Camper Spaces	13	None	5.00 dly
Tent Spaces	1	W/E (110)	12.00 dly
Tent Spaces	13 Gravel	None	5.00 dly
Yurt	1	E	15.00 dly

*Range 15 ' to 71 ', some pull-through.

SPT FACILITIES:			
	Camp Equip Rntl	Chapel/base	Falcon Trail
	Golf/base	Grills	Pavilions/fee
	Picnic Area	Playground	Port-a-Potties
	Rec Equip Rntl	Restrooms/nearby	Sewage Dmp Sta
	Snack Bar	Trails	

ACTIVITIES:			
	Fishing/license	Horseback Riding	Hunting/license
	Jogging	(Apr-Oct)	Swimming
	Snow Skiing		

Hunting and fishing on the Academy are very restricted, and limited to AD military on base and DoD and NAF full-time employees working on the Academy. There are many areas within an hour or so; state license required (available through Outdoor Recreation Center).

RESTRICTIONS: Pets allowed on leash; owner must clean up after pet. Check in 1200, check out 1200; 14-day limit. No open fires permitted. No picnicking in fam-camp area at any time. No laundry facilities on base. *Do not feed the wild animals. Trees, flowers, plants and nature's debris must remain undisturbed.* Quiet hours after 2200.

FLORIDA

BLUE ANGEL NAVY RECREATION PARK (FL36R1)
Corry Naval Station, Pensacola, FL 32511-5000

TELEPHONE NUMBER INFORMATION: Main installation numbers: Comm: 904-452-2000, DSN: 312-922-0111. Police for recreation park, Comm: 904-452-6508/6490.

LOCATION: Off base. From I-10 W of Pensacola, take Exit 2 (FL-297/Pine Forest Rd) S approximately 1 1/2 mi to Blue Angel Parkway ; S 8 mi, then W on US-98 for 3 mi. Watch for sign to Blue Angel Navy Recreation Park on L. Check in 1400. USMRA: page 39 (A-13). NMI: Corry Station, 8 mi NE. NMC: Pensacola, 8 mi E.

DESCRIPTION OF AREA: Situated on Perdido Bay amid oak trees and Spanish moss, the park offers spectacular camping, boating, swimming and picnic areas. As there are no currents or drop-offs in this part of the bay, its sandy bottom creates an ideal swimming area for children. 50 acres of the complex have been reserved for Boy Scout and other youth activities. Organized activities and annual events. Full range of support facilities at Corry Station.

SEASON OF OPERATION: Year round.

ELIGIBILITY: Active/Retired/DoD Civilians, and Guests.

RESERVATIONS: Recommended for rental campers. Address: Blue Angel Navy Recreation Park, 2100 Bronson Field Rd, Pensacola, FL 32506-5000. **Comm: 904-453-9435, FAX: 904-453-1147.**

CAMP FACILITIES:	NO UNITS	HOOKUPS	FEE
Campers	17 In Place	W/E (110/30A)	$15.00 dly
Camper/RV Spaces	138 Dirt/Gravel	W/E (110/30A)	7.00 dly
Tent Spaces, Primitive	Unlimited	None	3.00 dly

SPT FACILITIES:			
	BBQ Pits	Boat Launch	Boat Rntl
	Camp Equip Rntl	Catfish Pond	Country Store
	Dry Storage	Fishing Pier/hcp	Ice
	Jogging Trail	Laundry	LP Gas
	Paddle Boats	Pavilions/hcp	Pay Telephones
	Petting Zoo	Picnic Area	Restrooms/hcp
	Sewage Dmp Sta	Showers/hcp	Vending Mach
	Walking Trails		

"Mullet Train" trailer hayride on Saturday nights.

FLORIDA
BLUE ANGEL NAVY RECREATION PARK, continued

ACTIVITIES:	Boating	Deep-Sea Diving	Deep-Sea Fishing
	Fishing/license	Rec Equip Avail	Swimming
	Volleyball	Water Skiing	Windsurfing

RESTRICTIONS: Pets allowed on leash in park, no pets allowed in rental campers. Nominal admission charge for park. Absolutely NO firearms, bows and arrows, BB guns, or other items which could be considered to be weapons, and NO fireworks . Check out 0800-1100.

CAMP BLANDING RV PARK AND CAMPSITES
(FL45R1)
Camp Blanding Training Site, Starke, FL 32091-9703

TELEPHONE NUMBER INFORMATION: Main installation numbers: Comm: 904-533-3100, DSN: 312-904-3100. Police for campsites: Comm: 904-533-3462.

LOCATION: On post. From US-301 at Starke, take FL-16 E to FL-21. *OR* from US-17 at Green Cove Springs, take FL-16 W to FL-21. *OR* from I-95 at St Augustine, take exit 95 to FL-16 W to FL-21. S on FL-21 5 mi to post. Check in at MWR, Bldg 2540, 0800-1630. USMRA: page 38 (F-4). NMC: Jacksonville, 35 mi N.

DESCRIPTION OF AREA: Located on Kingsley Lake in Starke, Camp Blanding is 70,380-acre wildlife management area leased to the army as a training center in 1939. Additional 140,000 surrounding acres acquired for training purposes during World War II. There are 2 camping areas adjacent to each other. Basic campground (for trailers and tents) is wooded site on shores of Kingsley Lake, located on Avenue A South of NCO Lodge. Improvements have been made to campsite areas within last 2 years. Limited support facilities on post; full range available at Cecil Field NAS, 30 mi NE.

SEASON OF OPERATION: Year round.

ELIGIBILITY: Active/Retired/NG. Florida National Guard has preference.

RESERVATIONS: Required for RVs, with $12 deposit. Address: MWR—Morale, Welfare & Recreation Campsites, Camp Blanding Training Site, Route 1, Box 465, Starke, FL 32091-9703. **Comm: 904-533-3104, DSN: 312-533-3104.**

CAMP FACILITIES:	NO UNITS	HOOKUPS	FEE*
Lakeside Billeting			
Mobile Homes 2 bdrm	20		$30.00 dly
Quonset Huts	10		25.00 dly
RV Campground			
RV Spaces	15 Hardstand	W/S/CTV/E (110/220)	12.00 dly
Basic Campground			
Camper/Tent Spaces	50 Primitive	W	4.00 dly

*Fee does not include tax.

SPT FACILITIES:	Beach	Boat Ramps/	Grills
	Pavilions/fee	nearby	Picnic Area
	Playground	Rec Equip Rntl	Restrooms/hcp
	Sewage Dmp Sta	Showers/hcp	Sports Fields

ACTIVITIES: Boating   Hunting   Jogging
              Swimming

RESTRICTIONS: No pets allowed. 21-day limit. Check out 1200. Boaters should stay clear of swimming areas, fishermen and private residences. During summer months a limited number of spaces are available to users other than members of the Florida National Guard. Firearms must be registered with Range Control and at main gate.

COON'S CREEK RECREATION AREA (FL23R1)
MacDill Air Force Base, FL 33608-5000

TELEPHONE NUMBER INFORMATION: Main installation numbers: Comm: 813-828-1110, DSN: 312-968-1110. Police for recreation area, Comm: 813-828-3322.

LOCATION: On base. I-275 to exit 23B, Dale Mabry Highway (US-92). S approx 5 mi to main gate. Check in at marina adjacent to fam-camp after 1200. USMRA: page 38 (F-8) and page 53 (E,F-3,4). NMC: Tampa, 5 mi N.

DESCRIPTION OF AREA: Located on S end of installation in coastal peninsula area approx 2 mi from main base area. Recreation area consists of fam-camp, marina, beach, snack bar and pavilions. Fresh water lakes nearby, nature trail and an abundance of natural flora and fauna. Full range of support facilities on base.

SEASON OF OPERATION: Year round.

ELIGIBILITY: Active/Retired/DoD Civilians.

RESERVATIONS: Recommended, up to 90 days in advance; AD military have priority. $100 deposit (includes $10 processing fee) req to confirm resv of 10 or more days; $10 service fee for resv of less than 10 days. No resv accepted for full hookup sites 1-18 or partial sites 248-256. Visa & MasterCard are accepted. Address: Coon's Creek Recreation Area, PO Box 6825, MacDill AFB, FL 33608-5000. Include self-addressed envelope. **Comm: 813-828-4982/3864, DSN: 312-968-4982/3864.**

CAMP FACILITIES:	NO UNITS	HOOKUPS	FEE
Camper Spaces *	199 Paved/Dirt	W/S/E(110/30&50A)	$12.00 dly
Camper Spaces	57	W/E(110/30&50A)	9.00 dly
Tent Spaces	34 Dirt	None	2.50 dly

* 3 reserved for wheelchair guests

SPT FACILITIES:			
	Activity Room	Bait	Beach
	Boat Launch	Boat Rntl	Boat Slips
	Equipment Rntl	Golf	Grills
	Ice	Laundry	LP Gas
	Marina	Nature Trail	Pavilions
	Picnic Area	Playground	Restrooms
	Sewage Dmp Sta	Showers	Snack Bar
	Sports Fields	Swimming Pools	TV/Game Room

ACTIVITIES:			
	Fishing/license	Jogging	Sailing
	Swimming	Windsurfing	

FLORIDA
COON'S CREEK RECREATION AREA, continued

RESTRICTIONS: Pets allowed on short leash or in RV; owner must clean up after pet even in dog walk area. Pets without complete and current immunizations are not allowed on MacDill AFB and recreation area. Check out 1100. No open campfires. Firearms must be registered at Fam-Camp office.

DESTIN ARMY INFANTRY CENTER
RECREATION AREA (FL01R1)
Fort Benning, GA 31905-5065

TELEPHONE NUMBER INFORMATION: Main installation numbers: Comm: 706-544/545-2011, DSN: 312-784/835-2011. Police (Okaloosa County Sheriff) for recreation area, Comm: 904-651-7400/911.

LOCATION: Off post. In Destin FL. US-231 S to I-10, W to US-331, S to US-98, W to Benning Dr; R to area. *OR* I-10 to FL-85; S to Fort Walton Beach; US-98 E to Destin; L at Benning Dr to area. Check in at office 1600-2000. USMRA: page 39 (C-13). NMI: Eglin AFB FL, 17 mi N. NMC: Pensacola FL, 45 mi W.

DESCRIPTION OF AREA: Located on 15-acre site on Choctawhatchee Bay in Destin FL. Enjoy sparkling sugar-white quartz sands of Emerald Coast. Gulf of Mexico fishing and swimming areas approx 5 mi from recreation area. Area also offers golf at 6 public courses, 2 greyhound race tracks within 45 miles, Destin Fishing Museum, Gulfariam, Zoo, and Indian Temple Mound Museum. Full range of support facilities available at Eglin AFB.

SEASON OF OPERATION: Year round.

ELIGIBILITY: Active/Retired/DoD Civilians.

RESERVATIONS: Req for cabins, motel and charter boat; accepted for camper spaces; up to 6 mo in adv for AD at Ft Benning, 4 mo for others. Address: Destin Recreation Area, 557 Calhoun Ave, Destin, FL 32541. Comm: 904-837-2725; *Reservations, Comm: 800-642-0466. Information only, Comm: 904-837-6423, FAX Comm: 904-837-5706.*

CAMP FACILITIES:	NO UNITS	HOOKUPS	FEE
Duplex, 3 bdrm**	4		$42-57 dly*
Duplex, 2 bdrm**	18		36-49 dly
Motel***	34 Units		30-39 dly
Camper Spaces	43	W/S/E (110/30A)	8-12 dly****
Camper/Tent Spaces	23 Primitive	E/Central W	6.00 dly

*Includes immediate family only. Additional fee for guests. Off-season rates available 15 Oct-16 Mar.
**PB, kit, MW, CTV, linens, pots and pans. 5 rms equipped for handicapped.
***Refr, coffeepot.
**** $2 dly for electric air conditioner/heater.

FLORIDA
DESTIN ARMY INFANTRY CENTER REC AREA, continued

SPT FACILITIES:	Beach	Boat Launch	Boat Rntl
	Boat Slip Rntl	Deep-Sea Charter	Fishing Pier
	Game Room	Boat (48 ')	Grills
	Laundry	Marina	Party Boat
	Picnic Area	Playground	Restrooms
	Sewage Dmp Sta	Showers	TVRoom
	Swimming Pool	Vending Mach	
	Water Sports Equipment Rental		

ACTIVITIES:	Boating	Deep-Sea Fishing	Fishing/license
	Rec Equip Avail	Swimming	

RESTRICTIONS: No pets allowed. Check out 1100. No firearms allowed.

EGLIN FAM-CAMP (FL25R1)
Eglin Air Force Base, FL 32542-5000

TELEPHONE NUMBER INFORMATION: Main installation numbers: Comm: 904-882-6668, DSN: 312-872-1110. Police for fam-camp, Comm: 904-882-2502.

LOCATION: On base. From I-10 at Crestview take FL-85 S to Niceville and John Simms Blvd to East Gate. USMRA: page 39 (C,D-13). NMC: Pensacola, 40 mi W.

DESCRIPTION OF AREA: Located on a peninsula on the northern coast of the Gulf of Mexico in Ft Walton area off Choctawhatchee Bay. The fam-camp is part of the Post Recreation Area and is situated adjacent to the beach. Beautiful forested areas and fresh-water lakes also nearby. Full range of support facilities available at Eglin AFB.

SEASON OF OPERATION: Year round.

ELIGIBILITY: Active/Retired/DoD Civilians.

RESERVATIONS: No adv resv. Address: Recreation Services, 646 MWRSS/ MWRO, Eglin AFB, FL 32542-5000. Comm: 904-882-5058.

CAMP FACILITIES:	NO UNITS	HOOKUPS	FEE
Camper Spaces	22 Gravel	W/E (110/30A)	$10.00 dly/275 mo
Tent Spaces	10 Gravel	None	5.00 dly

SPT FACILITIES:	Beach	Boat Launch	Boat Rntl
	Chapel	Deep-Sea Charter	Gas
	Golf	Fishing Boat	Grills
	Laundry	Marina	Picnic Area
	Restrooms/hcp	Sewage Dmp Sta	Shoppette
	Showers/hcp	Sports Fields	Trails
	Outdoor Adventure Program		

ACTIVITIES:	Fishing/license	Hunting	Jogging
	Rec Equip Avail		

FLORIDA
EGLIN FAM-CAMP, continued

RESTRICTIONS: Pets allowed. 90-day limit. Postal boxes available for forwarding of personal mail.

JACKSONVILLE RV PARK (FL40R1)
Jacksonville Naval Air Station, FL 32212-5000

TELEPHONE NUMBER INFORMATION: Main installation numbers: Comm: 904-772-2345/2346, DSN: 312-942-2345. Police for RV park, Comm: 904-772-4539. DSN: 312-942-4529.

LOCATION: On base. Access from US-17 (Roosevelt Blvd) S of Jacksonville, near intersection with I-295. Check in at Auto Hobby Shop, Bldg 622, on Birmingham Ave, 0800 M-F, 0900 Sa-Su. USMRA: page 50 (B-6,7). NMC: Jacksonville, 9 mi N.

DESCRIPTION OF AREA: The RV park is located on Manatee Point on the St Johns River. There are many opportunities for water-related activities. Full range of support facilities available on base, many within walking distance.

SEASON OF OPERATION: Year round.

ELIGIBILITY: Active/Retired/Reserve/DoD Civilians at Jacksonville NAS.

RESERVATIONS: Accepted. Address: MWR, 622 Birmingham Ave, Box 14, Attn: RV Park, Naval Air Station, Jacksonville, FL 32212-5000. **Comm: 904-772-3227, DSN: 312-942-3227. FAX Comm: 904-772-3424.** Discounts available to holders of Golden Age and Golden Access Passports.

CAMP FACILITIES:	NO UNITS	HOOKUPS	FEE
Camper Spaces	8	W/S/E(110/220/30A)	$13.00 dly
Camper Spaces	4	W/E(110/220/30A)	10.00 dly
Camper/Tent Spaces	14	None	5.00 dly

SPT FACILITIES:			
	Clubs/nearby	Conv Store/nearby	Golf/base
	Grills	Marina/nearby	Picnic Area
	Restrooms	Sewage Dmp Sta	Showers

ACTIVITIES:		
	Boating	Fishing/license

RESTRICTIONS: Pets allowed on leash. Sa, Su & hol check in 0900-1700. After hours, go directly to RV park (located at Birmingham and Mustan); check in the following morning. Ask for handbook on MWR Department. 2-week limit. No firearms allowed.

LAKE FRETWELL RECREATION AREA (FL24R1)
Cecil Field Naval Air Station, FL 32215-5000
(Cecil Field NAS is mandated to close
under the 1993 Base Closure Law.)

TELEPHONE NUMBER INFORMATION: Main installation numbers: Comm: 904-778-5626, DSN: 312-860-5626. Police for rec area, Comm: 904-778-5626.

LOCATION: On base. Take Normandy Blvd (FL-228) exit off I-295; W to main gate. Recreation area approx 2 mi from gate. USMRA: page 38 (G-3). NMC: Jacksonville, 13 mi NE.

DESCRIPTION OF AREA: Located at Lake Fretwell. Full range of support facilities available on base.

SEASON OF OPERATION: Year round.

ELIGIBILITY: Active/Retired.

RESERVATIONS: Accepted up to 30 days in adv. Address: MWR Dept, Box 109, Bldg 200, C Avenue, NAS Cecil Field, FL 32215-0109. **Comm: 904-778-6112, DSN: 312-860-6112; FAX, Comm: 904-778-6636, DSN: 312-860-6636.**

CAMP FACILITIES:	NO UNITS	HOOKUPS	FEE
Camper Spaces	4 Hardstand	W/E(110/220/30A)	$10 dly/56 wkly
Tent Spaces	Only on or adjacent to camper spaces		

SPT FACILITIES:			
	Boat Rntl	Gas	Golf
	Grills	Nature Trail	Picnic Area
	Playground	Restrooms	Sewage Dmp Sta
	Showers	Sports Fields	Tennis Courts

ACTIVITIES:			
	Boating	Fishing	Hiking
	Racquetball	Rec Equip Avail	

RESTRICTIONS: Pets allowed on leash. No firearms allowed. No open fires in camping area.

LAKE PIPPIN, MAXWELL/GUNTER RECREATION AREA (FL12R1)
Maxwell Air Force Base, AL 36112-5000

TELEPHONE NUMBER INFORMATION: Main installation numbers: Comm: 205-953-1110, DSN: 312-493-1110. Police (Eglin AFB) for recreation area, Comm: 904-882-2502.

LOCATION: Off base. Near Niceville FL. From I-10 at Crestview take FL-85 S to Niceville. Take FL-20 E approx 6.5 mi to sign for Maxwell/Gunter Recreation Area. New Mid-Bay Bridge (toll) makes area easily accessible from both FL-20 and US-98. Check in at gate house 1700-2100. USMRA: page 39 (C,D-13). NMI: Eglin AFB FL, 15 mi N. NMC: Pensacola FL, 25 mi W.

DESCRIPTION OF AREA: Located on Choctawhatchee Bay on northern coast of Gulf of Mexico. Lovely wooded site on beach. Within driving distance of Pensacola, Panama City, Ft Walton Beach and fishing attractions. Easy access to full range of support facilities available at Eglin Air Force Base.

SEASON OF OPERATION: Year round.

FLORIDA
LAKE PIPPIN, MAXWELL/GUNTER RECREATION AREA, continued

ELIGIBILITY: Active/Retired/Active Reserve/NG/DoD Civ at Maxwell/Gunter AFB.

RESERVATIONS: Required with payment in full. Patrons must have receipt. Address: ITT Office, Bldg 834, Maxwell AFB, AL 36112-5000. **Comm: 205-953-5496, DSN: 312-493-5496.** (Recreation Area, *information only*, Comm: 904-897-2411.)

CAMP FACILITIES:	NO UNITS	HOOKUPS	FEE*
Mobile Homes**	30		$30.00 dly
Camper Spaces	16 Paved	W/E (110/50A)	11.00 dly
Tent Spaces	30 Gravel		5.00 dly

*Monthly rates avail 16 Oct-14 Mar.
**2 & 3 bdrm, ramp, heat, A/C, 1 or 1.5 PB; furn exc linens, blankets.

SPT FACILITIES:	Beach	Boat Launch	Boat Rntl
	Boat Storage	Grills	Laundry
	Picnic Area	Playground	Restrooms/hcp
	Sewage Dmp Sta	Showers/hcp	TV Rntl

ACTIVITIES:	Boating	Fishing/license	Hiking
	Jogging	Sailing	Swimming
	Water Skiing		

RESTRICTIONS: No pets allowed. Check out 1600. No open fires. Quiet hours after 2200. As facility is in an isolated area, check your supplies carefully before arriving. No firearms allowed.

MANATEE COVE CAMPGROUND (FL39R1)
Patrick Air Force Base, FL 32925-5000

TELEPHONE NUMBER INFORMATION: Main installation numbers: Comm: 407-494-1110, DSN: 312-854-1110.

LOCATION: On base. Take I-95 to exit 73 (Wickham Rd); E 3 mi to FL-404 (Pineda Causeway), L on South Patrick Drive to fam-camp office, Bldg 1659. Check in M-F 0700-1700, Sa-Su 1100-1700 (closed Federal hol); on-site host at other times. USMRA: page 38 (I-8). NMC: Melbourne, 10 mi S.

DESCRIPTION OF AREA: Located adjacent to Cape Canaveral Air Force Station and along the Banana River which is host to the remaining population of manatees. Conveniently located for visiting Disney World, Universal Studios, John F Kennedy Space Center, and many other popular attractions. Full range of support facilities available on base.

SEASON OF OPERATION: Year round.

ELIGIBILITY: Active/Retired/DOD Civilians (space available).

RESERVATIONS: Accepted up to 60 days in adv for AD; up to 30 days in adv for Ret; all others on a space-avail basis. Address: Fam-Camp, P.O. Box 4007, Patrick AFB, FL 32925-4007. **Comm: 407-494-4787, DSN: 312-854-4787.**

CAMP FACILITIES:	NO UNITS	HOOKUPS	FEE
Camper Spaces	16	W/E (110)	$10 dly/60 wkly
Camper Spaces	5 Overflow	None	5 dly/30 wkly
Camper Spaces	20 Grass	None	5 dly
Camper/Tent Spaces	Primitive	None	5 dly

SPT FACILITIES:			
	Boat Rntl*	Camp Eq Rntl/	Gas*
	Golf/on base	nearby	Grills
	Jon Boats	Laundry	Pavilions
	Picnic Area	Playground	Range (Archery/
	Restrooms/hcp	Sewage Dmp Sta	Skeet/Trap)
	Showers/hcp		

*At Boat House

ACTIVITIES:			
	Boating	Fishing/license	Jogging
	Sightseeing	Swimming	Water Skiing

RESTRICTIONS: Pets allowed on leash. 14-day limit. Check out 1200.

MARATHON RECREATION COTTAGES (FL28R1)
7th Coast Guard District
Miami, FL 33131-3050

TELEPHONE NUMBER INFORMATION: Main installation numbers: Comm: 305-536-5850.

LOCATION: On base. In the Florida Keys on US-1 (Overseas Highway) at mile marker 48 at Marathon. Enter recreation area from US-1. Check in after 1600 with OOD, Coast Guard Station Marathon, 1800 Overseas Highway (Comm: 305-743-3549. USMRA: page 39 (H-15). NMC: Miami, 111 mi NE.

DESCRIPTION OF AREA: Situated on Vaca Key in the heart of the Florida Keys. Topography is similar to that of islands in the eastern Caribbean. Beaches on Atlantic and Gulf sides. Excellent fishing. No support facilities available on base; full range at Key West Naval Air Station on Boca Chica Key, 40 mi S.

SEASON OF OPERATION: Year round.

ELIGIBILITY: Active/Retired/Reserve.

RESERVATIONS: No Adv Resv for RV spaces; required for cottages with full payment in adv, *by application only*, at least 8 wks in adv, if possible. **Application may be obtained by phone**; *reservations cannot be made by phone*. Address: Commander (aps-1), 7th CG District, Brickell Plaza Federal Bldg, 909 SE First Ave, Miami, FL 33131-3050. **Comm: 305-536-5850.** *For information on RV spaces*, Comm: 305-743-3549.)

LODGING: 4 cottages, 1 bdrm; 1 dbl bed, 2 sgl sofa beds, 1 rollaway bed; slp 5 adults; fully furn, including kit; A/C, TV. Bring extra towels. Recently renovated.
      FEE: $15.00-40.00 dly, depending on rank

FLORIDA
MARATHON RECREATION COTTAGES, *continued*

CAMP FACILITIES:	NO UNITS	HOOKUPS	FEE
RV Spaces	4 Paved	W/E (110)	$5.00 dly

SPT FACILITIES:		
	Boat Rental ($20.00)	Boat Dock
	Grills	Picnic Tables

ACTIVITIES:			
	Basketball	Bicycling	Boating
	Fishing/license	Hiking	Swimming/nearby
	Volleyball		

RESTRICTIONS: No pets allowed. 12-day limit, to include only 1 weekend for cottages. 14-day limit for RV spaces. No cribs provided. Check out 1200. Swimming not allowed on CG Station; diving and fishing areas accessible by boat. No firearms allowed. No waste dumping allowed.

OAK GROVE TRAILER PARK (FL09R1)
Pensacola Naval Air Station, FL 32508-5000

TELEPHONE NUMBER INFORMATION: Main installation numbers: Comm: 904-452-0111, DSN: 312-922-0111. Police for trailer park, Comm: 904-452-2453.

LOCATION: On base. I-10 to US-29; S to Pensacola; take Navy Blvd directly to Naval Air Station. USMRA: page 53 (B-4,5). NMC: Pensacola, 8 mi E.

DESCRIPTION OF AREA: Located in wooded area across from Naval Aviation Museum along a 1½ mi Gulf of Mexico beachfront with historic lighthouse in center. Old Ft Pickens can be viewed from along beach. Full range of support facilities available on base.

SEASON OF OPERATION: Year round.

ELIGIBILITY: Active/Retired.

RESERVATIONS: Required for cabins only, up to 90 days in adv with one day's deposit. Address: Oak Grove Park Recreation Dept, NAS Pensacola, FL 32508-5000. **Comm: 904-452-2535, DSN: 312-922-2535.**

CAMP FACILITIES:	NO UNITS	HOOKUPS	FEE
Cabins*	12		$30.00 dly
Camper Spaces	50 Dirt	W/E (110/30A)	9.00 dly
Tent Spaces	15 Dirt	None	4.00 dly

*1 bdrm, PB, kit; furn, including linens, dishes, pots, pans. 1 cabin reserved for handicapped.

SPT FACILITIES:			
	Boat Launch	Boat Rntl	Camp Equip Rntl
	Marina	Picnic Area	Rec Equip Rntl
	Restrooms	Sailing Facility	Sewage Dmp Sta
	Showers		

ACTIVITIES: Boating   Fishing/license   Swimming

RESTRICTIONS: No pets allowed in cabins; allowed on leash in camping area. No firearms allowed.

ORLANDO TRAVEL TRAILER PARK (FL21R1)
Orlando Naval Training Center, FL 32813-5000
(Orlando NTC is mandated to close under the 1993 Base Closure Law. A closure date has not been announced for Orlando Travel Trailer Park. Final base closure in phases 1995-1998.)

TELEPHONE NUMBER INFORMATION: Main installation numbers: Comm: 407-646-4111, DSN: 312-791-4111.

LOCATION: On base. At the NTC Annex, S Orlando. I-4 to FL-528 (toll road) exit; E to Tradeport Road exit; R on Tradeport Road to Express St; R, and follow signs. Check in at entrance to travel trailer park. USMRA: page 38 (H-7). NMC: Orlando, 12 mi S.

DESCRIPTION OF AREA: Minutes away from Magic Kingdom and EPCOT Center, Sea World, Church St Station, Wet n Wild. Busch Gardens, Cypress Gardens and Silver Springs within driving distance. Full range of support facilities available at NTC Annex, within 2 mi of trailer park.

SEASON OF OPERATION: Year round.

ELIGIBILITY: Active/Retired.

RESERVATIONS: *Accepted only for Active Duty on PCS and TDY orders;* others first come, first served. Address: Recreational Services, Travel Trailer Park, 3480 W 8th St, Orlando, FL 32827. Include self-addressed, stamped envelope. **Comm: 407-857-2120.**

CAMP FACILITIES:	NO UNITS	HOOKUPS	FEE*
Camper Spaces, 48'	38 Concrete	W/S/E (110/30A)	$ 9.00 dly/55.00 wk
Camper Spaces	13 Grass	W/E (110/30A)	7.50 dly/42.50 wk
Camper/Tent Spaces	10 Overflow	None	3.50 dly/20.00 wk

*Winter rates (Nov-Apr) slightly higher.

SPT FACILITIES:	Chapel	Gas	Golf
	Grills/concrete sites	Laundry	Picnic Area
		Playground	Restrooms/hcp
	Sewage Dmp Sta	Showers/hcp	

ACTIVITIES: Sightseeing

RESTRICTIONS: Pets allowed on leash; must not annoy others; must not be left alone in park; must use designated walking area. 14-day limit. Check out 1100. One car per family per site. Firearms, firecrackers and other explosives are not permitted in the trailer park. No ground fires. Quiet hours 2200-0800.

FLORIDA

PANAMA CITY CSS OUTDOOR
RECREATION/MARINA (FL07R1)
Panama City Coastal Systems Station, FL 32408-5000

TELEPHONE NUMBER INFORMATION: Main installation numbers: Comm: 904-234-4100, DSN: 312-436-4100. Police for rec area, Comm: 904-234-4373.

LOCATION: On base. Located on US-98 at the foot of the Hathaway Bridge in Panama City Beach. Check in at marina, Bldg 327, 1200-2400 (closed Tu-W). USMRA: page 39 (D-14). NMC: Panama City, adjacent.

DESCRIPTION OF AREA: Panama City Beach is considered one of the world's most beautiful beaches because of the brilliant white sand and emerald waters of the Gulf of Mexico. Water sports (jet skiing, sailing, boating, swimming, etc) attract tourists to the area. Limited support facilities available on base; full range available at Tyndall AFB, 35 mi E.

SEASON OF OPERATION: Year round; closed Tu: 1 Oct-1 Apr.

ELIGIBILITY: Active/Retired/Reserve/DoD Civilians at Coastal Systems Station

RESERVATIONS: Accepted. Address: Recreation Services, Coastal Systems Station, Panama City, FL 32408-5000. *For campers/boats*, call the Marina, **Comm: 904-234-4402 or write to address above.** List dates/times of arrival. A refundable cleaning deposit of $30 is required to hold a trailer reservation. FAX Comm: 904-234-4402.

CAMP FACILITIES:	NO UNITS	HOOKUPS	FEE
Mobile Homes 1 bdrm*	3		$40 dly/200 wkly
(Park Models)			
Camper Spaces	29 Hardstand	W/S/E (110/30A)	10 dly/65wkly
Boat Slips	13 Wet		65.00 mo
Boat Slips	35 Dry		35.00 mo

*Includes linens, pots and pans. *No pets.*

SPT FACILITIES:			
	Beach	Boat Ramp	Boat Rntl
	Camper Rntl	Camp Equip Rntl	Consol Mess
	Exchange	Gas	Golf Driving Rg
	Grills	Grocery/nearby	Gym
	Ice	Laundry/nearby	Marina
	Pavilions	Picnic Area	Playground
	Racquetball	Restrooms	Showers
	Sports Eq Rntl	Sports Fields	Swimming Pool
	Tennis Courts	Trails	Vending Mach

ACTIVITIES:			
	Bicycling	Boating	Canoe Trips
	Fishing/license	Horseshoes	Picnicking
	Rafting	Rec Equip Avail	Sailing
	Scuba Diving	Snorkeling	Swimming
	Tours	Water Skiing	

RESTRICTIONS: Pets allowed on leash, except in mobile homes. Check out 1200-2400. Campers already registered on Tu will not be asked to leave. Certification tests for boat rental given by appointment. No tent sites. No firearms allowed. Campfires are not permitted on sites.

RUCKER FLORIDA RECREATION AREA (FL10R1)
Fort Rucker, AL 36362-5000

TELEPHONE NUMBER INFORMATION: Main installation numbers: Comm: 205-255-6181, DSN: 312-558-1110.

LOCATION: Off post. Near Niceville FL. From I-10 at Crestview take FL-85 S through Eglin AFB to Niceville. E on FL-20. Located between Niceville and Freeport. Check in at rec area office 1400-1930 daily. USMRA: page 39 (D-13). NMI: Eglin AFB FL, 15 mi NW. NMC: Pensacola FL, 45 mi W.

DESCRIPTION OF AREA: Located on Choctawhatchee Bay in the Ft Walton area of Florida's northern Gulf of Mexico coast approx 100 mi from Ft Rucker. Sandy beach. Easy access to Destin Beach (13 mi) via new Mid-Bay bridge. Full range of support facilities at Eglin AFB.

SUPPORT FACILITIES: Year round.

ELIGIBILITY: Active/Retired/NG/Reserve/NG/DoD Civ/Ft Rucker Contractors.

RESERVATIONS: Required, with one night's deposit, up to 60 days in adv. Address: ITR Office, Bldg 9204, PO Drawer 620189, Ft Rucker, AL 36362-5000. **Comm: 205-255-9517/2997.** Discounts on campsites available to holders of Golden Age and Golden Access Passports.

CAMP FACILITIES:	NO UNITS	HOOKUPS	FEE
Mobile Homes, 2 bdrm*	15		$35-40 dly**
Mobile Homes, 3 bdrm*	3		45-50 dly**
Camper Spaces	20 Dirt	W/E (110)	8-10 dly
Tent Spaces	Open	None	6-8 dly

*A/C, fully furnished; bring towels, soap, dishwashing liquid, paper towels, etc.
**Reduced weekly and monthly rates available 1 Oct-31 Mar. Add fee of $3 dly for campsites for AC and electric heaters.

SPT FACILITIES:			
	Beach	Boat Launch	Boat Rntl
	Fast Food/nearby	Fishing Pier	Gas
	Ice	Laundry	Marina
	Picnic Area	Playground	Restrooms
	Sewage Dmp Sta	Showers	Store/Small
	Vending Mach		

FLORIDA
RUCKER FLORIDA RECREATION AREA, continued

ACTIVITIES: Fishing/license   Rec Equip Avail   Swimming
                     Water Skiing

RESTRICTIONS: No pets allowed. Check out 1100.

SHADES OF GREEN ON
WALT DISNEY WORLD® RESORT (FL49R1)
PO Box 22789
Lake Buena Vista, FL 32830

TELEPHONE NUMBER INFORMATION: Main installation number: Comm: 407-824-3600.

LOCATION: From Orlando take I-4 W to exit 26B, Walt Disney World. Follow Magic Kingdom Resort signs; go through Magic Kingdom toll booth. Stay in far R lane, following signs to Resort and hotels. L at first light (Seven Seas Dr), pass Polynesian Resort. At 3-way stop, turn R on Floridian Way. Driveway is first road on L (Magnolia Palm Dr). USMRA: page 38 (G-7). NMC: Orlando, 15 mi NE.

DESCRIPTION OF AREA: The Disney Inn at Walt Disney World in Orlando FL has been leased to serve as an Armed Forces Recreation Center (AFRC). It has 287 rooms, and has been renamed *"Shades of Green on Walt Disney World®️ Resort."* It opened in February 1994 and has been very popular with families because of large rooms and easy access to transportation to various parts of Disney World. Children love its Snow White theme. Built in 1973, the Inn is one of the older and smaller hotels, but has been impeccably maintained and has had recent renovations. It's across from the Grand Floridian and adjacent to Magnolia and Palm golf courses.

SEASON OF OPERATION: Year round.

ELIGIBILITY: Active/Retired/NG/Reserve/DoD Civilians.

RESERVATIONS: Required. Address: Shades of Green on Walt Disney World Resort, PO Box 22789, Lake Buena Vista, FL 32830. **Comm: 407-824-3600, FAX 407-824-3665.** Write for reservation and information packet.

FACILITIES: 288 large rooms each with 2 queen-size beds, sofa bed, PB. Outdoor pool, golf courses, tennis courts, and easy access to Walt Disney World transportation.

RATES	
E1-5, GS 1-7	$49.00 dly
E6-7, O1-2, WO-1, GS 8-12	73.00 dly
E8-9, O3-5, CW2-5, GS 13-15	85.00 dly
O6-10, GS-16 and up	92.00 dly

Rates are for 2 persons; $9 for each additional adult.

SIGSBEE RV PARK (FL37R1)
Key West Naval Air Station, FL 33040-5000

TELEPHONE NUMBER INFORMATION: Main installation numbers: Comm: 305-293-3700, DSN: 312-483-3700. Police for RV park, Comm: 305-293-2114.

LOCATION: On base. From US-1 in Key West, turn R on N Roosevelt Blvd; take first R after Searstown Plaza (Kennedy Dr) to Sigsbee Housing Area. Check in at marina. USMRA: page 39 (G-16). NMI: Key West NAS, 7 mi N. NMC: Key West, in city limits.

DESCRIPTION OF AREA: RV Park and tent spaces are located in Sigsbee Housing Area. The tent spaces are on the waterfront. Overflow camper spaces are on Trumbo Point in NW Key West. We have been told that it has never been necessary to turn anyone away. Excellent fishing, diving and snorkeling year round (best in Apr-Sep). Historical sites include Ft Zachary Taylor and Ernest Hemingway House. Limited support facilities at Trumbo Point; full range of facilities available at Sigsbee Park.

SEASON OF OPERATION: Year round.

ELIGIBILITY: Active/Retired/Reserved/DoD Civilians at Key West NAS.

RESERVATIONS: No adv resv except for wheelchaired disabled sites, which may be reserved for a 14-day stay. Address: MWR Dept, PO Box 9027, Naval Air Station, Key West, FL 33040-9001, ATTN: Sigsbee RV Park. Comm: 305-293-4434. FAX Comm: 305-293-2416.

CAMP FACILITIES:	NO UNITS	HOOKUPS	FEE
Camper Spaces	68 Concrete	W/S/E (110/30A)	$12.00 dly
Tent Spaces	Unlimited	Central W	6.00 dly
Camper Spaces at Trumbo Point (Dec-Apr)	200 Overflow	Central W	6.00 dly

SPT FACILITIES:	Beach	Boat Ramp	Boat Rntl
	Camper Rental	Commissary	Exchange
	Fishing Tackle	Gas	Grills
	Ice	Laundry	Lounge/Cafe
	Marina	Pay Telephones	Picnic Area
	Playgrounds	Restrooms	Sewage Dmp Sta
	Showers	Snorkel Gear	Sports Fields

ACTIVITIES:	Boating	Snorkeling	Swimming

RESTRICTIONS: Pets allowed on leash; must have complete and current immunizations; owner must clean up after pet. 14-day limit on spaces with hookups. Check out 1200. Quiet hours 2200-0800. No open campfires. Only one parking space is available per site.

FLORIDA

TYNDALL FAM-CAMP (FL26R1)
Tyndall Air Force Base, FL 32403-5000

TELEPHONE NUMBER INFORMATION: Main installation numbers: Comm: 904-283-1110, DSN: 312-523-1110.Police for fam-camp, Comm: 904-283-2254.

LOCATION: On base. US-231 S to Panama City; US-98 E to base. Fam-camp ¼ mi on R after crossing Dupont Bridge. USMRA: page 39 (E-14). NMC: Panama City, 11 mi W.

DESCRIPTION OF AREA: Located on the coast of the Gulf of Mexico with the Gulf on one side and East Bay on the other. Some sites have water views; all are larger than normal and shaded by oak trees with Spanish moss. Bird-watching is excellent. Water sports attract many tourists to the area. Full range of support facilities available on base.

SEASON OF OPERATION: Year round.

ELIGIBILITY: Active/Retired/DoD Civilians.

RESERVATIONS: No adv resv for campsites; resv for cottages accepted up to 90 days in adv. Address: Fam-Camp, 101 Fam-Camp Rd, Tyndall AFB, FL 32403-1045. **Comm: 904-283-2798, DSN: 312-523-2798.**

CAMP FACILITIES:	NO UNITS	HOOKUPS	FEE
Cottages, 2 bdrm, furn	3		$40 dly/240 wkly
Camper Spaces	19 Concrete	W/S/CTV/E (30A)	11.00 dly
Camper Spaces	17 Concrete	W/CTV/E(110/30A)	10.00 dly
Camper Spaces	14 Concrete	W/E (110/30A)	9.00 dly
Tent Spaces	8 Cleared	None	6.00 dly

Adequate overflow parking available, some with W/E.

SPT FACILITIES:			
	Archery	Beach	Boat Rntl
	Camp Equip Rntl	Chapel	Gas
	Golf	Grills	Laundry
	LP Gas	Marina	Mini Golf
	Nature Trail	Picnic Area	Quick Shop
	Racquetball	Restrooms	Sewage Dmp Sta
	Showers	Shuffleboard	Skeet Range
	Snack Bar	Sports Fields	Stables
	Tennis Courts	Water Sports Equip	

Work currently in progress on a new campground community center incorporating shower and laundry facilities, and an indoor recreation center with kitchen. All will be accessible to handicapped. Scheduled for completion in fall 0f 1994.

ACTIVITIES: Fishing/license Hunting/license Swimming

RESTRICTIONS: Maximum of 2 domestic pets allowed on leash. *No pets allowed in rental cottages.* No discharge allowed of firearms or fireworks.

GEORGIA

GORDON RECREATION AREA (GA04R1)
Fort Gordon, GA 30905-5000

TELEPHONE NUMBER INFORMATION: Main installation numbers: Comm: 706-791-0110, DSN: 312-780-0110. Police for rec area, Comm: 541-1057-EX-131.

LOCATION: Off post. Off GA-47 N of Leah. *From I-20 NW of Augusta,* take GA-28/104 exit (Washington Rd) W to Leah. *From I-20 W of Augusta at intersection with I-221,* take GA-47 (Appling) N to Leah. Signs clearly mark entrance. USMRA: page 37 (F-4). NMI: Ft Gordon, 25 mi S. NMC: Augusta, 25 mi SE.

DESCRIPTION OF AREA: Located on an 904-acre site with a 1200 mi shoreline along Thurmond Lake (formerly Clarks Hill Lake) on Georgia/South Carolina line. Ideal for wide range of outdoor activities in fresh-water lakes and rivers of the area. Savannah about 120 mi SE. Easy access to full range of support facilities available at Ft Gordon.

SEASON OF OPERATION: Mar-Oct. Marina closed Oct through Mar; limited number of cabins and mobile homes available Nov-Mar. Limited number of camper spaces with full hookups available year round for self-contained RVs; one primitive tent area available year round.

ELIGIBILITY: Active/Retired/Reserve/DoD Civilians.

RESERVATIONS: Required for mobile homes and cabins for a min of 2 nights; 1 night's deposit required 7 days in adv. May be made up to 45 days in adv for AD, 30 days in adv for others. Walk-ins accepted when cabins/mobile homes are available. Address: Ft Gordon Recreation Area, PO Box 67, Appling, GA 30802. **Comm: 706-541-1057/0063/0338.** Discounts for campsite rental are available to holders of Golden Age and Golden Access Passports.

CAMP FACILITIES:	NO UNITS	HOOKUPS	FEE
Cabins, 3 bdrm*	9		$35-45 dly
Mobile Homes, 3 bdrm*	8		30-35 dly
Bunk House, dbl rms**	1		5.00 ea pers dly
Camper Spaces	60 Gravel	W/S/E (110)	8.00 dly
Camper Spaces	30 Gravel	W/E	7.00 dly
Tent Spaces	50 Dirt	None	6.00 dly
Pioneer Camping Area (for large groups)	Primitive	None	1.00 ea pers dly 10.00 min dly

*Furnished
**Slp 24; TV, kit, W/D, common shower room.

SPT FACILITIES:			
	Adventure Ropes	Bath House	Beach/sumr
	Boat Launch	Boat Rntl	Boat Sheds/Slips
	Camp Equip Rntl	Country Store	Fish House
	Marina	Pavilions	Picnic Area
	Playground	Restrooms	Sewage Dmp Sta
	Showers	Trails	TV Room

GEORGIA
GORDON RECREATION AREA, continued

ACTIVITIES: Boating   Fishing/license   Hiking
                Picnicking   Swimming

RESTRICTIONS: No pets in cabins, mobile homes or swimming area. Allowed on leash in other areas; owners must clean up after pets. Ft Gordon boating safety card required for boat rental. Firearms, bows and arrows, explosives, fireworks and all sporting devices capable of causing death or injury are prohibited.

GRASSY POND RECREATION AREA (GA06R1)
Moody Air Force Base, GA 31699-5000

TELEPHONE NUMBER INFORMATION: Main installation numbers: Comm: 912-333-4211, DSN: 312-460-1110. Police, Comm: 912-333-5133 (sheriff's office).

LOCATION: Off base. From I-75 S of Valdosta, take exit 2; W on GA-376 (Clyatt-ville Rd). Immediately watch for signs and L turn to rec area. Check in for cabins after 1400. USMRA: page 37 (D-9). NMI: Moody AFB, 25 mi N. NMC: Valdosta, 16 mi N.

DESCRIPTION OF AREA: Located along a 275-acre pond surrounded by 500 acres of rolling, wooded terrain near Georgia/Florida line, Grassy Pond is a major fishing area offering a variety of facilities and activities. Record bass caught in Feb 92 weighed 14 lbs 14.5 oz. Full range of support facilities available at Moody AFB.

SEASON OF OPERATION: Year round, during daylight hours.

ELIGIBILITY: Active/Retired/DoD and NAF Civilians.

RESERVATIONS: Required for cabins. Address: Recreation Services, Grassy Pond, Rte 3, Box 10, Lake Park, GA 31636-5000. Comm: 912-559-5840, DSN: 312-460-1110 EX-559-5840. Discounts available to holders of Golden Age, Golden Access and Golden Eagle Passports.

CAMP FACILITIES:	NO UNITS	HOOKUPS	FEE
Cabins, slp 6*	6	All Electric	$25.00 dly
Camper Spaces	18 Gravel	W/E (110/30A)	10.00 dly
Tent Spaces	Many	None	5.00 dly

*PB, kit, linens, dishes, pots and pans; bring bath and kitchen towels, wash cloths, paper towels, detergent for dishes. **7 new cabins will be available in fall of 1994.**

SPT FACILITIES:			
	Boat Launch	Boat Rntl	Fishing Docks
	Fishing Tackle	Grills	Ice
	Laundry	Mail Service	Paddle Boats
	Pay Telephone	Picnic Area	Playground
	Rec Equip Rntl	Rec Room	Restrooms
	Sewage Dmp Sta	Shelter Rntl	Showers
	Snack Bar	Tackle/Bait	TV Room

Fishing docks and entry doors are equipped for handicapped.
Wide range of RV maintenance service and parts available in local area.

ACTIVITIES: Boating   Fishing/License   Horseshoes
                    Nature Trail

RESTRICTIONS: No pets allowed in cabins. No more than 2 pets per campsite; leash required; owner must clean up after pet. Quiet hours 2200-0800. Check out 1200. No firearms allowed.

HOLBROOK POND RECREATION AREA AND CAMPGROUND (GA19R1)
Fort Stewart, GA 31314-5000

TELEPHONE NUMBER INFORMATION: Main installation numbers: Comm: 912-767-1110, DSN: 312-870-1110. Police for recreation area and campground, Comm: 912-767-2822.

LOCATION: On post. From US-17 or I-95 S of Savannah take exit 15; W on GA-144 approx 17 mi; L on FS-48 at sign for Outdoor Recreation Service Center Bldg 8325, Check-in, 1130-1730. USMRA: page 37 (G-7). NMC: Savannah, 30 mi NE.

DESCRIPTION OF AREA: Located in Holbrook Pond area. Full range of support facilities available on main post, approx 6 mi away.

SEASON OF OPERATION: Year round.

ELIGIBILITY: Active/Retired/NG/Reserve/DoD Civilians.

RESERVATIONS: Accepted up to 30 days in adv with payment in full. Address: Community Recreation Division (AFZP-PAR), Outdoor Recreation, Bldg 622, Ft Stewart, GA 31314-5000. **Comm: 912-767-2717, DSN: 312-870-2717.** Discounts available to holders of Golden Age and Golden Access Passports.

CAMP FACILITIES:	NO UNITS	HOOKUPS	FEE
Camper Spaces	20 Hardstand	W/E (110/30A)	$ 5.00 dly
Tent Spaces	20 Primitive	Central Fresh W	2.50 dly

SPT FACILITIES:	Bait	Boat Rntl	Conv Store
	Gas/post	Golf/on post	Grills
	Ice	Laundry	Off-Road Veh
	Pavilions	Picnic Area	Playgrounds
	Restrooms	Sewage Dmp Sta	Showers
	Skeet/Trap Rg	Trails	Vending Mach

ACTIVITIES:	Boating	Fishing/license	Hiking
	Hunting/license		

RESTRICTIONS: Pets allowed on leash or physically restrained at all times. After hours, go directly to campground and check in the next day.

GEORGIA

LAKE ALLATOONA ARMY RECREATION AREA
(GA05R1)
Fort McPherson, GA 30330-5000

TELEPHONE NUMBER INFORMATION: Main installation numbers: Comm: 404-752-3113, DSN: 312-572-1110. Police for rec area, Comm: 404-752-3712/382-1234.

LOCATION: Off post. From I-75 N of Atlanta, take exit 122 E. Follow signs for approx 3 mi to entrance on L. Check in 1700 to closing. USMRA: page 37 (B-3). NMI: Dobbins AFB and Atlanta NAS, 15 mi S. NMC: Atlanta, 43 mi S.

DESCRIPTION OF AREA: Located on 99-acre site at Lake Allatoona reservoir. Full range of beach and water activities. Conveniently situated for sightseeing in Atlanta and surrounding area, including Stone Mountain Memorial State Park and Six Flags. Full range of support facilities available at Ft McPherson and Dobbins AFB in Atlanta.

SEASON OF OPERATION: Year round.

ELIGIBILITY: Active/Retired/Reserve/NG/DoD Civilians at Ft McPherson and Ft Gillem.

RESERVATIONS: *Required for lodging.* AD at Forts McPherson and Gillem have priority to make resv during first 10 days of any month and 3 succeeding months; all others may make resv for same period after 10th day. Address: Army Recreation Area, 40 Old Sandtown Rd, Cartersville, GA 30120. **Comm: 706-974-3413/9420.**

CAMP FACILITIES:	NO UNITS	HOOKUPS	FEE*
Apartment,3 bdrm**	3		$66.00 dly
Cabins, 2 bdrm/deluxe	2		57.00 dly
Cabins, 2 bdrm/hcp**	13		48.00 dly
Cabins, 1 bdrm/hcp**	8		39.00 dly
RV Spaces	13	W/S/E (110/30A)	10.00 dly
Tent Spaces	18	W/E (110/30A)	5.00 dly

*Off-season rates available 1 Oct-1 Mar.
**A/C; furn; MW, VCR, TV, bed linens, pots, pans, dishes and kitchen utensils. Bring towels, extra blankets, can opener, soap, detergent.

SPT FACILITIES:		
Basketball Ct	Bath Houses/hcp	Beach
Boat Launch	Fishing Piers	Game Room
Grills	Laundry	Marina
Miniature Golf	Pavilions	Picnic Area
Playgrounds	Restrooms	Sewage Dmp Sta
Showers	Trails	Volleyball Ct

ACTIVITIES:		
Boat Tours	Boating	Fishing/license
Horseshoes	Swimming	Water Skiing

RESTRICTIONS: No pets allowed. Motorcycles, minibikes, all-terrain vehicles and motor carts are prohibited. No open fires. 14-day limit 1 Apr-31 Oct. 2-day minimum on weekends from Memorial Day through Labor Day. Check in 1700 to closing. Family members under 18 must be accompanied by authorized adult sponsor to use the area. No firearms allowed.

LAKE ALLATOONA NAVY RECREATION SITE (GA01R1)
Atlanta Naval Air Station, Marietta, GA 30060-5000

TELEPHONE NUMBER INFORMATION: Main installation numbers: Comm: 404-421-5000, DSN: 312-925-5000. Police for recreational site, Comm: 404-421-5394, and/or Bartow County Sheriff.

LOCATION: Off base. From I-75 N of Atlanta, take exit 122 E. Follow signs for approx 3 mi to entrance on L. Check in 1300-1800. USMRA: page 37 (B-3). NMI: Atlanta NAS, Marietta, 20 mi SE. NMC: Atlanta, 40 mi SE.

DESCRIPTION OF AREA: Located in a 15-acre park near Lake Allatoona reservoir. Ideal spot for many outdoor recreational activities. Wide range of support facilities at Atlanta NAS.

SEASON OF OPERATION: Cabins: Year round; campgrounds: Apr-Oct.

ELIGIBILITY: Active/Retired/Reserve/DoD Civilians.

RESERVATIONS: Required (with non-refundable deposit for 1 day's stay) *for cabins and houseboat only.* Address: MWR Office, Bldg 402, Naval Air Station Atlanta, Marietta, GA 30060-5099; **Comm: 404-421-5502, DSN: 312-925-5502.** *Rec area,* Comm: 706-974-6309. Discounts available to holders of Golden Age, Golden Access and Golden Eagle Passports, and Senior Citizen Cards. VISA, MasterCard, and DISCOVER accepted.

CAMP FACILITIES:	NO UNITS	HOOKUPS	FEE
Cabins, 1 bdrm*	1		$34.00 dly**
Cabins, 2 bdrm*	6		41.00 dly**
Cabins, 3 bdrm*	2		48.00 dly**
"Liberty Belle" Houseboat			60.00 dly***
Camper, Pop-up	1	W/E (110)	15.00 dly
RV Camper Spaces	10 Paved	E (110)/Central W	8.00 dly
Tent Spaces	3 Dirt	Central W	5.00 dly

*A/C, furn, including color TV, MW, dishes, pots, pans and linens.
**Winter rates avail 1 Oct-31 Mar.
***Plus fuel.

GEORGIA
LAKE ALLATOONA NAVY RECREATION SITE, continued

SPT FACILITIES:	Beach	Boat Dock	Boat Rntl
	Game Room	Grills	Laundry
	Marina	Pavilions/fee	Picnic Areas
	Playground	Restrooms/hcp	Sewage Dmp Sta
	Showers	Softball	

ACTIVITIES:	Boating	Fishing/license	Swimming

RESTRICTIONS: No pets allowed. 14-day limit for RV spaces. Check out 0900-1100. No firearms allowed.

LAKESIDE FAM-CAMP (GA18R1)
Dobbins Air Reserve Base, GA 30069-5000

TELEPHONE NUMBER INFORMATION: Main installation numbers: Comm: 404-421-5000, DSN: 312-925-1110. Police for fam-camp, Comm: 404-421-4909.

LOCATION: On base. From I-75, S of Marietta, exit to GA-280. W 1½ mi to AFB. Entrance is on US-41 S. USMRA: page 49 (A-1). NMC: Atlanta, 15 mi S.

DESCRIPTION OF AREA: Offers many recreational and leisure activities. Conveniently located for sightseeing in Atlanta and surrounding area. Geese, ducks, beavers and other wildlife frequent the picnic/playground area adjacent to the fam-camp. Limited support facilities available on base; wide range available at Atlanta NAS, adjacent and to the E of Dobbins AFB.

SEASON OF OPERATION: Year round.

ELIGIBILITY: Active/Retired/Reserve/DoD Civilians.

RESERVATIONS: No adv resv. Address: Recreational Services, 94 SPTG/MWR, 1335 Dozer Circle, Bldg 558, Dobbins AFB, GA 30069-4510. Comm: 404-421-4870; DSN: 312-925-4870.

CAMP FACILITIES:	NO UNITS	HOOKUPS	FEE
Camper Spaces	16 Hardstand	W/E (110/30A)	$ 8.00 dly
		W	5.00 dly
Tent Spaces		None	4.00 dly

SPT FACILITIES:	Chapel/nearby	Grills	Grocery/nearby
	Picnic Area	Playground	Rec Center
	Restrooms/hcp	Sewage Dmp Sta	Showers/hcp
	Sports Fields	Tennis Courts	

ACTIVITIES:	Horseshoes	Jogging	Rec Equip Avail
	Volleyball		

RESTRICTIONS: Pets allowed on leash. No swimming or fishing allowed. Patrons should park RV on available site and report to Bldg 806 (Consolidated Club) to register.

LOTTS ISLAND ARMY/AIR FORCE TRAVEL CAMP (GA22R1)
Hunter Army Airfield, Savannah, GA 31409-5000

TELEPHONE NUMBER INFORMATION: Main installation numbers: Comm: 912-352-6521, DSN: 312-870-1110. Police for travel camp, Comm: 912-352-5916.

LOCATION: On post. From I-95 take Hunter Army Airfield exit; take GA-204 N approx 4 mi to sign on left for Rio Gate. L to stop sign; R to sign for Outdoor Recreation, then L to Bldg 8454. USMRA: page 37 (G-7). NMC: 5 mi NE.

DESCRIPTION OF AREA: Located at Lotts Island, the travel camp is convenient to the many water-related activities of the inland harbor. Full range of support facilities available on post.

SEASON OF OPERATION: Year round.

ELIGIBILITY: Active/Retired/NG on AD or ADT/Civilians at Ft Stewart and Hunter AAF.

RESERVATIONS: Accepted up to 30 days in adv with full payment. Address: Community Recreation Division (AFZP-PAR), Outdoor Recreation, Bldg 8454, HAAF, Savannah, GA 31409-5000. **Comm: 912-352-5722/5274/5916, DSN: 312-870-5722.**

CAMP FACILITIES:	NO UNITS	HOOKUPS	FEE
Camper/Tent Spaces	15	W only	$ 3.00 dly
Campers, Coleman Popup		A/C	20.00 dly

SPT FACILITIES:			
	Archery Rg	Boat Docks	Boat Rntl
	Camp Equip Rntl	Camper Rntl	Fishing Dock
	Golf	Grills	Ice
	Pavilions/fee	Picnic Areas	Restrooms
	Skeet Rg	Vending Mach	

ACTIVITIES:	Boating	Fishing	Hunting/license

RESTRICTIONS: Pets allowed on leash or physically restrained at all times. No firearms allowed.

ROBINS FAM-CAMP (GA07R1)
Robins Air Force Base, GA 31098-5000

TELEPHONE NUMBER INFORMATION: Main installation numbers: Comm: 912-926-1110, DSN: 312-468-1001.

LOCATION: On base. From US-129 take GA-247 E at Warner Robins to AFB. Check in at fam-camp. USMRA: page 37 (D-6). NMC: Macon, 16 mi N.

DESCRIPTION OF AREA: Fam-camp is situated at SE corner of installation adjacent to Luna Lake. Very rustic setting surrounded by trees. Full range of support facilities available on base.

GEORGIA
ROBINS FAM-CAMP, continued

SEASON OF OPERATION: Year round.

ELIGIBILITY: Active/Retired/DoD Civilians.

RESERVATIONS: Not required. Address: Outdoor Recreation (SVRO), Bldg 1305, Robins AFB, GA 31098-1469. **W-Sa only, Comm: 912-926-4500, DSN: 312-468-4500.** *Other days,* **Comm: 912-926-3193, DSN: 312-468-3193.**

CAMP FACILITIES:	NO UNITS	HOOKUPS	FEE
Camper Spaces	16	W/E (110/30A)	$ 6.00 dly
Tent Spaces	12	None	4.00 dly

SPT FACILITIES:			
	Bicycle Path	Chapel/nearby	Gas/nearby
	Golf/nearby	Picnic Areas	Playground
	Restrooms	Showers	

ACTIVITIES:	Bicycling	Fishing/license	Hiking

RESTRICTIONS: Pets allowed on leash. Firearms are prohibited, for hunting check with Outdoor Rec Comm: 912-926-4500.

UCHEE CREEK ARMY CAMPGROUND/MARINA (GA20R1)
Fort Benning, GA 31905-5000

TELEPHONE NUMBER INFORMATION: Main installation numbers: Comm: 706-545-2011, DSN: 312-835-2011. Police for campground/marina, Comm: 706-545-2222.

LOCATION: On post. Located on S side of Columbus. Accessible from US-80, I-185, US-27, US-280 and US-165. Clearly marked. Check in at facility. USMRA: page 37 (B-6). NMC: Columbus, 18 mi NW.

DESCRIPTION OF AREA: The geography and climate are ideal for most outdoor activities. National Infantry Museum on post. Full range of support facilities available on post.

SEASON OF OPERATION: Year round.

ELIGIBILITY: Active/Retired/DoD Civilians.

RESERVATIONS: Accepted. Address: Community Recreation Division, ATTN: ATZB-PAR-U (Uchee Creek Army Campground/Marina), Bldg 241, Baltzell St., Ft Benning, GA 31905-5226, **Comm: 706-545-4053/7238; DSN: 312-835-4053/7238.** VISA and MasterCard accepted.

CAMP FACILITIES:	NO UNITS	HOOKUPS	FEE
*Log Cabin, 16x26, Slp 6	10		$32-36 dly
*Log Cabin, 14x20, Slp 6	10		22-26 dly
**Log Cabin, 14x14, Slp 4	1		14-18 dly
**Log Cabin, 12x12, Slp 4	1		12-16 dly
Camper Spaces	38 Paved	W/S/E (110/20-50A)	9-10 dly
Camper Spaces	27	W/E (110\20-50A)	7-8 dly
Tent Area		None	5.00 dly

*AC, heat, PB, VCR, TV; kit with stove, refr, MW, utensils.
**No bath or kit.
Bring linens and towels.

SPT FACILITIES:	Boat Dock	Boat Launch	Boat Rntl
	Boat Slips	Bowling	Camp Equip Rntl
	Camper Rntl	Chapel	Country Store
	Fishing Pier	Gas/LP	Golf
	Grills	Ice	Laundry
	Marina	Multi-Courts	Party Boats
	Pavilion	Picnic Area	Playgrounds
	Restrooms/hcp	Sewage Dmp Sta	Showers/hcp
	Snack Bar	Sports Fields	Stables
	Swimming Pool	Trailer Rntl	Vending Mach
	Video Arcade		

ACTIVITIES:	Fishing/license	Hunting/license	Rec Equip Avail

RESTRICTIONS: Pets allowed on leash. Check out 1100. If staying over 72 hours, firearms must be registered at Country Store.

HAWAII

BARBERS POINT RECREATION AREA (HI01R6)
Barbers Point Naval Air Station, HI 96862-5000
(Barbers Point NAS is mandated to close under the 1993 Base Closure Law. A closure date has not been announced)

TELEPHONE NUMBER INFORMATION: Main installation numbers: Comm: 808-684-6266, DSN: 315-484-6266. Police for rec area, Comm: 808-684-6222/6223.

LOCATION: On base. I-H1 W to Barbers Point exit. Bear L at stop sign and go approx 1 mi and through main gate; turn R on Saratoga (traffic light). Check in at ITT office on L. *Campers* check in 1200-1700. *Cottage patrons only* check in 1400-1700 at ITT or at Security (on Enterprise) after 1700. USMRA: page 129 (C-7). NMC: Waipahu, 5 mi NE.

HAWAII
BARBERS POINT RECREATION AREA, continued

DESCRIPTION OF AREA: A small, but nice, facility located on SW coast of Oahu, 13 mi from Pearl Harbor and 29 mi from Honolulu. Enlisted cottages are on Nimitz Beach; Officer cottages, and campsites, are on White Plains Beach. Beaches excellent for surfing. Nearby attractions include: Pearl Ridge Phase I and II, Ala Moana Park, Wainae Beach parks, Pearl Harbor Park and Ice Palace (skating). Full range of support facilities available on base.

SEASON OF OPERATION: Year round.

ELIGIBILITY: Active/Retired/Reserve/DoD Civilians on Barbers Point.

RESERVATIONS: Required with payment. *No phone resv accepted for cottages.* Resv for campsites must be completed at least 5 working days in adv of use. Address: MWR, ITT and Reservations, Bldg 19, Naval Air Station, Barbers Point, HI 96862-5050. **Comm: 808-682-2019.**

CAMP FACILITIES:	NO UNITS	HOOKUPS	FEE
Cottages, 2 bdrm, furn	15 Enlisted		$40-45 dly
	7 Officer		45-50 dly
	2 VIP (06+)		45.00 dly
Camper/Tent Spaces	21	W	10-15 dly

SPT FACILITIES:	Beach	Bicycle Rntl	Cabanas
	Chapel	Gas	Golf
	Grills	Laundry	Mini Mart
	Picnic Area	Playground	Racquetball
	Rec Center	Restrooms	Showers
	Snack Bar	Sports Fields	Tennis Courts
ACTIVITIES:	Fishing/license	Rec Equip Avail	Scuba Diving
	Snorkeling	Surfing	Swimming

RESTRICTIONS: No pets allowed. No open fires. Cottages may not be used as a party facility. No glass bottles at beaches. Alcohol: beer only. Check out 1200 for campground. No firearms allowed.

BARKING SANDS BEACH COTTAGES (HI04R6)
Barking Sands Pacific Missile Range Facility
Kekaha, Kauai, HI 96752-0128

TELEPHONE NUMBER INFORMATION: Main installation numbers: Comm: 808-335-4111, DSN: 312-471-4111. Police for beach cottages, Comm: 808-335-4523.

LOCATION: On base. From airport at Lihue take HI-50 W approx 30 mi. Barking Sands is 6 mi past the town of Kekaha. Check in after 1400 at Rec Center, Bldg 1264. USMRA: page 129 (B-2). NMC: Waimea, 8 mi S.

DESCRIPTION OF AREA: Located on the picturesque "Garden Island" of Kauai near Captain Cook's Landing Place. Although the island is small, there are many scenic areas to explore. Waimea Canyon (the "Grand Canyon of Hawaii") is 12 mi from the base. Limited support facilities available on base.

HAWAII
BARKING SANDS BEACH COTTAGES, continued

SEASON OF OPERATION: Year round.

ELIGIBILITY: Active/Retired/Reserve/NG.

RESERVATIONS: Required, **by written application**, at least 60 days in adv. More requests are received than can be accommodated. Address: Beach Cottages Reservation, MWRPMRF, PO Box 128, Barking Sands, Kekaha, Kauai, HI 96752-0128. **Comm: 808-335-4752, DSN: 312-471-6752;** *VIP (06+) Cottages,* **Comm: 808-335-4255, DSN: 312-471-6255; M-F 0730-1600.**

BEACH COTTAGES:	NO UNITS	FEE*
2 Bdrm, PB, slp 6;	8	$40.00 dly
kit, refr, utensils,	2 VIP (06+)	$40.00 dly
MW, W/D, CTV		

*For 2 pers. $4 ea add pers. $65 after 7th day.

SPT FACILITIES:	Beach Club/all ranks	Grills
ACTIVITIES:	Fishing/license	Swimming

RESTRICTIONS: No pets allowed. Check out by 1000. No firearms allowed.

BELLOWS RECREATION AREA (HI02R6)
Bellows Air Force Station, HI 96795-1010

TELEPHONE NUMBER INFORMATION: Main installation numbers: Comm: 808-259-5941, DSN: None. Police for rec area, Comm: 808-259-5955.

LOCATION: On base. From Honolulu Airport or Hickam AFB, take I-H1 Freeway E to exit 21A (Pali Highway); N to HI-72, S to Waimanalo Town. AFS is on L. Check in after 1400. USMRA: page 129 (E-7). NMC: Kailua, 9 mi NW.

DESCRIPTION OF AREA: A seaside recreation facility on the southeast coast of the Island of Oahu, 16½ mi from the Honolulu business district. One of the oldest places of habitation in the Hawaiian Islands. 3 mi of beautiful beachfront. Some support facilities available on base; full range at Kaneohe MCAS, 10 mi NW.

SEASON OF OPERATION: Year round.

ELIGIBILITY: Active/Retired/DoD and NAF Civilians.

RESERVATIONS: Required with deposit. Resv may be made 45-90 days in adv; maximum time depends on branch of service and status. Address: Bellows Reservation Office, 220 Tinker Rd, Waimanalo, HI 96795-1010. **Comm: 808-259-8841. Toll Free from mainland 800-437-2607.**

HAWAII
BELLOWS RECREATION AREA, continued

BEACH COTTAGES:	NO UNITS	FEE
Studio	5	$30-40 dly
Backrow	44	45.00 dly
Oceanview	53	50.00 dly

102 cottages, furn, PB, kitchenette. All are equipped with TV, linens, towels, pots, pans, utensils and dishes. Porta cribs are available.

CAMP FACILITIES:	NO UNITS	HOOKUPS	FEE
Camper/Tent Spaces	44 Dirt	None	$ 5.00 dly

SPT FACILITIES:	Bath Houses	Beach	Beach Lounge
	Boat Rntl	BX	Camp Equip Rntl
	Gas	Golf Driv Range	Laundry
	Marina	Picnic Area	Restaurant
	Softball Field	Tennis Courts	

ACTIVITIES:	Billiards	Boating	Fishing
	Snorkeling	Swimming	

RESTRICTIONS: No pets allowed. 14-day limit. Hiking and hunting are prohibited on Bellows AFS. All overnight guests must be registered with the reservation office. The total number of people permitted to stay overnight in a cottage or campsite is 10. Check out 1200. Rental cars are *not* available on Bellows. Off-island visitors are advised to obtain rental cars for mobility. No firearms allowed.

HALE KOA HOTEL ARMED FORCES RECREATION CENTER (HI08R6)
2055 Kalia Road, Honolulu, HI 96815-1998

TELEPHONE NUMBER INFORMATION: Main installation numbers: Comm: 808-955-0555 (24 hrs dly); 800-367-6027, FAX 800-833-6060 (from CONUS only, 0800-1600 dly HI time, except federal holidays). Police for AFRC, Comm: 808-438-2532.

LOCATION: At 2055 Kalia Rd, Waikiki Beach, Honolulu. The installation (Ft DeRussy) is on Waikiki Beach, between Ala Moana Blvd, Kalakaua Ave and Saratoga Rd, approx 9 mi E of Honolulu International Airport. USMRA: page 131 (F-4). NMC: Honolulu, in city limits.

DESCRIPTION OF AREA: This morale-boosting, all-ranks hotel, has 14 stories with 419 guest rooms with views of the Pacific Ocean and Koolau Mountains. All rooms are identical in size and have private lanai, room-controlled A/C, and color TV. Coin-operated washers and dryers are available. Some rooms are handicapped accessible. Hotel has swimming pool, children's pool, landscaped gardens, and offers indoor and outdoor sports activities on beautiful Waikiki Beach.

HAWAII
HALE KOA HOTEL ARMED FORCES RECREATION CENTER, *continued*

Also available: cocktail lounges, snack bars, coffee house, fine dining in Hale Koa Room, live entertainment and dancing in Warriors Lounge; fitness center, sauna and locker rooms; post exchange, barber and beauty shops, jewelry shop, rental cars, and discount tour and travel desk. In addition, snorkeling, tennis, volleyball, sailboats, racquetball and paddle tennis are available. Private banquets, meetings and conferences may be arranged through the hotel's catering service. With its magnificent dining, cocktail and entertainment rooms, the Hale Koa is one of the island's most complete resorts. One of the world's largest shopping centers is nearby. Dress is resortwear and aloha attire at all times.

SEASON OF OPERATION: Year round.

ELIGIBILITY: Active and Retired Military Personnel, their dependents and family members. Ready and Selected Reserve Component Personnel with red/pink ID card and family members. Retired Reserve and NG Personnel with gray/blue ID card. Senior ROTC Cadets on extended AD. Cadets and Midshipmen of Service Academies. Active and Retired Commissioned Officers of the Public Health Service. Honorably discharged 100% Disabled Veterans and Medal of Honor Winners with current DD Form 1173. Foreign National Armed Forces and their immediate family members when assigned or attached to US military operation/ installation or on TDY to a DoD organization. DoD Civilians and uniformed full-time professional installation Red Cross Personnel, including dependents, residing on Hawaii military installations, and DoD Employees who perform on Hawaii. DoD Civilians on TDY to Hawaii or traveling to or from Hawaii on PCS orders. Others as specifically authorized by the General Manager or his designee. DoD Employees with civilian ID cards are authorized use of food and beverage facilities.

RESERVATIONS: Required with deposit; may be made up to 365 days in adv; maximum stay of 30 days. Address: Hale Koa Hotel, 2055 Kalia Road, Honolulu, HI 96815-1998. **Use phone numbers at top of listing.** Ask for free information packet. Some rooms specially fitted for handicapped.

1992-1993 DOUBLE RATES (FOR 2 PERSONS) ARE QUOTED BELOW

Categories (AD & Ret)*	I	II	III
Standard	$47.00	$60.00	$70.00
Superior	56.00	67.00	82.00
Park View	62.00	80.00	94.00
Ocean View	70.00	87.00	101.00
Ocean Front	82.00	98.00	109.00

Rates are based on room location (generally the higher floors and view reflect the higher rates). *Rates are subject to change on or before 1 Oct 1994.* Deduct $2 for single occupancy. Add $10 for each additional occupant. MOST rooms are furnished with two double beds, for a maximum occupancy of 4 persons. Children under 12 are free in parents' room if no additional beds are required. ONLY ocean front rooms have king-sized beds. Cribs are available at $4 daily.

*I: E-1 to E-5; II: E-6 to E-9, WO-1 to CW-3, 0-1 to 0-3; all TDY, TLA, DAV (must have DD 1173) and widows; III: CW-4, 0-4 to 0-10, foreign, others. Active and Retired (DD Form 2, Ret - gray or blue) and family members (DD 1173), all services, all ranks, family and guests meeting eligibility requirements.

HAWAII
HALE KOA HOTEL ARMED FORCES RECREATION CENTER, continued

Wide range of Hale Koa dinner shows throughout the week include Tuesday Night Magic, Tama's Polynesian Revue dinner show, Hale Koa Luau on the beach Mondays and Fridays.

NOTE: A 13-story tower addition to the Hale Koa with 396 rooms is under construction and is scheduled for completion in late 1995.

RESTRICTIONS: No pets allowed.

HICKAM HARBOR RECREATION AREA (HI07R6)
Hickam Air Force Base, HI 96853-5000

TELEPHONE NUMBER INFORMATION: Main installation numbers: Comm: 808-471-7110, DSN: 315-430-0111. Police for rec area, Comm: 808-449-6372.

LOCATION: On base. S coast of Oahu, next to Pearl Harbor. Follow I-H1 signs to Pearl Harbor/Hickam AFB; take Hickam exit through main gate (vehicles without military pass must check in); follow signs to Hickam Harbor/Beach. USMRA: page 131 (B,C-3). NMC: Honolulu, 6 mi E.

DESCRIPTION OF AREA: The Harbor was built from a marsh into 300 acres of picnicking and water sports paradise. Many outdoor recreational activities such as fishing (surf and big game), sightseeing, hiking and backpacking, body and bogey board surfing are possible year round. Recreation Equipment Issue is located in Bldg 1713, 900 Hangar Ave (Comm: 909-449-6870). *This is a recreation area; no camping facilities or overnight lodging are available.* Full range of support facilities on base.

SEASON OF OPERATION: Year round.

ELIGIBILITY: Active/Retired/DoD Civilians.

RESERVATIONS: Required for sailing lessons and some rentals. Address: Recreation Services, 15 MWRSS/MWRO, Hangar Ave, Hickam AFB, HI 96853--5246. Comm: 808-449-5215; DSN: 315-430-5215.

SPT FACILITIES:	Boat Launch	Boat Rntl	Cabanas/fee
	Marina	Picnic Areas/fee	Racquet Sports
	Rec Equip Rntl	Restrooms	Showers
	Snack Bars	Wheelchair Rmps	

Day use (1000-2200) of Cabanas, $10 & 20 per day.

ACTIVITIES:	Boating	Fishing	Golf/on base
	Kayaking	Sailing	Swimming
	Windsurfing		

RESTRICTIONS: No pets allowed. Alcohol is restricted and allowed in designated areas only, and by written permission of the Director of Outdoor Recreation. No firearms allowed.

KANEOHE BAY BEACH COTTAGES AND CAMPSITES (HI06R6)
Kaneohe Bay Marine Corps Air Station, HI 96863-5010

TELEPHONE NUMBER INFORMATION: Main installation numbers: Comm: 808-471-7110, DSN: 315-430-0110. Police for cottages and campsites, Comm: 808-257-2123.

LOCATION: On base. At the end of H-3 on windward side of Oahu. Clearly marked off Mokapu Blvd and Kaneohe Bay Dr. USMRA: page 129 (E-6). NMC: Honolulu, 14 mi SW.

DESCRIPTION OF AREA: Located in a secluded area overlooking beautiful Kaneohe Bay. Cottages are across the airstrip along the coastline, near Pyramid Rock. Campsites are near the northern area of the base in a sheltered cove with an excellent view. Full range of support facilities on base.

SEASON OF OPERATION: Year round.

ELIGIBILITY: Active/Retired/DoD Civilians.

RESERVATIONS: Required for studio units and cottages: up to 60 days in adv for AD stationed at Kaneohe Bay MCAS; up to 15 days in adv for all others. Address: TLF, Bldg 3038, MCAS Kaneohe Bay, HI 96863-5018; **Comm: 808-254-2806, DSN: 315-430-3513.** *Campsites address:* Special Services, Bldg 219, MCAS Kaneohe Bay, HI 96863-5000; Comm: 808-254-3230.

CAMP FACILITIES:	NO UNITS	HOOKUPS	FEE
Studio Units*	24		$40.00 dly
Cottages, 2 bdrm, furn	11		40.00 dly
Camper Spaces	4 Primitive	W	8.00 dly

*2 rooms are handicap capable.

SPT FACILITIES:			
	Beach	Chapel	Gas
	Golf	Grills	Marina
	Pavilion/fee	Picnic Area	Playground
	Rec Equip Rntl	Rec Center	Restrooms
	Short Stop	Showers	Snack Bar
	Sports Fields	Swimming Pool	Tennis Courts

ACTIVITIES:	Boating	Fishing	Scuba Diving

RESTRICTIONS: No pets allowed. 7-day limit for cottages.

KILAUEA MILITARY CAMP ARMED FORCES RECREATION CENTER (HI17R6)
Hawaii National Park, HI 96718-5000

TELEPHONE NUMBER INFORMATION: Main installation numbers: Comm: 808-967-7315, DSN: None. Police for rec center, Comm: 808-967-8378.

HAWAII
KILAUEA MILITARY CAMP ARMED FORCES REC CENTER, continued

LOCATION: On post. Off HI-11 approx 1 mi from Hawaii National Park, SW of Hilo on Island of Hawaii. Honolulu is 216 air miles NW. Scheduled bus from Hilo airport to Kilauea Military Camp (KMC), reservations required. USMRA: page 129 (I,J-6,7). NMC: Hilo, 32 mi NE.

DESCRIPTION OF AREA: This Joint Armed Forces Recreation Center is a mountain resort on the island of Hawaii in Hawaii Volcanoes National Park at an elevation of 4000 feet on the edge of active Kilauea Volcano. A 65° day is warm and morning temperatures below 50° are common. Limited support facilities available on base.

SEASON OF OPERATION: Year round.

ELIGIBILITY: Active/Retired/Reserve/NG/DoD Civilians and Retirees.

RESERVATIONS: Required: up to 90 days in adv for AD; up to 60 days in adv for Ret; up to 45 days in adv for all others. Address: KMC Reservations, Kilauea Military Camp, Hawaii National Park, HI 96718-5000. **Comm: 808-438-6707, 808-967-8333.**

LODGING: 58 units (cabins/apartments) with cable TV, refrigerators and fireplaces in all units; some cabins have fac for handicapped in PB. Fee includes up to 2 occupants per unit and use of scheduled bus for an unlimited number of guests to and from Hilo airport.

> FEE: $25-60 dly/$5 ea add pers.

SPT FACILITIES:

Cafeteria	Chapel	Conference Room
Dispensary	Fitness Center	Gas
General Store	Gift Shop	Golf
Laundry	Library	Miniature Golf
Multi-Purpose Ct	Playground	Post Office
Rec Lodge	Tennis Courts	Tour Service

ACTIVITIES:

Bicycling	Bowling	Hiking
Rec Equip Avail	Tours	

RESTRICTIONS: No pets allowed. Use of dispensary limited to emergency care.

WARNING: Venting gas surrounds the area as a result of volcanic acid. The sulfur fumes could be noxious or hazardous to people with heart or lung disorders.

WAIANAE ARMY RECREATION CENTER (HI05R6)
Army Support Command Fort Shafter, HI 96858-5000

TELEPHONE NUMBER INFORMATION: Main installation numbers: Comm: 808-471-7110, DSN: 315-430-0111.

LOCATION: Off post. On west coast of Oahu. Take I-H1 W to HI-93 (Farrington Hwy); N to Waianae. USMRA: page 129 (B-6). NMI: Schofield Barracks, 20 mi NE. NMC: Honolulu, 35 mi SE.

HAWAII
WAIANAE ARMY RECREATION CENTER, continued

DESCRIPTION OF AREA: Located along beach of Pokai Bay in once-quiet fishing and plantation village. One of the favorite swimming and fishing spots on Oahu. The facility is one of the finest on the island. Full range of support facilities at Schofield Barracks.

SEASON OF OPERATION: Year round.

ELIGIBILITY: Active/Retired/Reserve/DoD Civilians/Other Federal Employees.

RESERVATIONS: Required with dep: up to 90 days in adv for AD Army; up to 80 days in adv for other AD and Ret; up to 60 days in adv for Res and DoD Civ; up to 30 days for other Federal Employees. Address: Waianae Army Recreation Center, 85-010 Army Street, Waianae, HI 96792-5000. **Comm: 808-668-3636, 800-333-4158 (from mainland), or 800-847-6771 (from outer islands),** 0900-1600 M-F, Hawaiian time.

OCEANFRONT LODGING:	NO UNITS		FEE
Deluxe Cabins	6	2 bdrm	$55-70 dly
carpet, VCR	3	3 bdrm	65-75 dly
Standard Cabins	25	2 bdrm	40-55 dly
Studio	5	1 large rm	30-40 dly

A/C, kit, refr, color TV, deck, grill. 3 cabins constructed for handicapped.

SPT FACILITIES:	Beach	Club/all ranks	Conv/Pkg Store
	First Aid Sta	Grills	Pavilions/fee
	Picnic Area	Restrooms	Showers
	Snack Bar	Water Sports	Equipment Rental
ACTIVITIES:	Surfing	Snorkeling	Swimming

Outdoor sports facilities, 5-minute walk from camp.

RESTRICTIONS: No pets allowed. 14-day limit.

IDAHO

ISLAND PARK RECREATION AREA (ID05R4)
Idaho Falls Naval Administrative Unit, ID 84302-1613
This recreation area will be administered by Mountain Home Air Force Base begining in 1996. For more information call the number under reservations for Mountain Home Fam-Camp on page 79.

TELEPHONE NUMBER INFORMATION: Main installation numbers: Comm: 208-522-0767, FTS: 208-524-3214.

LOCATION: Off base. Near US-20 at Island Park. *Patrons must obtain keys at the Naval Administrative Unit in Idaho Falls by 2130 hours M-F, 1200 Sa.* From I-15 N of Idaho Falls, take exit 119 W to Skyline Dr; R to 1575 N Skyline. Directions to sites will be furnished at time of check-in. USMRA: page 98 (G-7). NMI: Hill AFB UT, 260 mi S. NMC: Idaho Falls, 80 mi S.

IDAHO
ISLAND PARK RECREATION AREA, continued

DESCRIPTION OF AREA: 6 trailers at 4 different locations in Island Park area: 2 units at **Pond's Lodge** within 1 mile of Buffalo River, North Fork of the Snake River, and Island Park Reservoir, which provide excellent fishing; 1 unit is at **Henry's Lake** which is nationally known for its trophy fish, yielding cutthroat, rainbow and brook trout near record size; **Lionshead Resort**, 8 miles from the West entrance to Yellowstone Park, has 1 unit—Hebgen Lake MT is 4 miles away and offers blue-ribbon trout fishing. Full range of support facilities at Hill AFB.

SEASON OF OPERATION: 15 May-15 Sep.

ELIGIBILITY: Active/Retired/Reserves (must have commissary card).

RESERVATIONS: Required; may be made up to 30 days in adv. Address: Navy MWR, 1575 North Skyline Dr, Idaho Falls, ID 83402-1613. **Comm: 208-522-0767.**

CAMP FACILITIES: Travel Trailers are 24, fully self-contained, sleep 6 adults and 2 children, and are equipped with cooking and eating utensils. All three areas offer snack bars/restaurants and game rooms. There are numerous hiking, bicycling and nature trails. *No pets are allowed in any of the facilities.*

Pond's Lodge

	NO UNITS	HOOKUPS	FEE
Travel Trailers	2	W/S/E	$15.00 dly

Facilities include a lodge with grocery store, restaurant, lounge and playground. Island Park Reservoir, 1 mile from the trailers, offers boating, water skiing, fishing and a free public boat ramp.

Henry's Lake

Travel Trailer	1	W/S/E	$15.00 dly

Facilities include commercial boat and float tube launching; the lodge has rental boats available.

Lionshead Resort

Travel Trailer	1	W/S/E	$15.00 dly

Mack's Inn

Travel Trailers	2	W/S/E	$15.00 dly

RESTRICTIONS: No pets allowed. Firearms must be licensed and registered.

MOUNTAIN HOME FAM-CAMP (ID03R4)
Mountain Home Air Force Base, ID 83648-5000

TELEPHONE NUMBER INFORMATION: Main installation numbers: Comm: 208-828-2111, DSN: 312-728-1110. Police for fam-camp, Comm: 208-828-2256.

LOCATION: On base. From I-84, take ID-67 12 mi SW to base and through Main Gate. R on first street; go 1/4 mi, turn R to Fam-Camp. Check in at Fam-Camp. USMRA: page 98 (C-9). NMC: Boise, 50 mi NW.

IDAHO
MOUNTAIN HOME FAM-CAMP, continued

DESCRIPTION OF AREA: Located in open country surrounded by mountains, close to Snake River. Sun Valley approx 100 mi NE. Excellent access to vast public lands and recreation. Ideal base for many sightseeing and recreational activities. Fam-camp facilities are handicapped accessible. Existing hardstand pads were renovated in 93-94 with landscape improvements. Full range of support facilities on base.

SEASON OF OPERATION: Year round.

ELIGIBILITY: Active/Retired.

RESERVATIONS: No adv resv. Address: 366 SG/SSRO, 615 Pine St, Mountain Home AFB, ID 83648-5000. Comm: 208-828-6333, DSN: 312-728-6333.

CAMP FACILITIES:	NO UNITS	HOOKUPS	FEE
Camper Spaces	22 Hardstand	W/S/E (110/20/30A	$10.00 dly
Tent Area	10	None	6.00 dly

SPT FACILITIES:			
	Chapel	Golf	Grills
	Ice	Laundry	Picnic Area
	Playground	Rec Equip Rntl	Restrooms
	Sewage Dmp Sta	Showers	Skeet/Trap Range
			nearby

MWR operates a marina 20 mi S of base with boat rentals and good fishing. Outdoor Recreation operates a very popular whitewater rafting program.

ACTIVITIES:		
	Fishing (Apr-Sep) Hunting	Sightseeing/
	Snow Skiing/nearby	ghost towns

RESTRICTIONS: Pets (2 per site) allowed on leash. Host on site in summer.

STRIKE DAM MARINA (ID02R4)
Mountain Home Air Force Base, ID 83648-5000

TELEPHONE NUMBER INFORMATION: Main installation numbers: Comm: 208-828-2111, DSN: 312-728-1110. Police for marina area, Comm: 208-828-2256, DSN: 312-728-2256.

LOCATION: Off base. From I-84 E of Boise, follow signs to Mountain Home AFB (on ID-67) and on to C J Strike Reservoir. USMRA: page 98 (B-9). NMI: Mountain Home AFB, 27 mi NE. NMC: Boise, 60 miles N.

DESCRIPTION OF AREA: Situated along Snake River and surrounded by mountains. Full support for water sports and picnic activities. Full range of support facilities Mountain Home AFB.

SEASON OF OPERATION: 15 Apr-Labor Day.

IDAHO
STRIKE DAM MARINA, continued

ELIGIBILITY: Active/Retired/DoD Civilians.

RESERVATIONS: Accepted up to 2 weeks in adv. Address: 366 MWRSS/MWRO, ATTN: Strike Dam Marina, Bldg 2800, Mountain Home AFB, ID 83648-5000. **Comm: 208-828-6333** (Outdoor Adventure Program).

CAMP FACILITIES: There is an open camping area without hookups; camper spaces with hookups are available at Mountain Home AFB.

SPT FACILITIES:	Boat Docks	Boat Launch	Boat Rntl
	Fishing Tackle	Game Room	Golf/on base
	Grills	Marina	Picnic Area
	Restrooms	Snack Bar	Water Sports Eq

ACTIVITIES:	Boating	Fishing/license	Jet Skiing
	Pontoon Boat/26 '	Sailing	Water Skiing
	Wind Surfing		

RESTRICTIONS: Pets allowed on leash. Day use only.

ILLINOIS

SCOTT FAM-CAMP (IL09R2)
Scott Air Force Base, IL 62225-5225

TELEPHONE NUMBER INFORMATION: Main installation numbers: Comm: 618-256-1110, DSN: 312-576-1110. Police for fam-camp, Comm: 618-256-3000.

LOCATION: On base. From I-64 at exit 19A (Scott AFB Exit); go S on IL-158. At 2d traffic light, turn L to base. Ask gate guard for directions to Gateway Community Activities Center (open 1000-2200). USMRA: page 64 (D-8). NMC: St Louis MO, 23 mi W.

DESCRIPTION OF AREA: Located E of St Louis metropolitan area near O'Fallon. Camp is situated in a wooded area adjacent to base lake and was completely redone in the summer of 1985. Full range of support facilities available on base.

SEASON OF OPERATION: Year round.

ELIGIBILITY: Active/Retired/Reserve/DoD Civilians.

RESERVATIONS: *Accepted up to 60 days in adv for incoming PCS only*. Address: Outdoor Rec, 375 SVS/SVRO, 506 Scott Dr, Room 227, Scott AFB, IL 62225-5225. **Comm: 618-256-2067, DSN: 312-576-2067.**

CAMP FACILITIES:	NO UNITS	HOOKUPS	FEE
Camper Spaces	12 Gravel	W/E (110)	$10.00 dly
Overflow	4 Primitive	None	10.00 dly

SPT FACILITIES:	Chapel	Gas	Golf
	Grills	Picnic Area	Racquet Sports
	Restrooms	Sewage Dmp Sta	Shoppette
	Skeet/Trap Rg	Sports Fields	Snack Bar/near
	Tennis Courts		

ACTIVITIES:	Fishing/base permit req	Rec Equip Avail

RESTRICTIONS: Pets allowed on leash; must have current and complete immunizations. 30-day limit. Check out 1100. Water hookups will not be left on continuously when temperatures are below freezing. No open campfires. Fee receipt must be displayed in window of vehicle. Quiet hours after 2200. Firearms prohibited.

INDIANA
CAMP ATTERBURY CAMPGROUNDS (IN07R2)
Camp Atterbury, Edinburgh, IN 46124-1096

TELEPHONE NUMBER INFORMATION: Main installation numbers: Comm: 812-526-9711, DSN: 312-786-2499.

LOCATION: On post. From I-65 S of Indianapolis take exit 76 (US-31) N; W at Hospital Rd 3 mi to main gate entrance. (Military or dependent ID req.) S into post; E on Headquarters Rd to S on Durbin St. Facilities on L. Check in 0730-1800. USMRA: page 65 (E-6,7). NMC: Indianapolis, 35 mi N.

DESCRIPTION OF AREA: Limited support facilities on post; full range available at Ft Benjamin Harrison, 55 mi NE.

SEASON OF OPERATION: Year round; no water or sewage Apr-Oct.

ELIGIBILITY: Active/Retired/Reserve/NG/DoD Civ/Camp Atterbury Employees.

RESERVATIONS: No adv resv. Address: Bldg 1, MWR, Camp Atterbury, Edinburgh, IN 46124-1096. Comm: 812-526-1101, DSN: 312-569-2101.

CAMP FACILITIES:	NO UNITS	HOOKUPS	FEE
Camper Spaces, 30'+	26 Gravel/Dirt	W/S/E(110/30A)	$ 5.00 dly*
Camper Spaces	Unlimited	None	3.00 dly
Tent Spaces	Unlimited	None	3.00 dly
*$1 non-official users fee per day per vehicle.			

SPT FACILITIES:	Grills	Ice	Laundry
	Nature Trail	Picnic Area	Playground
	Rec Equip	Restrooms/hcp	Shelters
	Showers/hcp	Swimming Pool	

Boat dock and boats avail for fishing at any of the 7 lakes and ponds on post.

ACTIVITIES:	Bicycling	Boating	Fishing/license
	Hiking		

RESTRICTIONS: Pets allowed on leash. Check out 1200. No ATV or off-road vehicles allowed.

INDIANA

CRANE MWR CAMPGROUNDS (IN06R2)
Naval Surface Warfare Center Division
300 Highway 361, Crane, IN 47522-5001

TELEPHONE NUMBER INFORMATION: Main installation numbers: Comm: 812-854-1225, DSN: 312-482-1225. Police for campgrounds, Comm: 812-854-3300.

LOCATION: On base. From IN-37 N of Bedford, take IN-58 W to Gate 1 (or IN-158 W to Gate 3). *OR* from US-231 W of Bedford, take AL-558 E to Gate 4. *It is best to use Gate 4 with a camper.* Check in at marina 0600-1800 dly. USMRA: page 65 (D-8). NMC: Bloomington, 32 mi NE.

DESCRIPTION OF AREA: Located on an 800-acre lake in an area offering fishing, hunting, boating and hiking: a sportsman's dream come true. The campgrounds are located adjacent to the marina. Full range of support facilities available on base.

SEASON OF OPERATION: Year round.

ELIGIBILITY: Active/Retired/NSWC Retired Civilians.

RESERVATIONS: No adv resv *except for annual / seasonal campsites which may be paid in adv, or before 15 Apr.* A minimum of 4 campsites will be kept open for daily/weekly rental. Address: MWR Campgrounds, NAVSURFWARCENDIV, 300 Highway 361, Crane, IN 47522-5001. Comm: 812-854-1743, DSN: 312-482-1743.

CAMP FACILITIES:	NO UNITS	HOOKUPS	FEE*
Camper Spaces	52	W/S/E	$ 5.00/10.00 dly
Tent Spaces	20 Primitive	None	3.00/5.00 dly

*Military/civilian; weekly, monthly and yearly rates avail.

SPT FACILITIES:	Bicycles	Golf	Grills
	Laundry	Marina	Port-a-Pottie
	Sewage Dmp Sta	Showers	Stove Rntl
	Tent Rntl	The Hut/lunch	Trailer Rntl
	Trails		

ACTIVITIES:	Boating	Fishing/license	Hiking
	Hunting/license		

RESTRICTIONS: Pets allowed on leash; owner must clean up after pet. Check out 0900. No firearms allowed. No open fires. Possession of fireworks is prohibited. Unlicensed motor bikes or mini-bikes are not permitted in campground. All campers without appropriate clearance for other activities must stay in immediate area of campground. Monthly campers allowed a max of 30 days on one site; may be rented for another month if there are no other prospective campers. All campers must display current RV plates.

INDIANA

DELAWARE LAKE CAMPGROUND (IN04R2)
Fort Benjamin Harrison, IN 46216-5000
(Fort Benjamin Harrison is mandated to close under the 1991 Base Closure Law. Delaware Lake Campground will close 30 September 1995. Final closure of the base is 10 July 1997.)

TELEPHONE NUMBER INFORMATION: Main installation numbers: Comm: 317-546-9211, DSN: 312-699-1110.

LOCATION: On post. I-465 E to Ft Harrison exit 40; E on 56th St. *OR* take IN-67/US-36 (Pendleton Pike) exit 42 to Post Rd; N to Ft Harrison. Check in at Outdoor Rec Office, Bldg 803, Glenn Rd, 0900-1800. USMRA: page 65 (E-5). NMC: Indianapolis, 10 mi SW.

DESCRIPTION OF AREA: Located in Delaware Recreation Area which also contains Delaware Lake and Duck Pond (picnic area) and is on N end of post between Shafter Ave and Lee Rd. Full range of support facilities available on post.

SEASON OF OPERATION: 1 May-1 Oct. No water or sewage when weather turns cold.

ELIGIBILITY: Active/Retired/NG/Reserve/DoD Civilians.

RESERVATIONS: Accepted. Address: Outdoor Recreation, Bldg 803, Ft Benjamin Harrison, IN 46216-5040. **Comm: 317-542-4997.**

CAMP FACILITIES:	NO UNITS	HOOKUPS	FEE
Camper Spaces	20 Gravel	W/S/E (110/220)	$ 9.00 dly
Tent Spaces	5 Primitive	None	5.00 dly

SPT FACILITIES:			
	Chapel	Gas	Gazebo/fireplace
	Golf	Grills	Paddle Boat Rntl
	Pavilions	Picnic Area	Playground
	Restrooms	Sewage Dmp Sta	Showers
	Racquet Sports at Physical Fitness Facility		

ACTIVITIES:			
	Fishing	Hiking	Jogging
	Rec Equip Avail	Swimming	

RESTRICTIONS: Pets welcomed. After duty hours, check in at Welcome Center, Bldg 609, Comm: 317-549-5506/5507. Cars, campers and motorcycles must be kept on concrete, blacktop or gravel. Quiet hours after 2300. No firearms allowed.

KENTUCKY
CAMP CARLSON ARMY TRAVEL CAMP (KY03R2)
Fort Knox, KY 40121-5000

TELEPHONE NUMBER INFORMATION: Main installation numbers: Comm: 502-624-1181, DSN: 312-464-0111. Police for travel camp, Comm: 502-624-2111 (emergency 624-0911.)

KENTUCKY
CAMP CARLSON ARMY TRAVEL CAMP, continued

LOCATION: On post. *From N*, exit from I-64 or I-71 in Louisville to I-265 (Gene Snyder Freeway); exit to US-31W; S to Ft Knox. *From S*, exit from I-65 at Elizabethtown/Ft Knox to US-31W, N to Ft Knox. Junction with US-60 is 1 mi N of main post entrance (Chaffee Rd). Check in at Travel Camp, 2½ mi W on US-60. USMRA: page 41 (I-3,4). NMC: Louisville, 30 mi N.

DESCRIPTION OF AREA: Camp Carlson was formerly the town of Grahamton, site of the longest operational textile mill in Kentucky. Full range of outdoor activities available. Patton Museum on post. Abraham Lincoln birthplace, Mammoth Cave National Park and Rough River State Park are among nearby attractions. Full range of support facilities available 5 mi from camp.

SEASON OF OPERATION: Year round.

ELIGIBILITY: Active/Retired/Reserve and NG on AD/DoD Civilians.

RESERVATIONS: Required for **cottages and cabins.** Address: Community Recreation Division, 1468A Third Street, Camp Carlson, Ft Knox, KY 40121-5000. **Comm: 502-624-4836, DSN: 312-464-4836.** Discounts available to holders of Golden Age, Golden Access and Golden Eagle Passports.

CAMP FACILITIES:	NO UNITS	HOOKUPS	FEE
Family Cottages*	4		$22.00 dly
Youth Cabins,	4		3 per bunk dly
18 bunks ea			
Camper Spaces	25 Gravel	W/E (110/30&50A)	9.50 dly
Camper Spaces	10 Gravel	None	7.00 dly
Tent Spaces	25 Improved	None	7.00 dly

*Bring linens and cooking utensils.

SPT FACILITIES:	Boat Rntl	Golf/on post	Grills
	Ice	Laundry	Picnic Area
	Playground	Restrooms	Sewage Dmp Sta
	Showers	Sports Fields	Trails
	Vending Mach		

ACTIVITIES:	Fishing/license	Hunting/license	Rec Equip Avail

RESTRICTIONS: Pets allowed on leash. Check out 1100. Tours or visits to the gold vault are not permitted.

EAGLES' REST/FLETCHERS FORK TRAVEL CAMP (KY04R2)
Fort Campbell, KY 42223-5000

TELEPHONE NUMBER INFORMATION: Main installation numbers: Comm: 502-798-2151, DSN: 312-635-1110. Police for travel camp, Comm: 502-798-7112.

EAGLES' REST/FLETCHERS FORK TRAVEL CAMP, continued

LOCATION: On post. From I-24 S of Hopkinsville take Fort Campbell exit; S on ALT US-41 to Gate 1; Lee Rd to stop light; L on Woodlawn Dr; R on Lafayette Rd to camp. USMRA: page 40 (F-7). NMC: Clarksville TN, 12 mi SE.

DESCRIPTION OF AREA: Located adjacent to Land-between-the-Lakes area, between Clarksville TN and Hopkinsville KY. Tennessee Valley Authority manages an extensive reservoir complex on the Tennessee River along KY/TN line. Unlimited water recreational opportunities. The official name of the rec area is "Wohali" which means "Eagle" in Cherokee. **Eagles' Rest** is the main travel camp area; **Fletchers Fork** (approx ½ mi away) is an overflow area where most spaces have hookups. Equipment rental center can supply outdoor recreation equipment for a wide variety of activities. Full range of support facilities available on post.

SEASON OF OPERATION: Year round.

ELIGIBILITY: Active/Retired/DoD Civilians.

RESERVATIONS: Resv required for log cabins; accepted for camper spaces with $7 deposit. Address: Community Recreation Div, Outdoor Recreation Br, Ft Campbell, KY 42223-5000, ATTN: AFZB-PA-CR-O, Army Travel Camp. **Comm: 502-798-3126/5590, DSN: 312-635-3126/5590.** Discounts available to holders of Golden Age Passports.

CAMP FACILITIES:	NO UNITS	HOOKUPS	FEE
Eagles' Rest			
Camper Spaces	22 Gravel	W/E (120/20A-30A)	$ 9.00 dly
Fletchers Fork			
Log Cabins*	4		20.00 dly
Camper Spaces	50 Primitive	W/E (120/30A)	9.00 dly

*AD at Ft Campbell have priority. Sgl rm, beds, slp 4 adults; patrons must furn all bedding and other supplies.

SPT FACILITIES:		
Boat Launch	Boat Rntl	Fishing Pier
Golf	Grills	Laundry
Nature Center	Picnic Area	Playground
Restrooms/hcp	Sewage Dmp Sta	Showers/hcp
Snack Bar	Sports Fields	Stables
Tennis Courts	Vending Mach	

ACTIVITIES:		
Bicycling	Boating	Fishing/license
Hiking	Hunting	Rec Equip Avail

RESTRICTIONS: Pets allowed on leash. 14-day limit. Firearms are permitted for hunting.

LOUISIANA

BARKSDALE FAM-CAMP (LA09R2)
Barksdale Air Force Base, LA 71110-5000

TELEPHONE NUMBER INFORMATION: Main installation numbers: Comm: 318-456-2252, DSN: 312-781-1110.

LOCATION: On base. From I-20 E of Bossier City, take Barksdale exit. From US-71 enter base S of Bossier City. Check in at fam-camp 0800-1700 M-Sa; after hours, pick site and check in following day. USMRA: page 79 (B-2). NMC: Shreveport, 3 mi SW.

DESCRIPTION OF AREA: Camp is situated in alternatingly open and wooded areas shaded by many oaks and hickories. 3 lakes (Flag, Moon and Harmen) on base offer opportunities for fishing, boating and water skiing. Also, Toledo Bend, Caddo, Cross and Bistineau Reservoir lakes are conveniently located for a variety of water-oriented recreation. Full range of support facilities available on base.

SEASON OF OPERATION: Year round.

ELIGIBILITY: Active/Retired/DoD Civilians.

RESERVATIONS: No adv resv. Address: Outdoor Recreation, 109 Barksdale Blvd West, Suite 201, Barksdale AFB, LA 71110-2164. Comm: 318-456-2636, DSN: 312-781-2636.

CAMP FACILITIES:	NO UNITS	HOOKUPS	FEE
Camper Spaces	12 Hardstand	W/E (110)	$ 6.00 dly
Camper Spaces	6 Overflow	None	2.50 dly

SPT FACILITIES:			
	Boat Launch	Boat Rntl	Chapel
	Gas	Golf	Grocery Store
	Laundry	Picnic Area	Playground
	Rec Equip Rntl	Restrooms	Showers/hcp
	Sewage Dmp Sta		

ACTIVITIES:			
	Boating	Fishing/license	Hiking
	Hunting/license	Water Skiing	

RESTRICTIONS: Pets allowed on leash. No swimming. $20 deposit for site tag and restroom key. Check out 1100. No firearms allowed.

NEW ORLEANS NAS CAMPGROUND (LA08R2)
New Orleans Naval Air Station, LA 70143-5000

TELEPHONE NUMBER INFORMATION: Main installation numbers: Comm: 504-393-3011, DSN: 312-363-3011. Police for campground, Comm: 504-393-3788/3265.

LOCATION: On base. From BUS US-90 S of New Orleans, take LA-23 S approx 8 mi to Belle Chasse, watch for sign to base on R. Check in at Auto Hobby Shop, Bldg 143, 0800-1600. USMRA: page 79 (H-7), page 90 (F-6). NMC: New Orleans, 10 mi N.

DESCRIPTION OF AREA: Campground is just minutes from famous French Quarter and downtown New Orleans. Wide range of support facilities on base.

SEASON OF OPERATION: Year round.

ELIGIBILITY: Active/Retired/Reserve/DoD Civilians.

RESERVATIONS: Accepted with deposit. Address: Morale Welfare and Recreation, Bldg 400, Naval Air Station, New Orleans, LA 70143-5012. **Comm: 504-393-3448, FAX: 504-393-5759, DSN: 312-363-3448/3142.** Discounts available to holders of Golden Age Passports.

CAMP FACILITIES:	NO UNITS	HOOKUPS	FEE
Mobile Home, 2 bdrm*	1	W/E (110/220/30A)	$25 dly
Camper Spaces	17 Gravel/Dirt		10 dly/50 wkly
Camping Trailers	3		20 dly/100 wkly
Tent Spaces			

*Linens, fully equipped kit.

SPT FACILITIES:			
	Chapel	Fitness Center	Gas
	Golf	Grills	Laundry/hcp
	NEX Branch	Picnic Area	Restrooms/hcp
	Sewage Dmp Sta	Showers/hcp	Skeet Range
	Sports Fields	Swimming Pool	Tennis Courts

ACTIVITIES:			
	Hunting	Jogging	Swimming
	Rec Equip Avail		

RESTRICTIONS: Pets allowed. No firearms allowed; must be checked with Security at front gate.

NEW ORLEANS NSA RV PARK (LA03R2)
New Orleans Naval Support Activity, LA 70142-5000

TELEPHONE NUMBER INFORMATION: Main installation numbers: Comm: 504-948-5011, DSN: 312-485-5011.

LOCATION: On base. On W bank of Mississippi. From I-10 in New Orleans take BUS US-90 across "Greater New Orleans Bridge" (also called "Westbank" and "Mississippi River Bridge"). Exit at first ramp for Gen DeGaulle W. L on Gen DeGaulle to 3rd light; L at Shirley Drive to NSA. Report to Officers' Housing, Bldg 700, by RV park. USMRA: page 90 (E-4). NMC: New Orleans, adjacent to base.

LOUISIANA
NEW ORLEANS NSA RV PARK, continued

DESCRIPTION OF AREA: Attractions along Mississippi River include boat cruises, zoo cruise, bus tours, plantations, museums and historic homes. Famous New Orleans French Quarter and Bourbon Street nearby. Full range of support facilities available on base, many within walking distance.

SEASON OF OPERATION: Year round.

ELIGIBILITY: Active/Retired/DoD Civilians.

RESERVATIONS: No adv resv. Address: Naval Support Activity, Bldg 128, New Orleans, LA 70142-5000. Comm: 504-361-2269, DSN: 312-485-2269.

CAMP FACILITIES:	NO UNITS	HOOKUPS	FEE
Camper Spaces	16 Hardstand	W/E (110/220)	$ 6.00 dly

SPT FACILITIES:	Camp Equip Rntl	Chapel	Gas
	Mini Mart	Picnic Area	Playground
	Racquetball	Rec Equip Avail	Restrooms\gym
	Sewage Dmp Sta	Showers/gym	Sports Fields
	Tennis Courts		

ACTIVITIES:	Fishing	Sightseeing	Tours

RESTRICTIONS: Pets allowed on leash. 30-day limit. As NSA is surrounded by the city of New Orleans, finding your way through the maze requires patience; watch for road signs.

NOTE: Discount tickets, tour info and a free gift available at ITT Office (modular bldg). Hours: M 1000-1400, Tu-F 1000-1700, Sa 0900-1400, closed Su and hol. Snack Bar at Bowling Center, Bldg 722, open 7 days a week.

SOUTH FORT MOBILE HOME PARK (LA14R2)
Fort Polk, LA 71459-5000

TELEPHONE NUMBER INFORMATION: Main installation numbers: Comm: 318-531-2911, DSN: 312-863-1110. Police for mobile home park, Comm: 318-531-2227.

LOCATION: On post. From US-171 at Leesville, S to Ft Polk entrance road, E to main gate. 1 block on Louisiana Ave, then R on Utah Ave. Check in at Magnolia Guest House, Bldg. 522, 1200-1800. USMRA: page 79 (C-4). NMC: Alexandria, 45 mi NE.

DESCRIPTION OF AREA: The mobile home park is located near the Bayne-Jones Army Community Hospital. The order of priority for use of the RV spaces is as follows: (1) AD military on PCS orders to/from the post; (2) visiting relatives and guests of patients in Bayne-Johnson Army Community Hospital, or military patients in an area hospital; (3) AD and retired (and other personnel receiving outpatient medical treatment) who must stay near the hospital; (4) friends and relatives visiting military personnel at Ft Polk; (5) military personnel in leave, pass or transient status; (6) retired military in transient status; and (7) other personnel in transient status who are entitled to dependency benefits. Full range of support facilities available on post.

SEASON OF OPERATION: Year round.

LOUISIANA
SOUTH FORT MOBILE HOME PARK, continued

ELIGIBILITY: Active/Retired/DoD Civilians/Selected Civilians (see "Description of Area" above).

RESERVATIONS: Required up to 60 days in advance. Address: Directorate of Engineers & Housing, Attn: Billeting Office, Bldg 522, Utah Ave, Ft Polk, LA 71459-7100. **Comm: 318-531-2941/4822.**

CAMP FACILITIES:	NO UNITS	HOOKUPS	FEE
RV Spaces	10 Grass	W/S/E(110/30A & 220/50A)*	$8.00 dly

*Vehicle owner is responsible for connection to outlets provided. Sewer connection must be sealed with a joint sealer (PVS or rubber gasket) to insure a leak-free connection. Owner responsible for furnishing materials necessary to accomplish these tasks.

RESTRICTIONS: Pets must be inoculated and registered in accordance with current regulations and must be controlled so as not to become a public nuisance or menace. No open fires outside of barbecue pits. Children must be supervised at all times. Patron must arrive prior to 1800 on day of reservation or it will be canceled. (Exception will be made if Guest House is informed of late arrival when reservation is made.) 30-day limit; extensions will be considered on a case-by-case basis. Check out 1100.

TOLEDO BEND RECREATION SITE (LA04R2)
Fort Polk, LA 71459-5000

TELEPHONE NUMBER INFORMATION: Main installation numbers: Comm: 318-531-2911, DSN: 312-863-1110. Police for recreation site, Comm: 318-531-6825.

LOCATION: Off post. Take US-171 N from Leesville; W on LA-111 at Anacoco; bear R onto LA-392. N on LA-191; L at Army Travel Camp sign. Check in at Operations Center 1500. USMRA: page 79 (B-4). NMI: Ft Polk, 45 mi SE. NMC: Alexandria, 60 mi NE.

DESCRIPTION OF AREA: Toledo Bend is the largest man-made lake in the South and 5th largest in the country. Excellent fishing and swimming area. Campsite located on 26 acres of wooded land. Hodges Gardens and Ft Jesup offer sightseeing opportunities. Full range of support facilities available at Ft Polk.

Ft Polk also operates **Alligator Lake Recreation Site** on LA-469 just north of North Fort. It covers approx 20 acres along a man-made lake. Ample space for picnicking and all sorts of sports. Lake itself offers paddle boating and some good fishing. Community Recreation Division operates a check-out center where boats, campers, camping equipment, fishing equipment, scuba gear and water skis can be rented. Equipment can be reserved in advance by calling Comm: 318-531-5332/5350.

SEASON OF OPERATION: Year round.

ELIGIBILITY: Active/Retired/Reserve/NG/DoD and NAF Civilians.

RESERVATIONS: Accepted up to 30 days in adv depending on status of sponsor. Address: Toledo Bend Recreation Site, HC 65 Box 75, Florien, LA 71429. **Comm: 318-531-1974.** *For info only,* Comm: 318-565-4235. Discounts to holders of Golden Age Passports.

LOUISIANA
TOLEDO BEND RECREATION SITE, *continued*

CAMP FACILITIES:	NO UNITS	HOOKUPS	FEE
Mobile Homes, 2 bdrm*	12	W/S/E (110)	$25.00 dly
Camper Spaces, 33 ft	15 Gravel	W/E (110)	5.00 dly
Tent Spaces	Unlimited	None	2.00 dly

*2 baths, sleeper sofa, TV, fully equipped Kit w/MW, pots, pans and utensils. Bring bed linens and towels.

SPT FACILITIES:	Beach	Boat Launch	Boat Rntl
	Cabanas	Fishing Eq Rntl	Fishing Pier
	Grills	Jet Skis	Marina
	Party Barges	Pavilions	Picnic Areas
	Playgrounds	Rec Equip Rntl	Restrooms
	Sewage Dmp Sta	Showers	Small Store/
	Vending Mach		sumr

ACTIVITIES:	Boating/safety card req	Hiking Swimming	Horseshoes Volleyball

RESTRICTIONS: Pets allowed on leash. Check out 1200 M-Sa, 1400 Su. No firearms allowed.

MAINE

ROCKY LAKE (ME01R1)
Cutler Naval Computer and Telecommunications Station
East Machias, ME 04630-5000
This facility was closed in February 1995.

SPRAGUE'S NECK (ME02R1)
Cutler Naval Computer and Telecommunications Station
East Machias, ME 04630-5000

TELEPHONE NUMBER INFORMATION: Main installation numbers: Comm: 207-259-8229, DSN: 312-476-7229. Police for camp area, Comm: 207-8226/2113.

LOCATION: On base. From US-1 in East Machias, take ME-191 S approx 7 mi to installation. Obtain directions, map and equipment from MWR. USMRA: page 18 (G-7). NMC: Bangor, 100 mi W.

DESCRIPTION OF AREA: Located in a wooded section in eastern corner of Maine, overlooking rugged Atlantic Coast in Machias Bay area. Very rustic. Wide range of support facilities available at Cutler NCU.

SEASON OF OPERATION: Year round, road conditions permitting.

ELIGIBILITY: Active/Retired/DoD Civilians.

RESERVATIONS: Required: up to 60 days in adv with 50% deposit. Address: MWR, Naval Computer and Telecommunications Station Cutler, East Machias, ME 04630-5000. **Comm: 207-259-8284, DSN: 312-476-7284.**

CAMP FACILITIES:	NO UNITS	HOOKUPS	FEE
Camper Spaces	10 Gravel	None	$ 2.00 dly
Rustic, 4-rm log cabin. Lights, stove, refrigerator; wood heat. *Running water & indoor sanitary fac 15 May-15 Sep.*		16 May-14 Sep 15 Sep-15 May	27.00 dly 22.00 dly

SPT FACILITIES:			
	Firearms Ranges	Fitness Ctr	Gas
	Grills	Gym	Laundry
	Picnic Area	Racquetball	Rec Equip Rntl
	Sports Fields	Tennis Courts	Trails

ACTIVITIES:			
	Canoeing	Clamming	Fishing
	Hiking	Hunting/license	Ice Skating
	Jogging	Sailing	Skiing/XC

RESTRICTIONS: Pets allowed. Fire permits required. Firearms must be registered at the gate.

WINTER HARBOR RECREATION AREA (ME04R1)
Winter Harbor Naval Security Group Activity, ME 04693-0900

TELEPHONE NUMBER INFORMATION: Main installation numbers: Comm: 207-963-5534, DSN: 312-476-9011.

MAINE
WINTER HARBOR RECREATION AREA, continued

LOCATION: On base. From I-95 at Bangor, take ALT US-1 S to Ellsworth; take US-1 N (traveling E) approx 20 mi to ME-186; S to Winter Harbor. Installation is 6 mi from Winter Harbor. Stop at Quarterdeck for directions. USMRA: page 18 (F-8). NMC: Bangor, 45 mi NW.

DESCRIPTION OF AREA: Rec area is located on Schoodic Point in the Winter Harbor section of Acadia National Park along Maine's rugged Atlantic Coast. Many nature and hiking trails, ponds, lakes, and ocean activities are within easy driving distance. Wide range of support facilities on base within walking distance.

SEASON OF OPERATION: Campground: 15 Apr-15 Oct; Cabins and trailers: Year round.

ELIGIBILITY: Active/Retired/DoD Civilians.

RESERVATIONS: Recommended. Up to 90 days in adv for cabins and trailers, May-Sep; no limit off season. Campground, no limit. Drop-ins as space is available. Address: MWR, 20 Dept, Naval Security Group Activity, Winter Harbor, ME 04693-0138 **Comm: 207-963-5537, DSN: 312-476-9287/9288**; or Comm: 207-963-5534-EX-287/288, DSN: 312-476-9011.

CAMP FACILITIES:	NO UNITS	HOOKUPS	FEE
Rec Cabins*	6		$35-45 dly
Mobile Homes*	5 Gravel		25-30 dly
Camper Spaces	5 Gravel	W/E (110/30A)	12.00 dly
Camper Spaces	1	None	12.00 dly
Tent Spaces	3	None	8.00 dly

*2 bdrm, linens, dishes, TV; 1 cabin equipped for handicapped.

SPT FACILITIES:	Camp Equip Rntl	Camper Rental	Chapel
	Golf/local	Grill	Hiking Trails
	Pavilion	Picnic Area	Playground
	Rec Equip Rntl	Restrooms	Showers
	Tennis Courts		

ACTIVITIES:	Boating	Fishing	Golf
	Hiking	Skiing (DH/XC)	Swimming
	Water Skiing		

RESTRICTIONS: Pets allowed in trailers only for an additional fee.

MARYLAND

ANDREWS FAM-CAMP (MD18R1)
Andrews Air Force Base, MD 20331-0001

TELEPHONE NUMBER INFORMATION: Main installation numbers: Comm: 301-981-1110, DSN: 312-858-1110. Security Police for fam-camp, Comm: 301-981-2001.

LOCATION: On base. E of Washington DC. From I-95 (east portion of Capital Beltway I-495), take exit 9 (Andrews AFB/Allentown Rd) to traffic light at end of ramp; L to main gate. Check in after 1100 at Outdoor Recreation, 1642 Brookley Ave. USMRA: page 42 (E-5). NMC: Washington DC, 12 mi NW.

DESCRIPTION OF AREA: Aerial gateway to Washington DC, home of "Air Force One," the President's aircraft. There is much to do in the way of entertainment, i.e., monuments, parks, museums, restaurants, theaters, zoo, etc. Two excellent 18-hole golf courses within walking distance of fam-camp. Full range of support facilities available on base.

SEASON OF OPERATION: Year round.

ELIGIBILITY: Active/Retired.

RESERVATIONS: Strongly recommended, up to 3 mo in adv, with MasterCard, VISA or DISCOVER credit cards. Address: Outdoor Recreation, 89th MWRSS/ MWRO, 1642 Brookley Ave, Andrews AFB, MD 20331-7002. Make checks payable Outdoor Recreation Center. **Comm: 301-981-4109.**

CAMP FACILITIES:	NO UNITS	HOOKUPS	FEE*
Camper Spaces	11 Dirt	W/S/E (110)	$14.00 dly
Camper Spaces	Overflow	None	8.00 dly
Tent Spaces	Open	None	6.00 dly

*Weekly and monthly rates avail.

SPT FACILITIES:		
Gas	Golf/base	Grills
Lake	Laundry	Picnic Area
Playground	Restrooms	Sewage Dmp Sta
Showers	Skeet Rg	TV Lounge

ACTIVITIES:	Fishing/license	Rec Equip Avail

RESTRICTIONS: Pets are allowed; owner is responsible for animal. 14-day limit; 30-day limit for PCS move. All firearms must be registered with security police. Check out 1100.

ANNAPOLIS FAM-CAMP (MD16R1)
United States Naval Academy/Annapolis Naval Station
Annapolis, MD 21402-5058

TELEPHONE NUMBER INFORMATION: Main installation numbers: Comm: 410-293-1000, DSN: 312-281-0111. Police for fam-camp, Comm: 410-267-2886.

LOCATION: On base. 35 mi NE of Washington DC. S of US-50/301; off MD-648. USMRA: page 48 (D,E-2,3). NMC: Annapolis, in city limits near city dock.

DESCRIPTION OF AREA: Scenic and historic Annapolis offers a walking tour of the Naval Academy Museum, city dock area, and much more. Full range of support facilities available at US Naval Academy and Naval Station.

SEASON OF OPERATION: Year round.

ELIGIBILITY: Active/Retired/DoD Civilians.

RESERVATIONS: Accepted. Address: Recreational Services, Bldg 89, Naval Station, Annapolis, MD 21402-5071. **Comm: 410-293-3580, DSN: 312-281-3580.** Discounts available to holders of Golden Eagle Passports.

MARYLAND
ANNAPOLIS FAM-CAMP, continued

CAMP FACILITIES:	NO UNITS	HOOKUPS	FEE
Camper Spaces	14 Hardstand	W/E (110)	$15.00 dly
Group Camping	1 Primitive		1.00 pers dly

SPT FACILITIES:			
	Boat Rntl	Camp Equip Rntl	Chapel
	Gas	Golf/Academy	Grills
	Marina	Mini Mart	Picnic Area
	Playground	Racquetball	Rec Center
	Restrooms	Sewage Dmp Sta	Showers
	Sports Fields	Swimming Pools	Tennis Courts

ACTIVITIES:	Crabbing	Fishing	Rec Equip Avail

RESTRICTIONS: Pets allowed on leash. No swimming. Firearms are prohibited.

GOOSE CREEK/WEST BASIN RECREATION AREA
(MD03R1)
Patuxent River Naval Air Warfare Center, Aircraft Division
MD 20670-5409

TELEPHONE NUMBER INFORMATION: Main installation numbers: Comm: 301-826-3000, DSN: 312-326-3000. Police for recreation area, Comm: 301-526-3911.

LOCATION: On base. From US-301, MD-5 or MD-4 SE to MD-235. Follow MD-235 to Lexington Park and Naval Air Station. Check in 1200 at Gymnasium, Bldg 458. USMRA: page 42 (F-7). NMC: Washington DC, 65 mi NW.

DESCRIPTION OF AREA: There are two campgrounds. One is at Goose Creek, located along the Chesapeake Bay on Cedar Point Rd; the other is West Basin, and is on Patrol Rd. The Naval Air Station offers a wide range of recreational facilities and a full range of support facilities.

SEASON OF OPERATION: Feb-Nov.

ELIGIBILITY: Active/Retired/Reserve.

RESERVATIONS: Required. Address: MWR Dept, Naval Air Warfare Center, Aircraft Division, Cedar Point Rd., Bldg 458, Patuxent River, MD 20670-5423. **Comm: 301-826-3508, DSN: 312-326-3508, FAX Comm: 301-826-3232.**_For information off season, Comm: 301-826-3508.)_ Ask for a recreation guidebook.

CAMP FACILITIES:	NO UNITS	HOOKUPS	FEE
Camper Spaces	14 Gravel	W/E (110)	$10.00 dly
Camper/Tent Spaces	46 Dirt	None	6.00 dly

Rental trailers, furn, slp 4,		
23' trailers, PB		40.00 dly
17' trailers, no bath		25.00 dly
15' trailers, no bath		15.00 dly

SPT FACILITIES:			
	Archery	Beach	Boat Launch
	Boat Rntl	Camp Equip Rntl	Gas
	Golf	Laundry	Marina
	Picnic Area	Playground	Racquetball

MARYLAND
GOOSE CREEK/WEST BASIN RECREATION AREA, continued

Rec Center	Sewage Dmp Sta	Skeet/Trap Rg
Sports Eq Rntl	Sports Fields	Stables
Tennis Courts	Trails	

ACTIVITIES:

Crabbing	Fishing/license	Hunting
Jogging	Swimming	Water Skiing

RESTRICTIONS: No pets allowed. No firearms allowed. Check out 1200.

RITCHIE OUTDOOR RECREATION CENTER (MD17R1)
Fort Ritchie, MD 21719-5010

TELEPHONE NUMBER INFORMATION: Main installation numbers: Comm: 301-878-1300, DSN: 312-988-1300, DC Area Line: 878-1300. Police for recreation center, Comm: 301-878-4212.

LOCATION: On post. Traveling N from Washington DC, take I-270 W to US-15; N to Thurmont; then MD-550 W to post. USMRA: page 42 (C-2). NMC: Hagerstown, 16 mi SW.

DESCRIPTION OF AREA: Historic Civil War sites surround the area. Close to Appalachian Trail. Snow ski area within short drive. Lakes on post offer fishing, swimming and boating. The lakes are on a "flyway"—many different waterfowl spend a few days. All facilities are handicap accessible. This is a recreation center; *no camping facilities are available.* Full range of support facilities on post.

SEASON OF OPERATION: Year round.

ELIGIBILITY: Active/Retired/DoD and NAF Civilians at Ft Ritchie.

RESERVATIONS: Address: Outdoor Recreation Center, Bldg 834, Attn: ASQNJ-P-CF-R, Ft Ritchie, MD 21719-5010. Comm: 301-878-4186, DSN: 312-277-4186.

SPT FACILITIES:

Bowling	Camp Equip Rntl	Community Ctr
Fishing Tackle	Gas	Golf
Gym	ITR/SATO	Pavilions
Picnic Area	Playground	Pool/Beach
Rec Equip Rntl	Skeet Range	Skill Dev Ctr
Sports Fields	Tennis Courts	Theater
Watercraft Rntl		

ACTIVITIES:

Boating	Fishing	Horseshoes
Skateboarding	Snow Sledding	Swimming

RESTRICTIONS: All pets must be leashed and under control of owner at all times.

SKIPPER'S POINT RECREATIONAL AREA (MD12R1)
Aberdeen Proving Ground, MD 21005-5001

TELEPHONE NUMBER INFORMATION: Main installation numbers: Comm: 410-278-5201, DSN: 312-298-1110. Police for rec area, Comm: 410-671-2222, DSN: 312-584-2222.

MARYLAND
SKIPPER'S POINT RECREATIONAL AREA, continued

LOCATION: On post. Located in the Edgewood Area. Take exit 4 (Edgewood/Bel Air) from I-95 to MD-24 E. Follow signs to Edgewood/Aberdeen Proving Ground gate. Turn L at first light on post; straight to L at second light; turn L at first street and go over railroad tracks; turn R and follow road to water. Check in before 1900. USMRA: page 42 (G-2,3). NMC: Baltimore, 35 mi W.

DESCRIPTION OF AREA: This is a primitive camping facility located on a gravel road beside the Bush River approx 10 mi from the Aberdeen Area of the Proving Ground. There are many attractions in nearby Havre de Grace, including Concord Point Lighthouse, Decoy Museum, Stafford Furnace, and the Susquehanna Museum. The Carter Mansion, Jersey Toll House, and Rock Mill Run are all in Susquehanna State Park. Limited support facilities in the Edgewood Area; full range available at Aberdeen Proving Ground.

SEASON OF OPERATION: Year round.

ELIGIBILITY: Active/Retired/Aberdeen Proving Ground Civilians.

RESERVATIONS: Strongly recommended. Address: USAAPGSA, Community Rec Div, Outdoor Rec Program, Aberdeen Proving Ground, MD 21010-5001. **Comm: 410-278-4124, DSN: 312-298-4124. FAX: 410-278-4124.** (*For information Memorial Day weekend-Labor Day weekend,* Comm: 410-612-0714.) Discounts available to holders of Golden Age, Golden Access and Golden Eagle Passports.

CAMP FACILITIES:	NO UNITS	HOOKUPS	FEE
Camper Spaces	6 Dirt	None	$ 5.00 dly
Tent Spaces	15 Dirt	None	3.50 dly

SPT FACILITIES:			
Boat Launch, 20'	Boat Rntl	Chapel*	
Gas*	Golf*	Grills	
Gymnasium*	Nature Trail	Pavilion	
Picnic Area	Playground	Port-a-Potties	

*Located in Edgewood Area, approx 2 mi away.

ACTIVITIES: Hiking

RESTRICTIONS: Pets allowed on a leash. No firearms allowed.

SOLOMONS NAVY RECREATION CENTER (MD05R1)
Solomons, MD 20688-0147

TELEPHONE NUMBER INFORMATION: Main installation numbers: Comm: 301-863-3566, DSN: 312-326-3566. From Washington DC, Maryland and Virginia: 800-NAVY-230.

LOCATION: On base. On the Patuxent River. From US-301 take MD-4 SE to Solomons; *OR* take MD-5 SE to MD-235, then MD-4 NE to Solomons. USMRA: page 42 (F-6). NMI: Patuxent River NAWC, 10 mi S. NMC: Washington DC, 65 mi NW.

DESCRIPTION OF AREA: Located in southern Maryland on the delta where the Patuxent River meets the Chesapeake Bay. Rustic and relaxing area that has retained its natural beauty. Campground and facilities encompass approx 260 acres with extensive frontage on river.

MARYLAND
SOLOMONS NAVY RECREATION CENTER, continued

Only Navy facility dedicated solely to recreation. Historic waterfront community. Local points of interest include Calvert Marine Museum, Cliffs of Calvert, Oyster Fleet, St Mary's City, Battle Creek Cypress Swamp, Naval Air Test & Evaluation Museum, area festivals, Point Lookout State Park and many other historical sites. Full range of support facilities available at Patuxent River NAWC.

SEASON OF OPERATION: Year round.

ELIGIBILITY: Active/Retired/Reserve/DoD Civilians.

RESERVATIONS: Required with payment in full. Resv procedures depend on branch of service and status. Camping resv processed by lottery system. For specific information contact Navy Recreation Center, PO Box 147, Solomons, MD 20688-0147. **Comm: 410-326-4216, 301-863-9074; DC, Maryland and Virginia: 800-NAVY-230. FAX Comm: 410-326-4280.**

CAMP FACILITIES: DD**	NO UNITS	HOOKUPS	FEE*
Camper Spaces	91	W/S/E (110/30A)	15-23 dly
Camper Spaces	150	W/E (120/20A)	12-18 dly
Camper Spaces	7	E (120/20A)	10-14 dly
Camper/Tent Spaces	56	None	7-10 dly
Tent Spaces	Overflow	None	6-8 dly
Tent Spaces	15 Group Sites	None	1.65-2.00 pers dly/ 17-25 min dly

*Includes 4 pers ($2.50 dly ea add pers), higher rate includes Leisure Value Package; weekly and monthly rates avail (dly only for DoD). 2 night min.

Apartments, Bungalows and Cottages, 1-5 bdrm (max 2 pers per bdrm/$2.50 dly ea add pers over 5 yrs of age), A/C, bath, kit, utensils, picnic tables, grill. No linens, pillows, soap, TV or telephones. Waterfront cottages are not heated.

	E1-E5**	E6-E9**	Officers**	DoD**
1 Bedroom	$30-34	$37-43	$45-51	$56-64
2 Bedroom	33-38	40-46	48-54	60-68
3 Bedroom	29-41	36-49	44-56	55-70
4 Bedroom	32-44	37-52	47-59	79-74
5 Bedroom	41-47	48-55	55-63	69-79

**Higher rate includes Leisure Value Package; mo rates avail (dly only for DoD). Cottage 19 equipped for handicapped.

SPT FACILITIES:		
Bait/Tackle	Ball Fields	Beach
Boat Launch	Boat Rntl	Boat Slip Rntl
Camper Rntl	Camp & Sports	Fish/Crab Pier
Gazebo	Equip Rntl	Grills
Ice	Marina	Miniature Golf
Party Pavilions	Picnic Area	Playground
Racquetball Ct	Restrooms	RV Storage
Sewage Dmp Sta	Showers	Softball Field
Swimming Pools	Tennis Courts	Video Arcade

ACTIVITIES:		
Basketball	Bicycling	Boating
Crabbing	Duck Hunting	Fishing/license
Horseshoes	Special Events	Swimming
Volleyball	Windsurfing	

MARYLAND
SOLOMONS NAVY RECREATION CENTER, continued

RESTRICTIONS: Pets are not allowed in lodging units; must have proof of shots and be registered at Reservation and Information Center; must be on leash and under positive control. 1 Apr-15 Oct: 7-day limit to include only 1 holiday weekend. Open fires prohibited except in group site areas where fire rings are provided. DoD Civilians can make reservations.

MASSACHUSETTS

CAPE COD VACATION APARTMENTS (MA13R1)
Coast Guard Air Station Cape Cod
Otis Air National Guard Base, MA 02542-5000

TELEPHONE NUMBER INFORMATION: Main installation numbers: Comm and FTS: 508-968-6300, DSN: 312-557-6300.

LOCATION: On base. Take Massachusetts Military Reservation exit off MA-28; S on Connley Ave approx 2 mi to Bourne gate. Inquire at gate. Check in at Temporary Quarters, Bldg 5204, 0800-1600 M-F. USMRA: page 17 (M-7). NMC: Boston, 50 mi NW.

DESCRIPTION OF AREA: Situated on Cape Cod, a famous New England vacation area. Limited support facilities available on base; wider range available at South Weymouth NAS, 40 mi NW.

SEASON OF OPERATION: Year round.

ELIGIBILITY: Active/Retired/Reserve.

RESERVATIONS: Required with payment: up to 90 days in adv for AD on PCS; up to 60 days in adv for AD on TDY or TAD. Vacationers 2 wks in adv 1 May-1 Oct; up to 30 days in adv for all others/other times. Address: Coast Guard Air Station, Temporary Quarters, Bldg 5204-Ent Street, Otis ANGB, MA 02542-5024. **Comm: 508-968-6461, DSN: 312-557-6461.**

LODGING:	NO UNITS	FEE*
Townhouse Apartments, 2 bdrm, slp 6	4	$19-64 dly
2 dbl beds & bunk bed; TV, kit, furn		
Kitchenette Units, 1 bdrm, LDR, kit, furn	4	17-56 dly
Suites, 2 bdrm, MW, refr, dinette, slp 5	16	17-56 dly
Single Quarters, PB, furn	3	15-51 dly

*Rates vary, depending on rank and duty status.

SPT FACILITIES:			
	Boat Rntl	Commissary	Dispensary
	Exchange	Fishing Tackle	Gas
	Golf/9 holes	Gym	Laundry
	Picnic Area	Playground	Stables
	Theater		

ACTIVITIES:			
	Boating	Fishing	Rec Equip Avail
	Swimming		

RESTRICTIONS: Pets allowed/$2.00 dly. 2-week limit for non-PCS. Check in after hours and weekends by prior arrangement and prepayment.

MASSACHUSETTS

CUTTYHUNK ISLAND RECREATIONAL HOUSING FACILITY (MA04R1)
First Coast Guard District
Boston, MA 02110-5000

TELEPHONE NUMBER INFORMATION: Main installation numbers: Comm and FTS: 617-223-8047/8375.

LOCATION: Off base. On Cuttyhunk Island. From I-195 or MA-6 at New Bedford, S to State Pier (near Elm St). Transportation to the island is via Cuttyhunk Boat Lines M/V ALERT (Comm: 508-992-1432). USMRA: page 17 (L-8). NMI: Newport Naval Education and Training Center, RI, 35 mi SW of New Bedford. NMC: New Bedford, 17 mi N.

DESCRIPTION OF AREA: The dwelling site, a former CG lifeboat station, is located about 17 mi S off the coast of New Bedford and just W of Martha's Vineyard. It is approx 300 yards from the ferry landing and is within easy walking distance of the local community. As the community is very small and depends on ferry service for delivery of supplies, prices will be understandably higher than on the mainland. A small grocery store is available on the island, but visitors are advised to bring adequate food and laundry supplies to meet most of their needs during their stay. Full range of support facilities at Newport Naval Education and Training Center, RI.

SEASON OF OPERATION: Year round.

ELIGIBILITY: Active/Retired.

RESERVATIONS: Required, *by application only*, **with adv payment.** Resv for summer season (Jun-Sep) must be made prior to 1 May; all other seasons as early as possible. During Jun-Aug the facility is *usually* filled with First CG District personnel, but availability is good the rest of the year. Address: Commander (APS), First Coast Guard District, 408 Atlantic Ave, Boston, MA 02110-5000. **Comm and FTS: 617-223-8047/8375.**

LODGING:
One 3-bdrm apartment, slp 8, furn; kit, bath; no TV
One 2-bdrm apartment, slp 5, furn; kit, bath; no TV

FEE:*
$285-500 wkly
285-500 wkly

*Rates vary, depending on rank.

SPT FACILITIES:	Bicycles	Laundry	Nature Trails
	Picnic Area	Playground	Rec Room
ACTIVITIES:	Boating	Fishing	Hiking
	Swimming		

RESTRICTIONS: *Lead paint hazard for children under age of 6.* No pets allowed. 1-week limit (Sa-Sa) in summer; in other seasons partial-week stays are allowed, based on ferry schedule. Preference is given to patrons desiring to stay a full week. Ferry runs daily 15 Jun-15 Sep, twice a week other months.

MASSACHUSETTS

FOURTH CLIFF FAMILY RECREATION AREA
(MA02R1)
Hanscom Air Force Base, MA 01731-5000

TELEPHONE NUMBER INFORMATION: Main installation numbers: Comm: 617-377-4441, DSN: 312-478-4441. Police for rec area, Comm: 617-545-1212 (local police).

LOCATION: Off base. I-95 or I-93 to MA-3, approx 10 mi S of Boston; S to exit 12; MA-139 E to Marshfield. 1.5 mi to Furnace St; turn L. Continue to "T" intersection; turn L on Ferry St. Stay on Ferry St to Sea St; R over South River Bridge; L on Central Ave, bear L at fork. (Do not go straight up hill on Cliff Rd.) Proceed to gate. Check in at Fourth Cliff Recreation Hall, Bldg 7, 1200 daily. USMRA: page 17 (M-4). NMI: South Weymouth NAS, 15 mi NW. NMC: Boston, 30 mi N.

DESCRIPTION OF AREA: Rec area is 56-acre seaside resort situated high on a cliff on the tip of a small peninsula overlooking the Atlantic Ocean on one side and scenic North River on the other. Easy access to Boston, Cape Cod, Martha's Vineyard, Nantucket Islands and a host of recreational activities. Limited support facilities available at S Weymouth NAS.

SEASON OF OPERATION: 16 units: Memorial Day-Columbus Day; 13 units: year round. Self-contained trailers can be accommodated year round.

ELIGIBILITY: Active/Retired/100% DAV/Reserve/DoD Civ.

RESERVATIONS: Required on credit card or with one nights dep. (Ask for map; check on refund policy.) Reservation procedure based on status of sponsor. Address: Fourth Cliff Recreation Area, 348 Central Ave., PO Box 479, Humarock, MA 02047. **Comm: 617-837-9269, 800-468-9547 (0900-1630 M-F).** Visa, MasterCard, and Diners Club accepted.

CAMP FACILITIES:	NO UNITS	HOOKUPS	FEE
Townhouses, 2 bdrm*	2		$70.00 dly **
Chalets, 2 bdrm*	11		70.00 dly
Cabins, furn, 1-3 bdrm*	3		45.00 dly**
Camper Spaces	8 Concrete	W/E (110/30A)	11.00 dly
	3 Concrete	E (110/30A)	11.00 dly
Tent Spaces	Unimproved	None	8.00 dly
Other veh used as sleeping quarters & parked overnight			8.00 dly

Cabins and Tent spaces avail in season only

* Furn, color TV, MW, Crib, highchair, linens, pots, pans, dishes, etc. Bring toiletries.
**Off-season rates available; folding cots may be rented.

SPT FACILITIES:	Beach	Dishwashing Fac	Grills
	Ice	Laundry/sumr	Picnic Area
	Pavilion*	Pay Telephone	Playground
	Rec Hall/sumr	Restrooms	Sewage Dmp Sta
	Showers	Snack Bar	

*May be rented for group picnics; reservation required.

MASSACHUSETTS
FOURTH CLIFF FAMILY RECREATION AREA, continued

ACTIVITIES: Fishing   Horseshoes   Rec Equip Avail
Summer and fall programs available.

RESTRICTIONS: Pets are not allowed inside any cabins or on the porches. In other areas, they must be leashed or tied at all times and must not annoy others. No open fires. Firearms and/or hunting equipment, to include all projectile-firing apparatus, are not allowed. Children will not be left unattended. Wildlife will not be captured, killed or harassed in any way. Visitor information display for local sights and attractions. Also, discount passes and season tickets may be available. Check out 1100. Call desk clerk at 617-837-6785 (before 1400 on weekdays and 1000 on Sundays and holidays) to make arrangements for other hours to check in or out and for off-season hours. *No checking in after 2300.*

HANSCOM FAM-CAMP (MA08R1)
Hanscom Air Force Base, Bedford, MA 01731-5000

TELEPHONE NUMBER INFORMATION: Main installation numbers: Comm: 617-377-4441, DSN: 312-478-4441. Police for fam-camp: (Base) Comm: 617-377-7100; (Bedford) Comm: 617-275-1212.

LOCATION: Off base. From I-95, exit 31B to MA-4/225; W for ½ mi to L on Hartwell Ave; R on McGuire Rd to end. Check in at Campground Office, Bldg T-208. USMRA: page 17 (J-3), page 24 (A-2). NMI: Hanscom AFB, 2 mi W. NMC: Boston, 20 mi SE.

DESCRIPTION OF AREA: Located in wooded section adjacent to base 6 mi from Concord Bridge (site of "the shot heard round the world") and other Revolutionary War historical sites. Easy drive to Boston and the cultural and social world of the city known as the "Hub of the Universe." Full range of support facilities on base.

SEASON OF OPERATION: Year round; no water 1 Nov-1 May.

ELIGIBILITY: Active/Retired/DoD Civilians at Hanscom AFB.

RESERVATIONS: Accepted. Address: Recreational Services, 647 MWRS/MWR, 98 Barksdale St, Attn: Fam-Camp, Hanscom AFB, Bedford, MA 01731-1807. **Comm: 617-377-4670. FAX Comm: 617-377-4670.** *(For information off season,* Comm: 617-377-3348.)

CAMP FACILITIES:	NO UNITS	HOOKUPS	FEE*
Camper Spaces, 60'+	16 Hardstand	W/S/E (110/50A)	$12.00 dly
Camper Spaces, 30'	19 Hardstand	W/S/E(110/20&30A)	12.00 dly
Camper Spaces	21 Gravel	W/E (110/20A)	10.00 dly
Tent Spaces	10	None	6.00 dly

*Weekly, monthly and winter rates available.

SPT FACILITIES:	Basketball	Boccie	Conv Store
	Ice	Laundry	LP Gas
	Picnic Area	Pay Telephones	Restrooms/hcp
	Sewage Dmp Sta	Showers/hcp	

ACTIVITIES:	Deep Sea Fishing	Horseshoes	Rec Equip Avail
	Sightseeing		

MASSACHUSETTS
HANSCOM FAM-CAMP, continued

RESTRICTIONS: Pets allowed on leash and in physical control; owner must clean up after pet. 14-day limit. Quiet hours 220-0700. Check out 1200. Firearms allowed only after Firearms Identification Document has been obtained from local Chief of Police.

ROBBINS POND TRAVEL CAMP (MA01R1)
Fort Devens, MA 01433-5000
(Fort Devens is mandated to close, under the 1991 Base Closure Law, a small national guard/reserve enclave will be retained. A closure date has not been announced for Robbins Pond Travel Camp, final closure of the base is 31 December 1996.)

TELEPHONE NUMBER INFORMATION: Main installation numbers: Comm: 508-796-3911, DSN: 312-256-3911. Police for travel camp, Comm: 508-796-3179.

LOCATION: On post. N of Worcester, from I-190 E on MA-2, or I-495 W on MA-2, to Jackson Gate. Jackson St to R on Patton Rd; bear L to Queenstown Rd; R on El Caney St. Check in at Outdoor Rec, Bldg 3546, 0900. USMRA: page 17 (I-3). NMC: Boston, 35 mi E.

DESCRIPTION OF AREA: Located on Robbins Pond with sandy beach extending from water's edge to shaded area. Natural habitat for wild ducks and geese which may be fed. Full range of support facilities available on post.

SEASON OF OPERATION: 1 Apr-15 Oct; electric only 16 Oct-31 Mar.

ELIGIBILITY: Active/Retired/Reserve/NG/DoD Civilians.

RESERVATIONS: Accepted 90 days in adv with half of total rental. Address: Outdoor Recreation, Community Recreation Division, Box 18, Ft Devens, MA 01433-5180. **Comm: 508-796-3255/2477, DSN: 312-256-3255/2477.** Discounts available to holders of Golden Age and Golden Access Passports.

CAMP FACILITIES:	NO UNITS	HOOKUPS	FEE
Camper Spaces	20 Dirt	W/E (110)	$ 8.00 dly
Camper Spaces	4 Dirt	W only	7.00 dly
Camper Spaces	10 Dirt	None	6.00 dly
Tent Spaces	6 Dirt	None	5.00 dly

SPT FACILITIES:			
	Beach	Boat Rntl	Camp Equip Rntl
	Chapel	Conv Store	Gas
	Golf	Grills	Laundry
	Picnic Area	Playground	Restrooms
	Sewage Dmp Sta	Showers	Snack Bar
	Sports Fields	Tennis Courts	

ACTIVITIES:			
	Fishing	Hunting	Racquetball
	Rec Equip Avail		

RESTRICTIONS: Pets allowed on leash; owner must clean up after pet. Open fires permitted in grills and fireplaces only. No firearms allowed. Check out 1200.

MICHIGAN

CAMP GRAYLING TRAILER PARK (MI08R2)
Camp Grayling, MI 49739-0001

TELEPHONE NUMBER INFORMATION: Main installation numbers: Comm: 517-348-7621, DSN: 312-722-8621.

LOCATION: On post. From I-75 at Grayling, take MI-72 W 4 mi. Check in with Trailer Park Supervisor. USMRA: page 66 (D-5). NMC: Traverse City, 54 mi W.

DESCRIPTION OF AREA: Located in the center of northern Michigan's vacationland and easily accessible to major highways and recreational areas that offer excellent in-season hunting and fishing opportunities, as well as camping, boating, golf, trailriding, skiing and snowmobiling. Camp Grayling is the largest National Guard training site in the country. The trailer park is located .1 mi from, and has access to, Lake Margrethe. Limited support facilities available on post; full range available at Wurtsmith AFB, 80 mi E.

SEASON OF OPERATION: 15 May-15 Sep.

ELIGIBILITY: Active/Retired/DOD Civilians.

RESERVATIONS: Required. Resv for entire season may be made during Dec for following year; resv for shorter periods may be made after 1 Jan for current year. Except for weekend rentals, a minimum deposit equal to half of total cost is required. Address: Camp Grayling Trailer Park, c/o Officers Club, Bldg 311, Camp Grayling, MI 49739-0001. **Comm: 517-348-7621-EX 3389.**

CAMP FACILITIES:	NO UNITS	HOOKUPS	FEE
Camper Spaces	70 Hardstand	W/S/E (110)	$ 9.00 dly
Tent Spaces	10 Gravel		9.00 dly

SPT FACILITIES:	Beach	Boat Launch	Boats
	Grills	Laundry/post	Picnic Area
	Restrooms	Showers	

ACTIVITIES:	Fishing	Swimming	

RESTRICTIONS: Pets at campsites must be caged or chained. $2 security deposit required. Motorized 2- and 3-wheeled vehicles are prohibited in trailer park. Quiet hours after 2300. Checkout 1400. Parents will be held responsible for the acts of their children at all times. Firearms must be registered and used only with the coordination of Camp Grayling Range Control.

LITTLE TROUT CAMPGROUND (MI11R2)
K. I. Sawyer Air Force Base, MI 49843-5000
(K.I. Sawyer AFB is mandated to close under the 1993 Base Closure Law. Little Trout Campground will close 31 August 1995. Final closure of the base is 30 September 1995.)

TELEPHONE NUMBER INFORMATION: Main installation numbers: Comm: 906-372-6511, DSN: 312-472-1110. Police for campground, Comm: 906-346-2677.

LOCATION: On base. In the MI Upper Peninsula. From US-41 W of Marquette, take MI-35 S to CR-480; E to CR-553; S to CR-460; E to main gate. *OR from US-41 SE of Marquette*, take CR-460 W to gate 2.

MICHIGAN
LITTLE TROUT CAMPGROUND, continued

Check in by 1700 at Outdoor Recreation, Bldg 504. USMRA: page 66 (C-2). NMC: Marquette, 23 mi NW.

DESCRIPTION OF AREA: Situated by Little Trout Lake in an area with beautiful lakes and mountain regions offering numerous opportunities for camping, hiking, fishing, backpacking, sightseeing and exploring. Blueberry picking in Jul and Aug. Full range of support facilities available on base.

SEASON OF OPERATION: 15 May-15 Oct.

ELIGIBILITY: Active/Retired/DOD and NAF Civilians.

RESERVATIONS: Accepted up to 90 days in adv with $10.00 deposit; in addition to name, address, phone and dates, specify type of equip, size, whether pulling a car, hookups needed, and number of adults/children. Address: Little Trout Campground, K. I. Sawyer Fam-Camp, 410 MWRSS/MWRO, Bldg 504, Ave A, K. I. Sawyer AFB, MI 49843-5000. **Comm: 906-372-2046, DSN: 312-472-2046.** (*Campground,* Comm: 906-372-2830, DSN: 312-472-2830.) Write or phone for descriptive brochure.

CAMP FACILITIES:	NO UNITS	HOOKUPS	FEE*
Camper Spaces	6 Gravel	W/E (110/220)	$10.00 dly
Tent Spaces	5	None	5.00 dly

*Weekly and monthly rates available.

SPT FACILITIES:			
	Beach*	Boat Rntl	Chapel/base
	Gas/base	Golf/base	Grills
	Laundry	Movie Theater	Picnic Area
	Restrooms/hcp	Sewage Dmp Sta	Shoppette
	Showers	Bldg 869	Ski Hill*
	Hiking & Snowmobile Trails*		

*Nearby

ACTIVITIES:			
	Bowling	Fishing	Hiking
	Skiing/DH&XC	Swimming	

RESTRICTIONS: Pets allowed on leash; not allowed in beach or picnic areas. Check out 1200. Pizza Hanger (906-372-7907) will deliver to fam-camp. Outdoor and recreational equipment, and housing appliance rental (906-372-2046).

POINT BETSIE RECREATION COTTAGE (MI04R2)
Coast Guard Group, Grand Haven, MI 49417-5000

TELEPHONE NUMBER INFORMATION: Main installation numbers: Comm: 616-847-4500.

LOCATION: Off base. From US-131 100 mi N of Grand Rapids, exit at Manton to MI-42; W to Mesick and MI-115 NW to last exit; W into town of Frankfort. CG Sta is at W end of main road in town. Check in after 1200 and get cottage key. Rec cottage is 5 mi N on MI-22. USMRA: page 66 (C-5). NMI: Traverse City Air Station, 45 mi E. NMC: Traverse City, 45 mi E.

DESCRIPTION OF AREA: Located in NW Michigan on eastern shores of Lake Michigan S of Sleeping Bear Dunes National Lakeshore. Crystal Lake and Betsie Bay resorts nearby. Full range of support facilities available at Traverse City Air Station.

SEASON OF OPERATION: Year round.

ELIGIBILITY: Active/Retired/Reserve.

RESERVATIONS: *Required by phone*: 60 days in adv for AD CG; 30 days for others. Address for information and adv payment: Morale Officer, USCG Group, 650 Harbor Dr, Grand Haven, MI 49417-5000. **Comm: 616-847-4530.**

LODGING: 1 Cottage, 2 bdrm, slp 6; fully furn, including gas grill, kitchen utensils, bed linens and blankets. No TV.
FEE: $15.00-25.00 dly

SPT FACILITIES: There are no support facilities at the cottage. The following facilities are nearby or within a short driving distance.

Boat Launch	Boat Rntl	Bicycle Route
Camping	Golf	Rec Equip Rntl

ACTIVITIES:

Boating	Fishing	Hunting
Skiing/DH&XC	Swimming	Water Skiing

RESTRICTIONS: No pets allowed. Check out 1000. 5-day limit in summer; 7-day limit in winter; weekly basis preferred. No telephone at cottage.

MISSISSIPPI

KEESLER FAM-CAMP (MS05R2)
Keesler Air Force Base, MS 39534-5000

TELEPHONE NUMBER INFORMATION: Main installation numbers: Comm: 601-377-1110, DSN: 312-597-1110. Police for fam-camp, Comm: 601-377-3040.

LOCATION: On base. From I-10 take I-110 S to US-90; W approx 5½ mi to Beauvoir Rd (before Coliseum); R 1½ to pass Rd; R 2½ mi to Jim Money Rd; L to Thrower Park Housing; R on Annex Rd ¼ mi. Check in with Host Camper. USMRA: page 43 (F-10). NMC: Biloxi, 2 mi E.

DESCRIPTION OF AREA: Mississippi Gulf Coast holds a wealth of history. In Biloxi, tours are available daily at Beauvoir, the home of Jefferson Davis. The marina is located off Ploesti Drive on Back Bay and offers a park, boating and fishing. Full range of support facilities available on base.

SEASON OF OPERATION: Year round.

ELIGIBILITY: Active/Retired/DoD Civilians.

RESERVATIONS: No adv resv. Address: Outdoor Recreation, 81 MWRSS/MWRO, Annex Rd., Keesler AFB, MS 39534-5225. Comm: 601-377-3160/3186/0002, DSN: 312-597-3160/3186/0002.

CAMP FACILITIES:	NO UNITS	HOOKUPS	FEE
Camper Spaces	20	W/S/E (110/30A)	$ 8.50 dly
Camper Spaces	Overflow	W/E (110/30A)	6.00 dly

MISSISSIPPI
KEESLER FAM-CAMP, continued

SPT FACILITIES:	Archery	Beach	Boat Rntl
	Camp Equip Rntl	Chapel	Fishing Eq Rntl
	Gas	Golf	Grills
	Laundry/nearby	Marina	Picnic Area
	Playground	Quick Shop/	Showers
	Snack Bar	nearby	Sports Fields
	Swimming Pool	Tennis Courts	Trailer Rntl
ACTIVITIES:	Bicycling	Boating	Fishing/license
	Hiking	Jogging	Rec Equip Avail
	Sailing	Swimming	

RESTRICTIONS: No open fires on beach without city approval. Firearms are allowed in camper with no permit required.

LAKE WALKER FAMILY CAMPGROUND (MS12R2)
Camp Shelby, MS 39407-5500

TELEPHONE NUMBER INFORMATION: Main installation numbers: Comm: 601-584-2000, DSN: 312-921-2000. Police for campground: Comm: 601-584-2477/2448.

LOCATION: On post. On US-49 S of Hattiesburg. Exit at "South Gate" and check in at Bldg 1480, 0730-1600. USMRA: page 43 (F-8). NMC: Hattiesburg, 10 mi N.

DESCRIPTION OF AREA: Located on the edge of the DeSoto National Forest, Camp Shelby is an hour's drive from the Gulf Coast and enjoys a mild climate year round. The campground is beside Lake Walker. Limited support facilities available on post; full range available at Gulfport Naval Construction Battalion Center, 60 mi S.

SEASON OF OPERATION: Year round.

ELIGIBILITY: Active/Retired/NG/Civilian Employees.

RESERVATIONS: Accepted up to 45 days in adv; from Apr-Aug troops training at Camp Shelby have priority. Address: Commander, Camp Shelby Training Site, Attn: GSO-SS, Camp Shelby, MS 39407-5500. **Comm: 601-584-2659, DSN: 312-921-2659, FAX Comm: 601-584-2339.** M-F 0730-1600.

CAMP FACILITIES:	NO UNITS	HOOKUPS	FEE
Camper/Tent Spaces	25 Paved	W/S/E (110)	$5.00 dly

SPT FACILITIES:	Grills	Picnic Area	Restrooms/sumr
	Showers/sumr	Tennis	

A second picnic area is at Dogwood Lake.

ACTIVITIES:	Fishing	Rec Equip Avail	Swimming

RESTRICTIONS: Pets allowed on 6' leash. Open fires are allowed only in designated areas. No firearms allowed.

MISSOURI

LAKE OF THE OZARKS RECREATION AREA
(MO01R2)
Fort Leonard Wood, MO 65473-5000

TELEPHONE NUMBER INFORMATION: Main installation numbers: Comm: 314-596-0131, DSN: 312-581-0131. Police for rec area, Comm: 314-346-3693.

LOCATION: Off post. *From I-70 at Columbia,* take US-54 SW to Linn Creek area; L at State Rd A for 6 mi to Freedom; L on Lake Rd A-5 for 4.7 mi to travel camp. *From I-44 NE of Springfield,* MO-7 NW to Richland; R on State Rd A and travel 19.8 mi to Freedom; R on Lake Road A-5 4.7 mi to travel camp. Check in at Rental Office, Bldg 528, after 1500. USMRA: page 81 (D-6). NMI: Ft Leonard Wood, 50 mi SE. NMC: Jefferson City, 40 mi NE.

DESCRIPTION OF AREA: Located on Grand Glaize Arm of the Lake of the Ozarks in the center of a State Wildlife Refuge. Situated on 360-acre reserve with excellent fishing and beautiful scenery. Nearby attractions include Osage Beach, Ozark Caverns, musical shows, theme park, water slides, helicopter rides, etc. Historical and recreational points of interest surround the area. Full range of support facilities available at Ft Leonard Wood.

SEASON OF OPERATION: 1 Apr-10 Oct (full season 27 May-5 Sep).

ELIGIBILITY: Active/Retired/NG/Reserve/DoD and NAF Employees.

RESERVATIONS: Required by phone or in person at the LORA office, Bldg 528 (16 Mar-26 May, 0900-1700 W-F; 27 May-5 Sep, 0900-1700 M-F), with full adv payment. Single night resv will not be made more than 5 days in adv for weekends or holidays. *No mail resv. Information address:* Ft Leonard Wood LORA, Route 1, Box 380, Linn Creek, MO 65052. **Comm: 314-346-5640.** Discounts to holders of Golden Age Passports.

CAMP FACILITIES:	NO UNITS	HOOKUPS	FEE
Duplex, 2 bdrm/linens*	2		$60-73 dly
Mobile Homes, 3 bdrm*			
deluxe w/linens	16		50-63 dly
Mobile Homes, 3 bdrm*	8		40-56 dly
Mobile Homes, 2 bdrm*	8		31-46 dly
Camper Spaces	16 Hardstand	W/E (110)	7-8 dly
Camper/Tent Spaces	21 Hardstand	None	4-7 dly

*A/C, kit, PB, color TV, sofa bed; furn, except cleaning supplies, bedding and towels.

SPT FACILITIES:

Beach	Boat Rntl	Boat/RV Storage*
Country Store	Grills	Laundry
Marina	Party Barges	Pavilion/fee
Picnic Area	Playground	Restrooms
Sewage Dmp Sta	Showers	Ski Boats
Water Sports Equipment Rental		

*By reservation

ACTIVITIES:

Boating	Fishing/license	Hiking
Special Events	Swimming	Water Skiing

MISSOURI
LAKE OF THE OZARKS RECREATION AREA, continued

RESTRICTIONS: Pets must be on leash or under voice control and have all shots (tags displayed); owner responsible for damage caused by pet. Check out F, Sa, Su 1100. No open fires. No swimming except in beach area.

MONTANA

MALMSTROM FAM-CAMP (MT01R3)
Malmstrom Air Force Base, MT 59402-5000

TELEPHONE NUMBER INFORMATION: Main installation numbers: Comm: 406-731-1110, DSN: 312-632-1110. Police for fam-camp, Comm: 406-731-3895.

LOCATION: On base. From I-15 take 10th Ave S exit to AFB. Check in at fam-camp; on-site fee station 24 hrs dly. USMRA: page 99 (E-4). NMC: Great Falls, 2 mi W.

DESCRIPTION OF AREA: Situated in open terrain surrounded by Highwoods and Little Belt range of the Rockies. Full range of support facilities available on base.

SEASON OF OPERATION: Mid May-Oct, depending on weather, for hookups. Year round for limited or no-hookup service.

ELIGIBILITY: Active/Retired/DoD Civilians/Sponsored Guests.

RESERVATIONS: No adv resv. Address: Outdoor Recreation, 43 MWRSS/MWRO, 500 76th St N, Malmstrom AFB, MT 59402-7515. Comm: 406-731-3263, DSN: 312-632-3263, FAX Comm: 406-761-8583.

CAMP FACILITIES:	NO UNITS	HOOKUPS	FEE*
Camper Spaces 30'	10 Gravel	W/S/E (110/30A)	$ 9.00 dly
Camper/Tent Spaces	5 Gravel	None	6.00 dly

*Reduced rates off-season.

SPT FACILITIES:	Chapel	Gas	Grills
	Pay Telephone	Picnic Area	Restrooms
	Sewage Dmp Sta	Showers/Arena	Snack Bar/near

ACTIVITIES:	Rec Equip Avail	Swimming	Tennis
	Programs such as fishing, floating, backpacking, etc.		

RESTRICTIONS: Pets allowed on leash and in physical control; owner must clean up after pet. 14-day limit when camp is at full occupancy. Check out 1200. No open fires except in grills. Quiet hours 2300-0700. On site camp host. Discharging of firearms prohibited on base; must comply with state laws and base regulations.

WAGNER'S GUEST RANCH AND CAMP (MT09R3)
228 75th Street North,
Malmstrom Air Force Base, MT 59402-5000

TELEPHONE NUMBER INFORMATION: Main installation numbers: Comm: 406-731-1110, DSN: 312-632-1110. Police servicing area (Browning Police Dept.), Comm: 406-338-5455 or 911.

MONTANA
WAGNER'S GUEST RANCH AND CAMP, continued

LOCATION: Off base. From I-15 N of Great Falls and Conrad, take MT-44 W to US-89; N to Duck Lake/Route 464 turnoff. E 1.3 mi to camp access road. Camp is approx 8 mi NE of St. Mary. Check in at Lodge 1300. USMRA: page 99 (C-2). NMI: Malmstrom AFB, 170 mi SE. NMC: Great Falls, 165 mi SE.

DESCRIPTION OF AREA: Located in the NW corner of the state, adjacent to Glacier National Park, about 20 mi from Canada. Park boasts 60 live Glaciers, 250 trout lakes, 1100 mi of trails and thousands of wildflowers. Mountain goats, deer, bears and many species of birds may be observed in their natural surroundings. Weather in Glacier area changes rapidly. Land is privately owned. Full range of support facilities available at Malmstrom AFB.

SEASON OF OPERATION: Late May-mid Sep.

ELIGIBILITY: Active/Retired/Reserve/DoD Civilians/Sponsored Guests.

RESERVATIONS: Advised up to 45 days in adv with payment. Address: Outdoor Recreation, 500 76th St North, Malmstrom AFB, MT 59402-7515. Attn: Glacier Military Campground Reservations. **Comm: 406- 731-3263, DSN: 312-632-3263.** No reservations accepted prior to middle of May.

CAMP FACILITIES:	NO UNITS	HOOKUPS	FEE
Camp Trailers, kit, bath			
18', slp 4*	2 In Place		$30.00 dly
24', slp 6*	2 In Place		35.00 dly
Mini Cabins, slp 4	4	None	25.00 dly
Wall Tents, slp 4,	2 In Place	E nearby	17.50 dly
wood stove, cots, tables			
RV Spaces	4 Gravel	W/S/E (110)	10.00 dly
Tent Spaces	Open	None	6.00 dly
*Refr, stove, heat, PB.			

SPT FACILITIES:		
Dining Facility	Grills	Lodge
Pay Telephone	Picnic Area	Restrooms
Sewage Dmp Sta	Showers/fee*	Small Store

*Availability of showers is restricted due to limited water supply.

ACTIVITIES:		
Fishing/fee	Hiking	Photography
Rec Equip Avail	Volleyball	

RESTRICTIONS: Pets allowed on leash; owner must clean up after pets. 14-day limit (when camp is fully occupied). Check out 1200. $10 cleaning/key deposit. Limited services in nearby town: gas, dining, groceries, etc. *As a minimum, you must provide your bedding, food, warm clothing. No electric blankets.* No firearms allowed. Additional facilities are under construction. Fires allowed in designated areas only.

NEBRASKA

OFFUTT FAM-CAMP (NE01R3)
Offutt Air Force Base, NE 68113-5000

TELEPHONE NUMBER INFORMATION: Main installation numbers: Comm: 402-294-1110, DSN: 312-271-1110. Police for fam-camp, Comm: 402-294-6110.

NEBRASKA
OFFUTT FAM-CAMP, *continued*

LOCATION: Off base. From I-80 in Omaha, take US-75 S to Bellevue. E on Mission Ave (NE-370); through town; R on Hancock St for 1.5 mi; L to base lake and fam-camp. Check in at Outdoor Rec Office in snack bar bldg (Castawaays) 0800-1700 M-F. USMRA: page 82 (J-5). NMC: Omaha, 8 mi N.

DESCRIPTION OF AREA: Located near state's eastern boundary with Iowa. Strategic Command Headquarters. Surrounding area open farm country. Full range of support facilities available on base.

SEASON OF OPERATION: Year round; electric only 8 Nov-15 Apr.

ELIGIBILITY: Active/Retired/DoD Civilians.

RESERVATIONS: Accepted up to 30 days in adv. Address: Outdoor Recreation—Fam-Camp, 55 MWRS/MWRO, Offutt AFB, NE 68113-2084. **Comm: 402-294-2108, DSN: 312-271-2108.**

CAMP FACILITIES:	NO UNITS	HOOKUPS	FEE
Camper Spaces	10 Gravel	W/S/E (110/30A)	$10.00 dly*
Tent Spaces	Wilderness		2.00 dly

*Winter Season (8 Nov-14 Apr), electric only, $5.

SPT FACILITIES:	Archery	Bait	Boat House
	Boat Launch	Boat Rntl	Chapel
	Gas	Golf	Grills
	Grocery/nearby	Gym/base	Indoor Track/base
	Laundry	Marina	Picnic Area
	Playground	Racquetball	Restrooms
	Showers	Skeet/Trap Rg	Snack Bar
	Sports Fields	Stables	Tennis Courts
ACTIVITIES:	Boating	Fishing/license	Hunting/license
	Rec Equip Avail		

RESTRICTIONS: Pets allowed on leash. After duty hours, check in with fam-camp host or call Comm: 402-294-2108 and leave message. If you do not check in by 2000, you will lose your reservation. Check out 1200. 14-day limit. Quiet hours 2200-0600. No campfires allowed. No swimming or wading in base lake. No firearms allowed.

NEVADA

FALLON RV PARK AND RECREATION AREAS
(NV05R4)
Fallon Naval Air Station, NV 89496-5000

TELEPHONE NUMBER INFORMATION: Main installation numbers: Comm: 702-426-5162, DSN: 312-830-2110.

LOCATION: On base. From US-50 at Fallon, take US-95 S for 3 mi; L on Union Ln, L on Pasture Rd to base; R on Churchill Ave to main gate. Check in Equipment Rental, Bldg 393, 0700-1500 (M), 1000-1700 (Tu-F), 0800-1200 (Sa). USMRA: page 113 (C-4). NMC: Reno, 61 mi W.

NEVADA
FALLON RV PARK AND RECREATION AREAS, *continued*

DESCRIPTION OF AREA: The RV park is on main base. Nearby Carson River and several lakes offer fishing, boating, swimming, and water skiing. Call MWR for special rates to Reno, ghost towns, Virginia City, and other points of interest. Full range of support facilities available on base.

SEASON OF OPERATION: Year round.

ELIGIBILITY: Active/Retired/DOD Civilians.

RESERVATIONS: Accepted with payment. Address: MWR Dept, Pony Express Outfitters, Naval Air Station, Fallon, NV 89496-5000. **Comm: 702-426-2598/2279, DSN: 312-830-2598/2279.**

CAMP FACILITIES:	NO UNITS	HOOKUPS	FEE
Camper Spaces	16 Primitive	E (120) Central W	$ 5.00 dly

SPT FACILITIES:	Pavilion	Restrooms*	Sewage Dmp Sta
*Closed winter months.			

ACTIVITIES:	Boating	Fishing	Sightseeing

RESTRICTIONS: Pets allowed on leash; owner must clean up after pet. No firearms allowed.

OFF BASE OUTDOOR RECREATION AREAS:

Rose Creek
Location: Off base. Area is located 70 mi S of base off US-95 NW of Hawthorne at Mt Grant. Check in on base (hours and location above) to obtain keys to gate and cabin, and driving directions. USMRA: page 113 (C-5). NMC: Reno, 75 mi NW.

Season of Operation: May-Oct, depending on weather.
Eligibility and Reservations: Same as above.

Facilities: 1 cabin, bunks for 9, living/sleeping area, fireplace, dining table, 1 SB with flush toilet, shower, hot water; kitchen has stove, refr, sink, hot water heater. Some dishes provided. *Bring towels and bedding.*   **FEE:** $25.00 daily

Activities: Fishing (cement fishing reservoir). Permit may be purchased in advance ($8.75 dly per person) at Bldg 393 on base; Nevada state fishing license also required.

Restrictions: No tents or camping allowed. No live bait can be used in reservoir. No firearms allowed.

Horse Creek:
Location: Off base. In Dixie Valley, approx 50 mi N and 25 mi NE of base. Check in on base (hours and location above) to obtain keys to gate and cabin. From US-50, 35 mi E of Fallon, take NV-121 (Dixie Valley Rd) N 17.5 mi to R onto Horse Creek Rd (no sign). Go 8.6 mi to the gate; R at fork to cabin. USMRA: page 113 (D-4). NMC: Reno, 120 mi SW.

Season of Operation: Apr-Nov, depending on weather.
Eligibility and Reservations: Same as above.

NEVADA
FALLON RV PARK AND RECREATION AREAS, continued

Facilities: 1 cabin, 3 dormitory rooms, living/dining area, 1 SB with shower, hot water, upstairs loft; kitchen has stove, refr, sink, hot water heater. *No dishes or other kitchen necessities; also bring towels and bedding.* Indoor/outdoor storage area. **FEE: $25.00 dly**

Activities: Fishing. Permit may be purchased in advance ($8 dly per person) at Bldg 393 on base; Nevada state fishing license also required.

Restrictions: No tents or camping allowed. No firearms allowed.

LUCKY SEVEN FAM-CAMP (NV04R4)
Nellis Air Force Base, NV 89191-5000

TELEPHONE NUMBER INFORMATION: Main installation numbers: Comm: 702-652-1110, DSN: 312-682-1110. Police for fam-camp, Comm: 702-652-2311.

LOCATION: Off base. From I-15 N of Las Vegas, exit E on Craig Rd to Las Vegas Blvd North (NV-604), R onto Range Rd (directly across from Nellis North Gate). *OR* From US-93/95 (Boulder Hwy) in Las Vegas, go N on Nellis Blvd approx 8 mi; continue N on Las Vegas Blvd North (NV-604). *From both routes,* continue to North Gate; turn L onto Range Rd directly across from gate. Follow fam-camp signs. Check in at fam-camp, Bldg 342. USMRA: page 113 (G-9). NMC: Las Vegas, 8 mi SW.

DESCRIPTION OF AREA: Located in desert Southwest with mountains on one side and Lake Mead National Recreation Area on the other. Easy drive to Grand Canyon. Las Vegas attractions nearby. Full range of support facilities available on base.

SEASON OF OPERATION: Year round.

ELIGIBILITY: Active/Retired/DoD Civilians/Guests.

RESERVATIONS: Accepted up to 90 days in adv. Address: 554 SS/SVRC, 5942 Swaab Blvd, Nellis AFB, NV 89191-5000. **Comm: 702-643-3060.** Discounts available to holders of Golden Age and Golden Access Passports.

CAMP FACILITIES:	NO UNITS	HOOKUPS	FEE
Camper Spaces	8 Hardstand*	W/S/E(20/30/50A)	$10.00 dly
Tent Spaces	2	None	4.00 dly

* When needed these can accommodate up to 8 add smaller campers with water and electric hookups only.

SPT FACILITIES:			
	Boat Rntl	Chapel	Gas
	Golf	Grills	Laundry
	Picnic Area	Racquetball	Restrooms
	Sewage Dmp Sta	Shoppette	Showers
	Sports Fields		

Scheduled for completion in 1994: Support facility with registration office, recreation/lounge area, kitchinette, laundry and restrooms.

ACTIVITIES:			
	Boating	Fishing	Rec Equip Avail
	Snow Skiing	Swimming	

RESTRICTIONS: Pets allowed on leash; owner must clean up immediately after pets. 14-day limit; may be extended if there is no waiting list. Alternate spaces, 60-day stays. No open fires.

NEW HAMPSHIRE

NEW BOSTON RECREATION AREA (NH04R1)
**New Boston Air Force Station,
317 Chestnut Hill Rd, Amherst, NH 03031-5000**

TELEPHONE NUMBER INFORMATION: Main installation numbers: Comm: 603-472-3911, DSN: 312-489-1550. Police for rec area, Comm: 603-472-3911, DSN: 312-489-2285.

LOCATION: On base. From I-293 at Manchester take NH-101 W, straight through a set of traffic lights; road becomes NH-114. L at next set of lights onto New Boston Rd for approx 7 mi. AFS is on the R. Check in/out at gate, 24 hours daily. USMRA: page 23 (F-10). NMI: Hanscom AFB MA, 50 mi SE. NMC: Manchester, 8 mi SE.

DESCRIPTION OF AREA: This 2500-acre recreation area is considered to be the best-kept secret in New England. It has 5 stocked ponds and a marina with canoes, rowboats and paddleboats for rent. Fishing at Deer Pond is limited to children 15 years of age and under; no license required. Joe English Hill is great for rock climbing; on a clear day one can see the Prudential Center in Boston. Improvements will continue to be made as funds become available. Full range of support facilities available at Hanscom AFB MA.

SEASON OF OPERATION: Memorial Day - Columbus Day.

ELIGIBILITY: Active/Retired/Reserve/NG/DOD Civilians.

RESERVATIONS: Suggested, with 50% of total cost. Address: New Boston Air Force Station, 317 Chestnut Hill Rd., ATTN: MWR, Amherst, NH 03031-1514. **Comm: 603-471-2452/2234, DSN: 312-489-1550-EX-2452/2234.**

CAMP FACILITIES:	NO UNITS	HOOKUPS	FEE
Mobile Homes, 2 bdrm*	3	W/S/E	$30.00 dly
Camper Spaces	12	W/E(110/220)	10.00 dly
Camper/Tent Spaces	42	None	3.00 dly
Pop-up Campers	5	W/E	15.00 dly

* Furn, except linens and towels

SPT FACILITIES:

Boat Rntl	Camp Store/small	Grills
Ice	Marina	Picnic Area
Playground	Port-a-Potties	Rec Equip Rntl
Sewage Dmp Sta	Showers	Sports Fields
Trails	Vending Mach	

Large picnic area at Deer Pond, accommodating 150-200, has:

Beach/small	Grills	Pavilion
Horseshoes	Volleyball	w/electricity

ACTIVITIES:

Bicycling	Boating	Fishing/license*
Hiking	Jogging	Rock Climbing
Skiing (XC)	Snowmobiling	Soccer
Softball	Tennis	

* MWR $5 Guest Fee per person for length of stay.

RESTRICTIONS: Pets allowed on leash. No firearms allowed.

NEW JERSEY

BARNEGAT RECREATION COTTAGE (NJ06R1)
Maintenance and Logistics Command Atlantic
Governors Island, NY, NY 10004-5098

TELEPHONE NUMBER INFORMATION: Main installation numbers: Comm and FTS: 212-668-7032. Police for rec cottage, Comm: 212-668-7813.

LOCATION: Off base. On northern tip of Long Beach Island NJ. Exit 63 off Garden State Pkwy; NJ-72 E to Ship Bottom; R (S) 5 mi to Long Beach. Check in with caretaker after 1300. USMRA: page 19 (F-8). NMI: Ft Dix and McGuire AFB, 40 mi NW. NMC: Camden, 65 mi W.

DESCRIPTION OF AREA: Converted Coast Guard lighthouse near beautiful beach between Barnegat Bay and Atlantic Ocean. Full range of support facilities available at Ft Dix and McGuire AFB.

SEASON OF OPERATION: Year round.

ELIGIBILITY: Active/Retired/Reserve.

RESERVATIONS: Required, *by application only*, with payment in full, starting mid-Apr. Address: Commander (ps), Maintenance and Logistics Command Atlantic, Governors Island, Bldg 400, New York, NY 10004-5098. **Comm and FTS: 212-668-7813.** (*For information only:* Caretaker Barnegat Recreation Cottage, Barnegat Light, NJ 08006-9999, Comm: 609-494-9800.)

LODGING: 4-apartment beach house; community kitchen and dining room; fully furnished *except* bed linens, blankets, towels and pans.
           FEE: $22-30 dly; $3 for each add person over age of 12.

SPT FACILITIES: Beach   Laundry   Picnic Area

ACTIVITIES: Fishing   Swimming

RESTRICTIONS: No pets allowed. 7-day limit, to include only one weekend. Check out 1200. No campers/trailers allowed in the area.

BRINDLE LAKE TRAVEL CAMP (NJ04R1)
Fort Dix, NJ 08640-5111

TELEPHONE NUMBER INFORMATION: Main installation numbers: Comm: 609-562-1011, DSN: 312-944-1011, FTS: 484-1011.

LOCATION: On post. Take exit 7 off NJ Turnpike; S on NJ-68, which leads to post. L on Wrightstown/Cookstown Rd to Hockamick Rd to Brindle Lake Rd. Check in at Bldg 9905 at Brindle Lake (first bldg when you enter) or Bldg 6045 (Outdoor Recreation) on post. USMRA: page 19 (E,F-6). NMC: Trenton, 20 mi NW.

DESCRIPTION OF AREA: Wooded site located on a 30-acre lake 7 mi from main area of post. Full range of support facilities available on post.

SEASON OF OPERATION: Year round.

ELIGIBILITY: Active/Retired/DoD Civilians.

NEW JERSEY
BRINDLE LAKE TRAVEL CAMP, continued

RESERVATIONS: Accepted. Address: Outdoor Recreation, Bldg 6045, Ft Dix, NJ 08640-5110. **Comm: 609-562-6667, DSN: 312-944-6667, FTS: 484-6667.**

CAMP FACILITIES:	NO UNITS	HOOKUPS	FEE
Camper/Tent Spaces	10 Grass	None	$ 5.00 dly

SPT FACILITIES:	Camp Equip Rntl	Grills	Lodge/fee
	Picnic Areas	Port-a-Potties	

ACTIVITIES:	Firearms Ranges	Fishing/license	Rec Equip Avail

RESTRICTIONS: Pets allowed on leash; owner must clean up after pets.

LAKE DENMARK RECREATION AREA (NJ02R1)
Picatinny Arsenal, NJ 07806-5000

TELEPHONE NUMBER INFORMATION: Main installation numbers: Comm: 201-724-4021, DSN: 312-880-4021. Police for rec area, Comm: 201-724-6666.

LOCATION: On post. I-80 to NJ-15; N 1 mi to post on R. Security ID check required. Check in for mobile homes in Bldg 3050 on Main Rd; for RV and tent sites in Bldg 439 on Whittemore Ave; 1000-1300 M-F. USMRA: page 19 (E-2). NMC: Dover, 2 mi S.

DESCRIPTION OF AREA: Situated in a picturesque area in northern New Jersey, one hour W of New York City. Limited support facilities available on post.

SEASON OF OPERATION: Year round; no water in RV/tent spaces 15 Oct-30 Apr.

ELIGIBILITY: Active/Retired/DoD civilians.

RESERVATIONS: Required. Address *for mobile homes*: Community Recreation Branch, Attn: ITT Office, Bldg 3050, Picatinny Arsenal, NJ 07806-5000; **Comm: 201-724-4014, DSN: 312-880-4014.** *For RV and tent spaces,* Community Recreation Branch, Attn: Outdoor Recreation, Bldg 439, Picatinny Arsenal, NJ 07806-5000; **Comm: 201-724-4484, DSN: 312-880-4484, FAX Comm:201-724-6801.**

CAMP FACILITIES:	NO UNITS	HOOKUPS	FEE
Mobile Homes*	12		$20-30 dly
RV Spaces	3 Gravel	W/E (110)	7.00 dly
RV Spaces	15 Gravel	None	5.00 dly
Tent Spaces	16	None	5.00 dly

*1 2-bdrm, 11 3-bdrm, furn, including dishes, pots and pans, TV; linens on request. Must leave in clean condition.

SPT FACILITIES:	Laundry	Picnic Area	Restrooms
	Showers		

ACTIVITIES:	Boating	Fishing/license + Arsenal Permit

RESTRICTIONS: No pets allowed in new mobile homes; allowed in other areas and must be under control at all times. Trailer availability limited. Security ID check required. Hunting permitted with NJ state license and Arsenal permit with briefing.

NEW JERSEY

LAKE LAURIE CAMPGROUND (NJ14R1)
Willow Grove Naval Air Station, PA 19090-5010

TELEPHONE NUMBER INFORMATION: Main installation numbers: Comm: 215-443-1000, DSN: 312-991-1000.

LOCATION: Off base. In Cape May NJ. Campground entrance is on US-9, 2 mi N of junction with end of Garden State Parkway. USMRA: page 19 (D-10). NMI: Cape May Coast Guard Training Center, 5 mi SE. NMC: Vineland, approx 50 mi NW.

DESCRIPTION OF AREA: This well-planned recreation area is located at Lake Laurie in southern New Jersey close to beaches. Wide range of support facilities available at Cape May Coast Guard Training Center.

SEASON OF OPERATION: Mid-May - mid-Sep.

ELIGIBILITY: Active/Retired/Reserve/Civilian Employees at Willow Grove NAS *only*.

RESERVATIONS: Reservations *must be made in person at Willow Grove NAS ITT Office, Willow Grove PA,* with $50 dep. *No phone or mail reservations taken.* Resv taken beginning mid April for AD at Willow Grove NAS; all others after 1 May. Receipt required to check in. Address for information: Recreation Services, Bldg 2, Naval Air Station, Willow Grove, PA 19090-5010. Comm: 215-443-6082, DSN: 312-991-6082.

CAMP FACILITIES:	NO UNITS	HOOKUPS	FEE
Campers	2	W/S/E (110)	$ 70-90 dly/ 140-160 wkly

Patrons must bring their own cookware, dishes, eating utensils, detergent, toilet articles and bedding.

SPT FACILITIES:		
Beach	Boat Rntl	Camp Store
Fire Rings	Firewood/fee	Ice
Laundry	Miniature Golf	Picnic Area
Playground	Rec Room	Restrooms
Showers/fee	Snack Bar	Swimming Pool
Tennis Courts		

ACTIVITIES:		
Boating	Swimming	

RESTRICTIONS: No pets allowed. Quiet hours 2200-0800. Motorcycles and minibikes are not permitted. No more than 1 car at each site. All small children must be supervised at all times. *No* hot water in campers. Insect control fogging at dusk each evening.

McGUIRE FAM-CAMP (NJ07R1)
McGuire AFB, NJ 08641-5000

TELEPHONE NUMBER INFORMATION: Main installation numbers: Comm: 609-724-1100, DSN: 312-440-0111. Police for fam-camp, Comm: 609-724-2001.

LOCATION: On base. New Jersey Turnpike to exit 7; S on NJ-68 and follow signs to McGuire AFB through Gate 1. Report to Outdoor Recreation, 2415 Vandenberg, 0900-1800. USMRA: page 19 (E-6). NMC: Trenton, 15 mi NW.

DESCRIPTION OF AREA: Small, cozy campground set on 3½ acres of beautiful trees and fields. Surrounding areas have many U-PICK farms with fresh vegetables and fruits. Full range of support facilities available on base.

SEASON OF OPERATION: Year round.

ELIGIBILITY: Active/Retired/Reserve/DoD Civilians.

RESERVATIONS: Accepted with deposit. Address: Outdoor Recreation, 2415 Vandenberg, Attn: Fam-Camp, McGuire AFB, NJ 08641-5012. **Comm: 609-724-2145, DSN: 312-440-2145.**

CAMP FACILITIES:	NO UNITS	HOOKUPS	FEE
Camper Spaces	6 Hardstand	W/E (110/220)	$ 6.00 dly
Camper spaces	Overflow	None	4.00 dly
Tent Spaces	Unlimited	None	2.00 dly

SPT FACILITIES:			
	Gas	Golf/on base	Grills
	Picnic Area	Playground	Quik Shop
	Restrooms/hcp	Sewage Dmp Sta	Showers/hcp

ACTIVITIES:		
	Recreation Equipment Available	Tours
	Weekend Tours Available	

RESTRICTIONS: Small pets allowed on leash. Check out 1200. No wood fires. No firearms allowed.

The fam-camp is going to be relocated and upgraded. Contact Outdoor Recreation for current status and availability. Phone number and address listed under "Reservations" above.

WILDWOOD CAMPGROUND (NJ12R1)
Coast Guard Training Center, Wildwood, NJ 08260-0060

TELEPHONE NUMBER INFORMATION: Main installation numbers: Comm: 609-898-6900. Police for campground, Comm: 609-523-7212.

LOCATION: On base. Take Garden State Parkway to southern end. L at first light and over toll bridge (50¢); 1 mi to Training Center on R. Check in at Administration Bldg after 1300. USMRA: page 19 (D-10). NMC: Atlantic City, approx 50 mi N.

DESCRIPTION OF AREA: Situated along 2 mi of superb beach on a peninsula in SE New Jersey. Many water sports available. Wide range of support facilities at Cape May Coast Guard Training Center, 5 mi S.

SEASON OF OPERATION: 1 May-15 Oct.

ELIGIBILITY: Active/Retired.

RESERVATIONS: Required at least 90 days in adv. Address: Commanding Officer (MWR), Coast Guard Training Center, Cape May, NJ 08204-0060. **Comm: 609-898-6922.**

CAMP FACILITIES:	NO UNITS	HOOKUPS	FEE
Camper Spaces	8 Gravel	W/E (110/30A)	$10.00 dly
Tent Spaces*	8	None	5.00 dly

*Based on 6x10 ' tent; larger tents should be noted when making reservation.

NEW JERSEY
WILDWOOD CAMPGROUND, continued

SPT FACILITIES:	Beach	Beach Hut	Restrooms
	Pay Telephone	Picnic Area	Sewage Dmp Sta
	Showers		

ACTIVITIES:	Fishing	Horseshoes	Jogging
	Swimming	Tennis	Volleyball

RESTRICTIONS: No pets allowed. 10-day limit. Tents not allowed in camper area; screen tents not allowed along a camper. No parking of automobiles or other vehicles in camping area—park in beach parking lots only. No open fires. No firearms allowed.

NEW MEXICO

HOLLOMAN FAM-CAMP (NM06R3)
Holloman Air Force Base, NM 88330-5000

TELEPHONE NUMBER INFORMATION: Main installation numbers: Comm: 505-475-6511, DSN: 312-867-1110. Police for fam-camp, Comm: 505-475-7171.

LOCATION: On base. 10 mi SW of Alamogordo off US-70. Turn L immediately inside main gate on Mesquite Rd. Fam-camp is on L near entrance. Check in Bldg 2395, M-F 0800-1700, Sa 0800-1200, Su 1300-1630; closed hol. USMRA: page 114 (D-7). NMC: El Paso TX, 90 mi S.

DESCRIPTION OF AREA: Situated on open, semi-arid terrain with few trees, but surrounded by shrubs. Nearby attractions include Space Center Hall of Fame, planetarium, zoo, White Sands National Park, horse racing and winter sports. Full range of support facilities available on base.

SEASON OF OPERATION: Year round.

ELIGIBILITY: Active/Retired/DoD Civilians.

RESERVATIONS: No adv resv. Address: Holloman Fam-Camp, Bldg 2395, 49 SVC/SVRO, Holloman AFB, NM 88330-5000. Comm: 505-475-5369, DSN: 312-867-5369.

CAMP FACILITIES:	NO UNITS	HOOKUPS	FEE
Camper Spaces	12 Gravel	W/S/E (110)	$10.00 dly
			60 wk/150 mo

SPT FACILITIES:	Chapel	Gas	Golf
	Laundry	Picnic Area	Playground
	Racquet Sports	Rec Center	Restrooms
	Showers	Swimming Pool	Trails

ACTIVITIES:	Rec Equip Avail	Snow Skiing/29 mi

RESTRICTIONS: Pets allowed on leash; must have current immunizations; owner must clean up after pet. $25 fine for camping without a permit. No open campfires. After duty hours, select your site, then check in with fam-camp host. Check out 1200. Quiet hours 2000-0800.

KIRTLAND FAM-CAMP (NM07R3)
Kirtland Air Force Base, NM 87117-5000

TELEPHONE NUMBER INFORMATION: Main installation numbers: Comm: 505-844/846-0011, DSN: 312-244/246-0011. Police for fam-camp, Comm: 505-846-7926.

LOCATION: On base. From I-40 E of Albuquerque take Exit 164; S on Wyoming Blvd to AFB. Go thru gate to "M" St; R to third building on R (Bldg 20410). Check in at MWR Suppply/Outdoor Recreation, M-F 0700-1700, Sa 0800-1200, after hours drop box. USMRA: page 114 (D-4). NMC: Albuquerque, adjacent to base.

DESCRIPTION OF AREA: Located adjacent to base housing. Sandia and Manzano mountains are E of base. Sandia Crest Recreation Area and aerial tram nearby. Full range of support facilities available on base.

SEASON OF OPERATION: Year round.

ELIGIBILITY: Active/Retired/Reserve/DoD Civilians.

RESERVATIONS: No adv resv. Address: Outdoor Recreation, 377 SVS, 2000 Wyoming Blvd SE, Kirtland AFB, NM 87117-5000. Comm: 505-846-1275/1499, DSN: 312-246-1275/1499.

CAMP FACILITIES:	NO UNITS	HOOKUPS	FEE
Camper Spaces	20 Hardstand	W/S/E(110/220/30A)	$10.00 dly
Camper Spaces	3	W	6.00 dly
Camper Spaces	29	None	5.00 dly

2 spaces equipped for handicapped

SPT FACILITIES:	Boat Rntl	Chapel/base	Gas
	Golf/base	Grills	Laundry
	Picnic Area	Playgrounds	Restrooms
	Sewage Dmp Sta	Showers	

ACTIVITIES:	Hiking	Outdoor Sports

RESTRICTIONS: Pets must be on leash—*no exceptions;* owner must clean up after pets immediately. 7-day limit. Quiet hours 2200-0600. No generators 2200-0600. Check out 1100. No vehicle washing. Must sign in before using any facilities. No firearms allowed.

VOLUNTEER PARK TRAVEL CAMP SITE (NM08R3)
White Sands Missile Range, NM 88002-5000

TELEPHONE NUMBER INFORMATION: Main installation numbers: Comm: 505-678-2121, DSN: 312-258-2211.

LOCATION: On post. On US-70 E of Las Cruces. Entry to installation controlled by Military Police; visitor pass required. USMRA: page 114 (D-6,7,8). NMC: Las Cruces, 25 mi SW.

NEW MEXICO
VOLUNTEER PARK TRAVEL CAMP SITE, continued

DESCRIPTION OF AREA: Many outdoor sports to be found within 100-mi radius. To E is Cloudcroft ski area; horse racing at Ruidoso Downs; Apache Indian Reservation with Ski Apache, a first-class ski area; and Inn of the Mountain Gods, a resort of international repute. El Paso, where you can cross border into Mexico, is to S. To N are Caballo and Elephant Butte Lakes featuring state-operated recreational areas with RV facilities, boating, water skiing, fishing and swimming. Full range of support facilities on post.

Tours to Trinity Site, location of world's first nuclear explosion, are conducted on first Sa in Apr and first Sa in Oct. Arrangements may be made through Public Affairs Office, Bldg 122. Comm: 505-678-1134/1135/1700.

SEASON OF OPERATION: Year round.

ELIGIBILITY: Active/Retired/DoD Civilians.

RESERVATIONS: Accepted. Address: White Sands Missile Range, NM 88002-5035, ATTN: STEWS-DP-AR. **Comm: 505-678-1713, DSN: 312-258-1713.**

CAMP FACILITIES:	NO UNITS	HOOKUPS	FEE
Camper Spaces	8 Gravel	W/E (110)	$ 6 dly/36 wkly

SPT FACILITIES:	Chapel	Fitness Trail	Golf/9 holes
	Grills	Pavilion	Picnic Area
	Sewage Dmp Sta		

Showers planned for the near future.

ACTIVITIES:	Fishing/license	Hiking	Hunting/license*
	Snow skiing		

*Special hunts only; license available on base.

RESTRICTIONS: Pets allowed on leash.

NEW YORK

GRIFFISS FAM-CAMP (NY15R1)
Griffiss Air Force Base, NY 13441-5000

TELEPHONE NUMBER INFORMATION: Main installation numbers: Comm: 315-330-1110, DSN: 312-587-1110. Police for fam-camp, Comm: 315-330-7174, DSN: 312-587-7174.

LOCATION: On base. N of Rome on NY-46. Exit to Griffiss AFB, NY-49/365. Check in at Billeting Office, Bldg 704. Fam-camp at W end of base on Perimeter Rd by golf course. USMRA: page 21 (K-5). NMC: Rome, adjacent.

DESCRIPTION OF AREA: Located in Rome-Utica area. Delta Lake, with many recreational areas, is 4 mi away. Full range of support facilities available on base.

SEASON OF OPERATION: 15 May-15 Oct with hookups; 16 Oct-14 May without hookups.

ELIGIBILITY: Active/Retired/DoD Civilians.

RESERVATIONS: No adv resv. Address: Lodging Office, 416 SV/SVMH, 574 Wright Dr, Bldg 704, Griffiss AFB, NY 13441-4629. Comm: 315-330-4391, DSN: 312-587-4391.

CAMP FACILITIES:	NO UNITS	HOOKUPS	FEE
Camper Spaces	10 Gravel/Dirt	W/E (110/20A)	$ 10.00 dly*

*$5 dly without hookups

SPT FACILITIES:	Chapel	Gas	Golf
	Picnic Area	Playground	Port-a-Pottie
	Rec Equip Rntl	Restrooms	Sewage Dmp Sta
ACTIVITIES:	Fishing	Swimming	Tennis

RESTRICTIONS: 7-day limit, then space available. Call Security Police Comm: 315-330-7174 for information on firearms.

LAKESHORE TRAVEL PARK (NY13R1)
Seneca Army Depot, Romulus, NY 14541-5001
(This facility has seen a drawdown of support facilities.
Commissary, BX, Gas Station are now closed.)
(Closure not under Base Closure Law.)

TELEPHONE NUMBER INFORMATION: Main installation numbers: Comm: 607-869-1110, DSN: 312-489-5110. Police for travel park, Comm: 607-869-1448.

LOCATION: Off post. Seneca Army Depot is located 12 mi S of intersection of US-20/NY-96A near Geneva. Take NY-96A S; go 2½ mi after passing large "Troop Entrance, Gate 3" sign, through railroad underpass; R on Kennedy Rd (1st street) 1 mi to end. Turn L. (Sign on R indicating you are entering government property.) Bear L at fork; check in 1400-1630 M-F at travel park office on R. USMRA: page 20 (H-7). NMC: Rochester, 55 mi NW.

DESCRIPTION OF AREA: Located on shore of Seneca Lake at Lake Housing Area in center of New York's Finger Lakes Region. Seneca Lake, lake-trout capital of the world, approx 42 mi long and 2 mi wide and is largest of Finger Lakes. See Senecca white deer and visit NY State wineries. Area offers some of best fishing and hunting in the country. Full range of support facilities on post.

SEASON OF OPERATION: Year round.

ELIGIBILITY: Active/Retired/DoD Civilians.

RESERVATIONS: Required for mobile homes; accepted for campsites. Address: Seneca Army Depot, ATTN: SDSSE-PER (Travel Park), Route 96, Romulus, NY 14541-5001. **Comm: 607-869-1211, DSN: 312-489-5211.** Discounts *(for campsites only)* to holders of Golden Age, Golden Access and Golden Eagle Passports.

CAMP FACILITIES:	NO UNITS	HOOKUPS	FEE
Mobile Homes, 3 bdrm*	9		$40.00 dly
Mobile Homes, 2 bdrm*	10		40.00 dly
Camper Spaces	6	W/E (110/15A/30A)	10.00 dly
Camper Spaces	2	E (110/15A/30A)	10.00 dly
Tent Spaces	Many	None	8.00 dly

NEW YORK
LAKESHORE TRAVEL PARK, continued

*A/C; furn exc for bath and kitchen towels.

SPT FACILITIES:	Boat Launch Picnic Area Sewage Dmp Sta	Boat Rntl Playground Showers	Laundry Restrooms
ACTIVITIES:	Fishing Swimming	Rec Equip Avail Water Skiing	Snow Skiing

RESTRICTIONS: No pets allowed in mobile homes. Check out 1030. Office open daily Memorial Day weekend-Labor Day weekend; M-F off season.

REMINGTON POND RECREATION AREA (NY14R1)
Fort Drum, NY 13602-5000

TELEPHONE NUMBER INFORMATION: Main installation numbers: Comm: 315-772-6900, DSN: 312-341-6011. Police for rec area, Comm: 315-772-5156.

LOCATION: On post. From I-81 at Watertown, take exit 48; NY-3 NE to gates 1, 2 or 3. USMRA: page 21 (J-3). NMC: Watertown, 9 mi SW.

DESCRIPTION OF AREA: Beautiful area offering every recreational pursuit. Many tourist attractions such as Sackets Harbor Battleground (site of the War of 1812), Thousand Islands, Lake Ontario, Canada, Dry Hill ski area and white- water rafting. Full range of support facilities on post.

SEASON OF OPERATION: 1 Apr-15 Oct.

ELIGIBILITY: Active/Retired/Reserve/NG.

RESERVATIONS: Accepted. Address: Commander, 10th Mountain Div (LI) and Ft Drum, ATTN: AFZS-PA-CRD, Outdoor Recreation Center, NY State Route 26, Bldg P-11115, Ft Drum, NY 13602-5018. Comm: 315-772-5169, DSN: 312-341-5169. Ask for monthly calendar. Discounts to holders of Golden Age, Golden Access and Golden Eagle Passports.

CAMP FACILITIES: Camper/Tent Spaces	NO UNITS 6 Wilderness	HOOKUPS None	FEE $ 6.00 dly
SPT FACILITIES:	Beach Dock/floating Paddle Boats Rec Equip Rntl Skeet Range	Boat Rntl Golf Driv Range Pavilions Restrooms	Chapel Grills Picnic Area Showers
ACTIVITIES:	Canoeing Swimming	Fishing/license Windsurfing	Hunting/license

RESTRICTIONS: Pets allowed on leash. 14-day limit. No sewage dump station. State hunting and fishing licenses and post fishing permits available at Outdoor Recreation Center. No motorized boats permitted.

ROUND POND RECREATION AREA (NY04R1)
United States Military Academy, West Point, NY 10996-5000

TELEPHONE NUMBER INFORMATION: Main installation numbers: Comm: 914-938-4011, DSN: 312-688-1110. Police for rec area, Comm: 914-938-3333

LOCATION: Off post. 5 mi W of West Point on NY-293. Exit 16 from I-87; follow US-6 E to NY-293; continue E to rec area. USMRA: page 28 (C-4); 21 (M-10). NMI: US Military Academy, 5 mi E. NMC: New York City, 50 mi SE.

DESCRIPTION OF AREA: Located on Academy property in a rocky, wooded area near the old Ramapo mines. A delightful place with a natural spring-fed pond. Full range of support facilities available at US Military Academy.

SEASON OF OPERATION: 15 Apr-15 Nov.

ELIGIBILITY: Active/Retired/Reserve/DoD Civilians.

RESERVATIONS: Required: up to 180 days in adv for AD; up to 120 days in adv for Retired Military; up to 90 days in adv for Reserve and DoD Civilians working at West Point or Stewart Army Subpost. Address: Round Pond, Bldg 622, West Point, NY 10996-1985. **Comm: 914-938-2503, DSN: 312-688-2503.**

CAMP FACILITIES:	NO UNITS	HOOKUPS	FEE
Camper Spaces	26	W/E (110/20&30A)	14.00 dly
Tent Spaces	20	None	8.00 dly

Permanent camper sites available.

Lake Frederick Area, 6 mi from Round Pond:
A-Frames, slp 20	10	35.00 dly
Scout Camping		

SPT FACILITIES:	Bait Shop	Boat Rntl	Gas/LP
	Hiking Trail	Marina	Pavilions
	Picnic Area	Rntl Center	Playground
	Restrooms	Sewage Dmp Sta	Showers

ACTIVITIES:	Fishing/license	Rec Equip Avail	Swimming

RESTRICTIONS: Pets allowed on leash in camp area only. Quiet after 2230. Parties are not allowed in the tent area or camper sites. No firearms allowed.

TEAM PLATTSBURGH FAM-CAMP (NY10R1)
Plattsburgh Air Force Base, NY 12903-5000

TELEPHONE NUMBER INFORMATION: Main installation numbers: Comm: 518-565-5000, DSN: 312-689-5000.

LOCATION: On base. From US-9 in Plattsburgh, E on New York Rd through Plattsburgh Barracks Gate, to US Oval, to Club Rd; follow signs to Billeting Office, Bldg 381, to check in (24 hrs dly) and obtain directions to fam-camp. USMRA: page 21 (N-2). NMC: Plattsburgh, in city limits.

DESCRIPTION OF AREA: The base is located along Lake Champlain, the 6th greatest lake in the world. Visit Lake Placid and Canada. The fam-camp is located on the new part of the base on the outskirts of a peaceful, wooded area. It is easily accessible to the many, myriad support facilities available on base.

SEASON OF OPERATION: 15 Apr-15 Oct, depending on the weather.

ELIGIBILITY: Active/Retired.

NEW YORK
TEAM PLATTSBURGH FAM-CAMP, *continued*

RESERVATIONS: Accepted (priority is given to AD, Ret, and Medal of Honor recipients, in that order). Address: Billeting Office, 380th SVS, Bldg 381, Plattsburgh AFB, NY 12903-5000. **Comm: 518-565-7614.** *For information only:* Outdoor Recreation, 380th SVS, Bldg 652, Plattsburgh AFB, NY 12903-5000; Comm: 518-565-7395, FAX: 518-565-5070.

CAMP FACILITIES:	NO UNITS	HOOKUPS	FEE
Camper Spaces, 2 hcp	10 Paved	W/E(110/220)	$5.00 dly
Tent Spaces	10 Open	None	3.00 dly

SPT FACILITIES:			
	Archery	Boat Rntl	Camper Rntl
	Golf	Grills	Gym/pool
	Laundry	Marina/nearby	Picnic Area
	Playground	Restrooms/hcp	Sewage Dmp Sta
	Showers/hcp	Snack Bar	

Also: Nature, physical fitness and ski trails; trips oriented to outdoor activities.

ACTIVITIES:			
	Boating	Fishing/license	Golf
	Jogging	Snow Skiing (XC)	Swimming
	Water Skiing		

RESTRICTIONS: Pets allowed on leash; owner must clean up after pet. 7-day limit. Check out 1200.

THAYER HOTEL (NY05R1)
United States Military Academy, West Point, NY 10996-5000

TELEPHONE NUMBER INFORMATION: Main installation numbers: Comm: 914-446-4731, 800-247-5047; DSN: 312-688-2632.

LOCATION: On post. 11 mi S of Newburgh. From S, take I-87 N to exit 13N (Palisades Parkway) to Bear Mountain traffic circle. From N, take I-87 S to exit 17 (Newburgh) to traffic light, L on NY-17K to US-9W, R to West Point; *OR* take I-84 to US-9W S. Follow signs to West Point; hotel is just beyond the gate. USMRA: page 21 (M,N-10), 28 (D-3). NMC: New York City, 50 mi S.

DESCRIPTION OF AREA: Historic US Military Academy on the Hudson River. The hotel is operated under direction of Superintendent, US Military Academy. Full range of support facilities available at US Military Academy.

SEASON OF OPERATION: Year round.

ELIGIBILITY: Open to the public

RESERVATIONS: Preferred. Address: Hotel Thayer, U.S. Military Academy, West Point, NY 10996-0016. **Comm: 914-446-4731, 800-247-5047; DSN: 312-688-2632.**

LODGING: The Hotel Thayer has 200 guest rooms in addition to dining rooms and facilities for groups. Desk operation: 24 hours daily.

FEE:		
	Single	$ 65-85 dly
	Double	70-90 dly
	Suites	105-155 dly

SUPPORT FACILITIES: The Academy has a full range of support and recreational facilities available. Snow skiing from 15 Dec-1 Mar, weather permitting. Handicap facilities available.

ACTIVITIES: Many sightseeing and entertainment opportunities at the Academy and in nearby towns/cities. Golf, tennis, and swimming in pool in season. Murder Mystery and other theme weekends. Summer vacation packages.

RESTRICTIONS: No pets allowed.

NORTH CAROLINA

CAPE HATTERAS RECREATIONAL QUARTERS
(NC09R1)
Cape Hatteras Coast Guard Group, Buxton, NC 27920-0604

TELEPHONE NUMBER INFORMATION: Main installation numbers: Comm: 919-995-6435.

LOCATION: On base. From US-158 or US-64, take NC-12 to Buxton (approx 50 mi S of Nags Head). E on Old Lighthouse Rd, .5 mi to base. Check in with motel manager until 1600; pick up key in administration bldg 1600-2000. USMRA: page 45 (P-3). NMC: Elizabeth City, 110 mi NW.

DESCRIPTION OF AREA: On the Outer Banks of NC in the Cape Hatteras National Seashore. Beautiful bathing beach and ocean fishing. Site of famous Wright brothers' first airplane flight, 50 mi N. Beach is 100 yards from facility. A sick bay with a corpsman is available for medical emergencies M,W,F 0830-1200. Full range of support facilities available at Norfolk Naval Base VA, 150 mi NW.

SEASON OF OPERATION: Year round.

ELIGIBILITY: Active/Retired/Reserve/Civil Service and CG Civilians.

RESERVATIONS: Required with adv payment: 30-90 days in adv by mail or phone. Address: Cape Hatteras Recreational Quarters, CG Group Cape Hatteras, PO Box 604, Buxton, NC 27920-0604. **Comm: 919-995-6435 (0800-1200 M-F).**

LODGING: Furn, A/C, color CTV, small refr. Maid svc. Off-season rates avail.

6 Units	Slp 5, rollaway avail, comm kit	$25-32 dly
1 Suite**	Slps 7, kit	37-52 dly
1 VIP Suite (04+)	Slps 5, kit	55.00 dly

**MW, dishes, toaster, pots & pans.

SPT FACILITIES:

Beach	Dining Facility	Grills
Medical Clinic	Picnic Area	PX/small with
Showers/outside	Sports Field	grocery section
Tennis Court	Trails	Theater

There are marinas in Hatteras Inlet area, 11 mi S. Sunfish, surfboards, jet skis, fishing gear, and most items for water sports can be rented in the area.

NORTH CAROLINA
CAPE HATTERAS RECREATIONAL QUARTERS, continued

ACTIVITIES: Fishing   Water Sports

RESTRICTIONS: No pets allowed. 7-day limit. No open fires allowed. If pets are found in rooms, patron will be asked to leave. This is a seasonal area for shops, stores, etc; many close during winter months.

CHERRY POINT MWR FAM-CAMP (NC04R1)
Cherry Point Marine Corps Air Station, NC 28533-5000

TELEPHONE NUMBER INFORMATION: Main installation numbers: Comm: 919-466-2811, DSN: 312-582-1110.

LOCATION: On base. On NC-101, E of US-70, between New Bern and Morehead City. Upon arrival call Special Services Officer at 466-4232 (Station Duty Officer after hours) for additional info. USMRA: page 45 (N-4). NMC: Jacksonville, 45 mi SW.

DESCRIPTION OF AREA: Located near Neuse Waterway and Outer Banks area; surrounded by Croatan National Forest. Fam-camp within walking distance of full range of support facilities available on base.

SEASON OF OPERATION: Year round.

ELIGIBILITY: Active/Retired.

RESERVATIONS: No adv resv. Address: ITT Director, MWR, PSC 8009, Cherry Point, NC 28533-0009. Comm: 919-466-2197/2172, DSN: 312-582-2197.

CAMP FACILITIES:	NO UNITS	HOOKUPS	FEE
Camper Spaces	15	W/S/E (110/220)	$10.00 dly

SPT FACILITIES:			
	Boat Rntl	Camper Rntl	Camp Equip Rntl
	Chapel	Gas	Golf
	Grills	Laundry	Marina
	Picnic Area	Pig Cooker Rntl	Racquetball
	Sewage Dmp Sta	Snack Bar	Sports Fields
	Tennis Courts		

ACTIVITIES:	Arts/Crafts	Fishing/license	Hunting/license

RESTRICTIONS: Small pets allowed on leash. Boat rental available at Slocum Creek Marina only; permits must be obtained from Recreation Dept.

FORT FISHER AIR FORCE RECREATION AREA
(NC13R1)
Seymour Johnson Air Force Base, NC 27531-5000

TELEPHONE NUMBER INFORMATION: Main installation numbers: Comm: 910-458-6723.

LOCATION: Off base. On US-421 S of Wilmington NC, go through Carolina and Kure Beaches to Ft Fisher AF Rec Area. Check in 1600 at Reception Center. USMRA: page 45 (L-6). NMI: Camp Lejeune, 70 mi NE. NMC: Wilmington NC, 20 mi NW.

NORTH CAROLINA
FORT FISHER AIR FORCE RECREATION AREA, continued

DESCRIPTION OF AREA: Ft Fisher is located on Pleasure Island between Cape Fear River and Atlantic Ocean. Its history predates Civil War. Beaches within walking distance. Numerous local attractions: NC Aquarium at Ft Fisher; parks, fishing and museums nearby. No support facilities available at recreation area; full range available at Camp Lejeune.

SEASON OF OPERATION: Year round.

ELIGIBILITY: Active/Retired/Reserve/NG/DoD Civilians.

RESERVATIONS: Accepted with adv payment or confirmation with major credit card. May be made up to 90 days in adv for AD Air Force; up to 85 days for all other AD; up to 75 days for ret mil; up to 60 days for all others. Address: Ft Fisher AF Recreation Area, PO Box 380, Kure Beach, NC 28449. **Comm: 910-458-6546/ 6549.** Reservations for groups are welcomed during non-peak use periods; discounts are available subject to size of group, length of stay and time of year.

CAMP FACILITIES:	NO UNITS	HOOKUPS	FEE*
Beach Cottage, slp 12**	4		$60-125 dly
Beach Cottage, slp 6-8**	18		40-115 dly
Exec Cottage, slp 6**	4		60-125 dly
Mobile Home, slp 8	6		50-85 dly
River Marsh Landing	2 executive suites		30-65 dly
(no children under 12)	6 executive rooms		20-50 dly
Lodge Suites, SB, slp 4	6 suites		25-45 dly
Lodge Suites, SB, slp 4	7 suites		30-55 dly
Lodge Rooms, SB, slp 2	27 rooms		15-30 dly
Camper Spaces	16 Hardstand	W/S/E(110/220/30A)	8-15 dly
Tent Spaces	20		4-10 dly

*Rates vary depending on season and day of week; add charge for extra pers.
**Color CTV, W/D.

SPT FACILITIES:	Beach	Boat Ramp	Camp Equip Rntl
	Exercise/Wght Rm	General Store	Gift/Beach Shop
	Jacuzzi	Kennel (resv/fee)	Laundry
	Picnic Area	Racquetball	Restaurant
	Rec Center	Rec Equip Rntl	Restrooms
	Sauna	Sewage Dmp Sta	Showers
	Sports Fields	Swimming Pool	Tennis Courts

ACTIVITIES:	Beach	Boating	Canoeing
	Clamming	Fishing	Petting Zoo
	Rec Equip Avail/	Sailing	Sightseeing
	Swimming		

RESTRICTIONS: No pets allowed in lodges or suites. Pets allowed on leash in cottages and fam-camp only; $25 fee for pets in cottages; owner must clean up after pet; kennel available. No children under 12 in executive quarters. Check out 1100.

NEW RIVER MCAS MARINA (NC07R1)
New River Marine Corps Air Station, Jacksonville, NC 28545-5000

TELEPHONE NUMBER INFORMATION: Main installation numbers: Comm: 910-451-1113, DSN: 312-484-1113.

NORTH CAROLINA
NEW RIVER MCAS MARINA, continued

LOCATION: On base. Off US-17 S of Jacksonville. USMRA: page 45 (L,M-5). NMC: Jacksonville, 2 mi NE.

DESCRIPTION OF AREA: Situated along New River. Offers water sports, recreational and picnic areas. Improvements to the facilities at the camping area are currently under construction. Wide range of support facilities available on base.

SEASON OF OPERATION: Year round.

ELIGIBILITY: Active/Retired.

RESERVATIONS: Accepted. Address: Recreation Director, Marine Corps Air Station, New River, Jacksonville, NC 28545-5000. **Comm: 910-451-6578, DSN: 312-484-6578, FTS: 910-451-6578.**

CAMP FACILITIES:	NO UNITS	HOOKUPS	FEE
Camper Spaces, max 20 ', self-cont	6 Primitive	W	$ 3.00 dly
Tent Spaces	Primitive	None	3.00 dly

SPT FACILITIES:		
Beach	Boat Launch	Boat Rntl
Boat Slip Rntl	Camp Equip Rntl	Gas
Grills	Marina	Picnic Area
Restrooms	Showers	Sports Fields
Trails	Water Sports Equipment Rental	
Patio Room at Marina for parties, by reservation		

ACTIVITIES:		
Boating	Fishing	Hunting/license
Jet Skiing	Softball	Swimming
Volleyball	Water Skiing	

RESTRICTIONS: No pets allowed on beach; allowed on leash in camping area. Call ahead to coordinate visit.

ONSLOW BEACH CAMPSITES AND RECREATION AREA (NC14R1)
Marine Corps Base, Camp Lejeune, NC 28542-5000

TELEPHONE NUMBER INFORMATION: Main installation numbers: Comm: 919-451-1113, DSN: 312-484-1113.

LOCATION: On base. Main gate is off NC-24 6 mi E of junction with US-17. Campsites are located approx 10 mi from gate on NC-172. Clearly marked. USMRA: page 45 (M-5). NMC: Wilmington, 45 mi SW.

DESCRIPTION OF AREA: Located on an island between Inner Coastal Waterway and Onslow Bay. Campsites are on beach or in wooded area. Many commercial fishing and beach areas are also available. ITT Office on base has information on rec activities and discount tickets. Full range of support facilities available on base.

SEASON OF OPERATION: Year round.

ELIGIBILITY: Active/Retired.

RESERVATIONS: Accepted up to 30 days in adv. Address: MWR Activity, Director of Special Services, Camp Lejeune, NC 28542-5000, ATTN: Cabin & Cottages. **Comm: 919-451-7473/7502, DSN: 312-484-7473/7502.**

CAMP FACILITIES:	NO UNITS	HOOKUPS	FEE
Mobile Homes*	18		$6.00-19 sumr/
Apts, eff, 1 bdrm*	8 (E1-E5)		4.50-15 winter
Beach Houses*	3		
Camper Spaces (Area 1)	28	W/S/E (30A)	6.00 dly**
Camper Spaces (Area 2)	28	W/S/E (30A)	5.00 dly**
Tent Spaces (Area 3)	18	W/E	5.00 dly

*For use of AD; PB, furn, TV, dishes, pots, pans and linens; fees apply to all three facilities.
**Rate applies for stays up to 7 days.

SPT FACILITIES:	Bait/Tackle	Boat Dock	Boat Launch
	Bogey/Surfboards	BX/adjacent	Fishing Eq Rntl
	Fishing Pier	Golf/on base	Grills
	Marina/on base	Picnic Area	Playground
	Restrooms	Sewage Dmp Sta	fenced
	Showers	Snack Bar	

Areas 1 and 3 have all the facilities listed above. Area 2 is located in a wooded area and only has a restroom and showers.

ACTIVITIES: Deep-Sea Fishing Swimming

RESTRICTIONS: Pets allowed on leash; must be under positive control.

ROGERS BAY FAMILY CAMPWAY (NC16R1)
Seymour Johnson Air Force Base, NC 27531-5000

TELEPHONE NUMBER INFORMATION: Main installation numbers: Comm: 919-736-5400, DSN: 312-488-1110.

LOCATION: Off base. 6.5 mi N of Surf City on NC-210. USMRA: page 45 (L,M-5). NMI: Camp Lejeune, 15 mi N. NMC: Wilmington, 45 mi S.

DESCRIPTION OF AREA: Situated on SE shore of NC. Great area for water sports. All sites are less than 50 yards from Atlantic Ocean in shaded area. Inland Waterway on W side of campway. Full range of support facilities available at Camp Lejeune.

SEASON OF OPERATION: 1 Mar-30 Nov. Off season by special agreement.

ELIGIBILITY: Active/Retired/Reserve/ DoD and NAF Civilians.

RESERVATIONS: Required, in person, with $25 deposit; up to 60 days in adv for AD at Seymour Johnson AFB; up to 30 days in adv for others. Address: MWR Logistics, 4MWRS/MWRO, 1165 Martin Street, Seymour Johnson AFB, NC 27531-5225. Comm: 919-736-5263/6135, DSN: 312-488-5263.

NORTH CAROLINA
ROGERS BAY FAMILY CAMPWAY, continued

CAMP FACILITIES:	NO UNITS	HOOKUPS	FEE*
Travel Trailers/slp 5	Total of...	W/S/E (110/30A)	$35-40 dly
Travel Trailers/slp 7	6 Gravel		45-50 dly

*Weekly rates available.

SPT FACILITIES:			
	Beach/public	Boat Launch	Chapel
	Gas & LP	Laundry	Quick Shop
	Restrooms	Sewage Dmp Sta	Showers
	Teen Ctr/wknd	Video Game Rm	

There are several fishing piers in local area.
Facilities for handicapped include ramps, stalls, parking and eating.

ACTIVITIES:	Boating	Fishing	Swimming
	Water Skiing		

RESTRICTIONS: Pets allowed on leash; cannot remain in trailer or campgrounds unattended. A cleaning deposit of $15 ($25 with pet) is required.

SEYMOUR JOHNSON FAM-CAMP (NC08R1)
Seymour Johnson Air Force Base, NC 27531-5000

TELEPHONE NUMBER INFORMATION: Main installation numbers: Comm: 919-736-5400, DSN: 312-488-1110. Police for fam-camp, Comm: 919-736-6412/6413.

LOCATION: On base. Take US-70 to Seymour Johnson exit in Goldsboro. Take Berkeley Blvd to base. Check in and out at Billeting Office. USMRA: page 45 (L-3). NMC: Raleigh, 50 mi NW.

DESCRIPTION OF AREA: Fam-camp is surrounded by heavily forested areas and is within walking distance of many of the support facilities available on base.

SEASON OF OPERATION: Year round.

ELIGIBILITY: Active/Retired.

RESERVATIONS: No adv resv. Address: Recreation Services, 4 MWRS/MWRO, Seymour Johnson AFB, NC 27531-5225. Comm: 919-736-5405, DSN: 312-488-6705.

CAMP FACILITIES:	NO UNITS	HOOKUPS	FEE
Camper Spaces	8 Hardstand	W/S/E (110)	$10.00 dly

SPT FACILITIES:			
	Chapel	Gas	Golf
	Grills	Laundry	Picnic Area
	Pistol Range	Quick Shop	Racquetball
	Rec Center	Skeet/Trap Rg	Snack Bar
	Sports Fields	Tennis Courts	

ACTIVITIES:	Jogging	Rec Equip Avail
	Nature Interpretive Trail	

RESTRICTIONS: Pets allowed on leash only.

NORTH CAROLINA

SMITH LAKE ARMY TRAVEL CAMPGROUND (NC12R1)
Fort Bragg, NC 28307-5000

TELEPHONE NUMBER INFORMATION: Main installation numbers: Comm: 919-396-0011, DSN: 312-236-0111. Police for campground, Comm: 919-396-0391.

LOCATION: On post. Take I-95 to Business Loop I-95/US-301 to Owen Drive (changes to All-American Freeway) to Gruber Rd exit. R to dead end at Murchison Rd; L on first paved road .5 mi to travel camp on L. *OR* from US-401 (Fayetteville Bypass) exit to NC-210; N to Smith Lake. Check in at cabin at gate to picnic area 0730-1700. USMRA: page 45 (I,J-4). NMC: Fayetteville, 5 mi SE.

DESCRIPTION OF AREA: JFK Special Warfare Museum and 82d Airborne Division Museum on post; Pinehurst Resort is nearby. Full range of support facilities available on post.

SEASON OF OPERATION: Year round.

ELIGIBILITY: Active/Retired/Reserve on AD/DoD and MWR civilians with letter of authorization.

RESERVATIONS: No adv resv. Address: DCA, Rec Branch, Outdoor Recreation, Smith Lake, Ft Bragg, NC 28307-5000. Comm: 919-396-5979, DSN: 312-236-5979. Discounts available to holders of Golden Age and Golden Access Passports.

CAMP FACILITIES:	NO UNITS	HOOKUPS	FEE
Camper Spaces	13 Gravel	W/S/E (110/50A)	$8 dly/40 wkly
Camper Spaces	11 Gravel	W/E (110/30A)	7 dly/35 wkly

SPT FACILITIES:			
	Beach	Boat Rntl	Camp Equip Rntl
	Chapel/on post	Gas	Golf/on post
	Grills	Ice	Laundry
	Pay Telephone	Picnic Area	Restrooms
	Sewage Dmp Sta	Showers	Water Ski Lift

ACTIVITIES:	Fishing/license	Golf	Swimming/sumr

RESTRICTIONS: Pets allowed on leash in campground only; must be kept under control at all times; no pets in picnic area. Check out 1200. No fishing 1 May-30 Sep when the ski lift is in operation.

WEEKSVILLE CAMPSITES (NC15R1)
Coast Guard Support Center, Elizabeth City, NC 27909-5000

TELEPHONE NUMBER INFORMATION: Main installation numbers: Comm and FTS: 919-338-3941. Police for campsites, Comm: 919-335-6398.

LOCATION: On base. From US-17 in Elizabeth City take NC-34 (Halstead Blvd/Weeksville Rd) S to main gate of Center. USMRA: page 45 (O-1). NMC: Portsmouth VA, 50 mi N.

DESCRIPTION OF AREA: Located off the Albemarle Sound 1.5 blocks from beach. Attractions include the Outer Banks and Kitty Hawk. Wide range of support facilities available on base.

SEASON OF OPERATION: Year round.

NORTH CAROLINA
WEEKSVILLE CAMPSITES, continued

ELIGIBILITY: Active/Retired.

RESERVATIONS: Accepted up to 60 days in adv (very busy Apr-Sep). Address: CGES Office, Bldg 7, Coast Guard Support Center, Elizabeth City, NC 27909-5000. **Comm and FTS: 919-335-6548.**

CAMP FACILITIES:	NO UNITS	HOOKUPS	FEE
Mobile Homes, 2 bdrm, slp 6, furn, color TV	6		$20.00 dly
Camper Spaces	4 Gravel	W/S/E (110)	3.00 dly

SPT FACILITIES:	Beach	Boat Ramp	Boat Rntl
	Camp Equip Rntl	Country Store	Fitness Trail
	Gas	Grills	Gym
	Laundry	Medical Clinic	Picnic Area
	Playground	Racquetball	Rec Equip Rntl
	Restrooms	Sewage Dmp Sta	Tennis Courts

ACTIVITIES:	Boating	Fishing	Swimming

RESTRICTIONS: No pets allowed. No firearms allowed.

NORTH DAKOTA

GRAND FORKS FAM-CAMP (ND01R3)
Grand Forks Air Force Base, ND 58205-5000

TELEPHONE NUMBER INFORMATION: Main installation numbers: Comm: 701-747-3000, DSN: 312-362-3000. Police for fam-camp, Comm: 701-747-5351.

LOCATION: On base. From I-29 take US-2 W for 14 mi to County Road B-3 (Emerado/Air Base); 1 mi to AFB. Check in at Bowling Center, Bldg 202, 0800-1700. USMRA: page 83 (I-3). NMC: Grand Forks, 20 mi SE.

DESCRIPTION OF AREA: Located in an open area. Wide variety of recreational activities available. 2-hour drive to Canada. Full range of support facilities available on base.

SEASON OF OPERATION: 1 May-1 Oct.

ELIGIBILITY: Active/Retired/DoD Civilians.

RESERVATIONS: No adv resv. Address: Fam-Camp, 319 SVS/SVRO, 400 Eilson St, Grand Forks Air Force Base, ND 58205-5000. **Comm: 701-747- 3050.**

CAMP FACILITIES:	NO UNITS	HOOKUPS	FEE
Camper Spaces	21 Gravel	W/S/CTV/E*	$10.00 dly

*10 sites 50 AMP, 10 sites 35 AMP.

SPT FACILITIES:	Boat Rntl	Camp Eq Rntl	Camper Rntl
	Chapel	Fishing Eq Rntl	Gas
	Golf	Grills	Laundry
	Picnic Area	Playground	Restrooms
	Showers		

ACTIVITIES: Boating/nearby   Fishing/license   Hiking
                  Hunting/license

RESTRICTIONS: Pets allowed on leash. Check out 1200. For information on hunting and fishing contact the ND Fish and Game Dept. No firearms allowed.

OHIO

WRIGHT-PATTERSON FAM-CAMP (OH03R2)
Wright-Patterson Air Force Base, OH 45433-5000

TELEPHONE NUMBER INFORMATION: Main installation numbers: Comm: 513-257-1110, DSN: 312-787-1110. Police for fam-camp, Comm: 513-257-6516.

LOCATION: On base. S of I-70, off Routes OH-4, OH-444; *OR* I-675 at Fairborn. Fam-camp is approx 4 mi from Gate 8C, Visitor Center. Take Schuster to stop sign and L on Wright Ave; L on Skeel Ave approx 1 mi to Hebble Creek Rd; approx 1½ mi to fam-camp. Report to fam-camp area and select site. Fam-camp has a host Camper. USMRA: page 67 (B-7). NMC: Dayton, 8 mi NE.

DESCRIPTION OF AREA: Home of world's largest and most complete military aviation museum and Wright Brothers Memorial. Full range of support facilities available on base.

SEASON OF OPERATION: Year round; no water in winter.

ELIGIBILITY: Active/Retired.

RESERVATIONS: No adv resv. AD on PCS are given priority. Address: Outdoor Recreation, 645 SPTG/MWPO, 5215 Thurlow St, Ste 2, Wright-Patterson AFB, OH 45433-5542. Comm: 513-257-9889, DSN: 312-787-9889. *Fam-camp, for information only,* Comm: 513-257-2579, DSN: 312-787-2579.

CAMP FACILITIES:	NO UNITS	HOOKUPS	FEE
Camper Spaces	16-20 Concrete	W/E (110/220)	$ 5.00 dly
		E (110/220)	3.00 dly
Tent Spaces	Unlimited	None	1.00 dly

SPT FACILITIES:			
	Beach	Chapel	Gas
	Golf	Lakes (3)	Mini Marina
	Picnic Lodge/fee	Quick Shop	Racquet Sports
	Rec Center	Sewage Dmp Sta	Snack Bar
	Sports Fields		

ACTIVITIES:			
	Bicycling	Boating	Fishing/stocked
	Jogging	Kayaking	Rec Equip Avail
	Sailboarding		

RESTRICTIONS: Pets allowed on leash. Fishing and hunting in area near campsites are not permitted except according to WPAFBR 126-2. Canopy over gas pumps at BX cannot accommodate vehicles over 9' in height.

OKLAHOMA

ALTUS FAM-CAMP (OK06R3)
Altus Air Force Base, OK 73523-5000

TELEPHONE NUMBER INFORMATION: Main installation numbers: Comm: 405-481/482-8100, DSN: 312-866-1110. Police for fam-camp, Comm: 405-481-7444.

LOCATION: On base. Located off US-62 S of I-40 and W of I-44. From US-62 traveling W from Lawton, turn R at 1st traffic light in Altus and follow road, bearing R at fork, to main gate NE of Falcon Rd. Check in at Bowling Center, 24 hrs dly. USMRA: page 84 (E-5). NMC: Lawton, 56 mi E.

DESCRIPTION OF AREA: The Museum of the Western Prairie (history of SW Oklahoma) is located 5 min from base. There is a public rec area at Lake Altus, 17 mi N on US-283. Full range of support facilities available on base.

SEASON OF OPERATION: Year round.

ELIGIBILITY: Active/Retired/DoD Civilians.

RESERVATIONS: Accepted. Address: Altus AFB Fam-Camp, 443 SPTG/MR, Bldg 418, Altus AFB, OK 73523-5000. **Comm: 405-481-6704, DSN: 312-866-6704.**

CAMP FACILITIES:	NO UNITS	HOOKUPS	FEE
Camper Spaces	4 Gravel	W/S/E (110)	$ 8.00 dly
Camper Spaces	3 Gravel	E (110)	8.00 dly

SPT FACILITIES:	Chapel	Family Bowling	Gas
	Golf/9 holes	Picnic Area	Port-a-Potties
	Sewage Dmp Sta	Showers/gym	Sports Fields

ACTIVITIES:	Jogging	Rec Equip Avail	Tennis

RESTRICTIONS: Pets allowed on leash. Check out 1200. Signature required for action to be taken in the event of severe weather.

MURPHY'S MEADOW (OK07R3)
McAlester Army Ammunition Plant, OK 74501-5000

TELEPHONE NUMBER INFORMATION: Main installation numbers: Comm: 918-421-2011, DSN: 312-956-2011.

LOCATION: On post. Off US-69 S of McAlester. USMRA: page 84 (I-5). NMC: Tulsa, 90 mi N.

DESCRIPTION OF AREA: Located in SE Oklahoma on the shores of Brown Lake. Mostly rolling pastureland with timber-covered hills and creek bottoms. Great area for vacationing: many lakes offer fishing, boating and water sports. 30-min drive to Lake Eufaula, 3d largest artificial lake in the US. The small community of Savannah, approx 2 mi away, provides the essentials not available on post. Limited support facilities available on post within walking distance of camp; full range of facilities available at Tinker AFB, 116 mi NW.

SEASON OF OPERATION: 15 Jan-1 Oct.

ELIGIBILITY: Active/Retired/DoD Civilians.

RESERVATIONS: Recommended. Address: McAlester Army Ammunition Plant, ATTN: SMCMC-PTC, McAlester, OK 74501-5000. **Comm: 918-421-3484/2673, DSN: 312-956-6780.** Discounts available to holders of Golden Age and Golden Access Passports.

CAMP FACILITIES:	NO UNITS	HOOKUPS	FEE
Camper Spaces	17 Gravel	W/E (110/30A)	$ 5.00 dly
Camper Spaces	17 Overflow	W/E (110/30A)	5.00 dly
Camper/Tent Spaces	Primitive	None	3.00 dly

SPT FACILITIES:			
	Auto Hobby Shop	Boat Launch	Boat Rntl
	Community Club	Golf Driv Range	Grills
	Health Clinic	Pavilions	Picnic Area
	Playground	PX/small	Restrooms/hcp
	Sewage Dmp Sta	Shoppette	Showers/hcp
	Snack Bar/	Softball Field	Tennis Court
	limited dining		

ACTIVITIES:	Boating	Fishing/license	Rec Equip Avail

RESTRICTIONS: No pets allowed. No swimming. No water skiing. Nonresidents do not require a fishing license for overnight stay.

TINKER FAM-CAMP (OK08R3)
Tinker Air Force Base, OK 73145-5000

TELEPHONE NUMBER INFORMATION: Main installation numbers: Comm: 405-732-7321, DSN: 312-884-1110.

LOCATION: On base. Off I-40, 5 mi E of Oklahoma City. Enter Gate 1 off Air Depot Blvd. Ask for directions to Outdoor Recreation, Bldg 5935. USMRA: page 84 (G-4). NMC: Oklahoma City, 5 mi W.

DESCRIPTION OF AREA: Located in the midst of Oklahoma City/Midwest City metropolitan area. Fam-Camp is situated in well-developed recreation area offering 2 fishing ponds. Full range of support facilities available on base.

SEASON OF OPERATION: Year round.

ELIGIBILITY: Active/Retired/DoD Civilians.

RESERVATIONS: No adv resv. Address: Outdoor Recreation, 654 ABG/SVRO, Tinker AFB, OK 73145-5000. Comm: 405-734-2289, DSN: 312-884-2289.

CAMP FACILITIES:	NO UNITS	HOOKUPS	FEE
Camper Spaces	29 Hardstand	W/E(110/220/30A)	$10.00 dly
Camper Spaces	Overflow	None	4.00 dly
Tent Spaces	5	None	4.00 dly

SPT FACILITIES:			
	Chapel	Gas	Golf
	Laundry	Picnic Areas	Playgrounds
	Restrooms	Sewage Dmp Sta	Showers/hcp

ACTIVITIES:	Fishing		

RESTRICTIONS: No swimming or boating in ponds. Firearms are prohibited.

PENNSYLVANIA

LETTERKENNY ARMY TRAVEL CAMP (PA10R1)
Letterkenny Army Depot, Chambersburg, PA 17201-4150

TELEPHONE NUMBER INFORMATION: Main installation numbers: Comm: 717-267-8111, DSN: 312-570-5110. Police for travel camp, Comm: 717-267-8800.

LOCATION: On post. From I-81 take exit 8. W on PA-997 to gate 6. Clearly marked with signs for depot. Check in at travel camp (located along Pennsylvania Ave) 0800-1200 M-F, 1 Apr-31 Oct; at Security Desk, Bldg 500, other hours. USMRA: page 22 (E-7). NMC: Harrisburg, 50 mi NE.

DESCRIPTION OF AREA: Beautiful Cumberland Valley of Pennsylvania. Near historic Gettysburg and Antietam Battlefields and Caledonia State Park; also within driving distance of Hershey, Lancaster, Reading outlet stores, and other places of interest. Sites have large oak trees. Some support facilities available on base within walking distance; full range at Carlisle Barracks, 30 mi N.

SEASON OF OPERATION: 1 Apr-31 Oct.

ELIGIBILITY: Active/Retired/Reserve/DoD Civilians.

RESERVATIONS: Recommended with 50% deposit (payable to: IMWRF). Address: Letterkenny Army Depot, Attn: Travel Camp (SDSLE-BA), Chambersburg, PA 17201-4150. **Comm: 717-267-9494, FAX: 717-267-9887; DSN: 312-570-9494/8968.** Discounts available to holders of Golden Age Passports.

CAMP FACILITIES:	NO UNITS	HOOKUPS	FEE
Camper Spaces	8 Concrete	W/E (110/30A)	$12.00 dly/60 wkly
Tent Spaces	Many	None	5.00 dly/25 wkly

SPT FACILITIES:			
	Chapel	Fitness Trail	Golf
	Grills	Laundry	Nature Trail
	Picnic Area	Playground	Rec Bldg
	Rec Equip Rntl	Restrooms	Sewage Dmp Sta
	Showers		

ACTIVITIES:			
	Boating	Fishing/license	Jogging
	Swimming	Tennis	

RESTRICTIONS: Pets allowed on leash; owner must clean up after pet; animals may not be left unattended. Check out 1100. No firearms allowed.

SOUTH CAROLINA

SHADY OAKS FAMILY CAMPGROUND (SC12R1)
Charleston Air Force Base, SC 29404-5000

TELEPHONE NUMBER INFORMATION: Main installation numbers: Comm: 803-566-6000, DSN: 312-673-2100.

LOCATION: On base. From I-26 exit E to West Aviation Ave; continue through 2d traffic light; R on Arthur Rd around runway through gate to Outdoor Rec Center located 50' from gate. USMRA: page 44 (H-8). NMC: Charleston, 5 mi SE.

DESCRIPTION OF AREA: Situated near wooded picnic area in one of the country's most picturesque and historic seaport cities. Full range of support facilities available on base.

SEASON OF OPERATION: Year round.

ELIGIBILITY: Active/Retired/DoD Civilians.

RESERVATIONS: No adv resv. Address: Outdoor Recreation Center, 437 SVS/SVRO, Charleston AFB, SC 29404-5000. Comm: 803-566-5271/5270, DSN: 312-673-5271.

CAMP FACILITIES: Camper Spaces	NO UNITS 23 Concrete	HOOKUPS W/E (110)	FEE $10 dly
SPT FACILITIES:	Boat Rntl Nature Trails Playground Showers	Chapel Pavilions Restrooms/hcp Tennis Courts	Grills Picnic Area Sewage Dmp Sta
ACTIVITIES:	Fishing	Rec Equip Avail	Swimming

RESTRICTIONS: Pets allowed. Fam-camp parking is not authorized for Space-A travelers.

SHAW WATEREE RECREATION AREA (SC05R1)
517 Lane Avenue
Shaw Air Force Base, SC 29152-5000

TELEPHONE NUMBER INFORMATION: Main installation numbers: Comm: 803-668-8110, DSN: 312-965-1110.

LOCATION: Off base. Off SC-97 NW of Camden. Accessible from I-77 and I-20. Check in at recreation area 24 hours daily. USMRA: page 44 (G-5). NMI: Shaw AFB, 39 mi E. NMC: Columbia, 35 mi S.

DESCRIPTION OF AREA: Situated in peaceful, quiet, 23-acre, wooded area bordering Lake Wateree. Full range of support facilities available at Shaw AFB and Ft Jackson.

SEASON OF OPERATION: Year round.

ELIGIBILITY: Active/Retired/DoD Civilians.

RESERVATIONS: Required. Address: Carolina Pines Billeting Office, 2030 Baron Dekalb Rd, Camden, SC 29020. **Comm: 803-668-3710, DSN: 312-965-3710.**

CAMP FACILITIES: Cabins, 2/3 bdrm/hcp* Camper Spaces Tent Spaces	NO UNITS 4 13 Many	HOOKUPS W/E (110/30A)	FEE $45-65 dly 9.00 dly 5.00 ea tent dly

*Fully equipped, including TV/VCR, linens, dishes, pots & pans, and mw.

SOUTH CAROLINA
SHAW WATEREE RECREATION AREA, continued

SPT FACILITIES:	Bait/Retail	Bathhouse	Boat Launch
	Sales Store	Boat Rntl/	Grills
	Ice	Ski, fishing	Marina/hcp
	Picnic Area	Playground	Pontoon Boat/fee
	Restrooms	Sewage Dmp Sta	Showers
	Water Sports Equipment Rental		

ACTIVITIES:	Fishing/license	Swimming	Water Skiing

RESTRICTIONS: No pets allowed in cabins; allowed on leash in camping area. Roped-off swimming area with sandy beach. Gates closed 2200-0600. Firearms allowed during hunting season with notification of Site Manager at area.

SHORT STAY (SC02R1)
Charleston Naval Station, SC 29408-5000

TELEPHONE NUMBER INFORMATION: Main installation numbers: Comm: 803-743-4111, DSN: 312-563-4111.

LOCATION: Off base. On Lake Moultrie. Take US-52 N from Charleston. Follow the signs. Check in 1500. USMRA: page 44 (H-8). NMI: Charleston NS, 35 mi S. NMC: Charleston, 30 mi S.

DESCRIPTION OF AREA: Situated on a 55-acre peninsula at southern tip of Lake Moultrie. Excellent freshwater fishing. Children's and family programs during summer months. Full range of support facilities at Charleston Naval Station.

SEASON OF OPERATION: Year round.

ELIGIBILITY: Active/Retired/Reserve/DoD Civilians.

RESERVATIONS: Accepted (minimum age 21). Address: ITT Office, Naval Station (Code 15), Charleston, SC 29408-5000. **Comm: 803-743-5233, DSN: 312-563-5233.** *For information call the rec area*, Comm: 803-743-5608, DSN: 312-563-5608. Write for brochure.

CAMP FACILITIES:	NO UNITS	HOOKUPS	FEE*
Villas, 3 bdrm, slp 6	12		$38-56 dly
Villas, 2 bdrm, slp 4**	24		30-45 dly
Cabins, slp 4**	12		33-50 dly
Camper Spaces	13 Waterfront	W/E (110/30A)	8-12 dly
Camper Spaces	70 Wooded	W/E (110/30A)	7-11 dly
Camper/Tent Spaces	25 Primitive	None	4-8 dly

*Rates vary depending on status of sponsor and season; weekly and monthly rates.
**Villas and cabins fully equipped, including kit, PB, color TV; 2 2-bdrm villas and 1 cabin for handicapped.

SPT FACILITIES:	Bait/Tackle	Beach	Boat Rntl
	Conv Store	Fishing Piers/hcp	Game Room
	Gas	Grills	Ice
	Laundry	Marina	Miniature Golf
	Pavilions/fee	Picnic Area	Playground

Rec Center	Restrooms	Sewage Dmp Sta
Showers	Snack Bar	

Conference Room/seats 200; 4 Pavilions/seat 200-375

ACTIVITIES:

Fishing	Horseshoes	Rec Equip Avail
Swimming	Volleyball	

RESTRICTIONS: No pets allowed in villas or cabins; allowed on leash in campground. Admission fee for day users. Check out 1100.

WESTON LAKE RECREATION AREA AND TRAVEL CAMP (SC03R1)
Fort Jackson, SC 29207-5000

TELEPHONE NUMBER INFORMATION: Main installation numbers: Comm: 803-751-7511, DSN: 312-734-1110. Police for rec area, Comm: 911.

LOCATION: On post. From I-20 N of Fort take exit 80 onto Clemson Rd; L on Percival Rd (SC-12), then R onto Wilcat Rd; drive 7 mi across Ft Jackson, then L on Leesburg Rd (SC-262) 2.5 mi to Weston Lake Recreation Area on L. Leesburg Rd (SC-262) is also accessible from US-76/378 S of post *AND* from US-601 E of post. Ft Jackson is located 12 mi E of Columbia on SC-262 (Leesburg Rd). Travel camp is 4.5 mi E of main post on SC-262. Check in at Operations Center, Bldg M-2631, by 1630/1900, depending on season. USMRA: page 44 (G-6). NMC: Columbia, 12 mi SW.

DESCRIPTION OF AREA: Located adjacent to 240-acre lake with lots of wildlife to watch, from deer to black squirrels. Site offers wide range of outdoor activities. Museum and Ernie Pyle Media Center located on post. Columbia, the state capital, offers varied sightseeing, including zoo, Capitol and Coliseum. Full range of support facilities available on post.

SEASON OF OPERATION: Year round. Call or write for hours of operation.

ELIGIBILITY: Active/Retired/Reserve/NG/DoD Civilians.

RESERVATIONS: Required **for cabins and duplex**; taken for current and following months. Not accepted for travel camp. Address: Weston Lake Recreation Area, Rec Division, Ft Jackson, SC 29207-5000. **Comm: 803-751-LAKE, DSN: 312-734-LAKE.**

CAMP FACILITIES:	NO UNITS	HOOKUPS	FEE
Cabins, 4 bdrm*	1		$40.00 dly
Cabin, 3 bdrm*	2		40.00 dly
Cabin, 2 bdrm*	2		25.00 dly
Duplex, 1 bdrm*	1		20.00 dly
Kamping Kabins	2		15.00 dly
Camper Spaces	13 Hardstand	W/S/E (110/30A)	10.00 dly
Camper Spaces	5 Hardstand	W/E (110/30A)	8.00 dly
Tent Spaces	10 Improved	W/E (110/30A)	4.00 dly

*PB, kit, furn; color TV, MW, stove, dishes, pots, pans. Linens available/fee. Lakefront cabins come with use of rowboat.

SOUTH CAROLINA
WESTON LAKE RECREATION AREA AND TRAVEL CAMP, continued

SPT FACILITIES:	Beach/sumr	Boat Ramps	Boat Rntl
	Golf	Grills	Laundry
	Marina	Miniature Golf	Nature Trail
	Picnic Area/hcp	Playground	Pontoon Boat
	Restrooms	Sewage Dmp Sta	Showers
	Skeet Range	Sports Fields	Swing/wheelchair
	Trails	Group Meeting Facilities Avail	

ACTIVITIES:	Boating	Fishing	Hunting
	Jet Ski	Rec Equip Avail	Swimming/sumr

RESTRICTIONS: No pets allowed in cabins or rec area; allowed on leash in travel camp. Hunting and fishing require state and post permits. Nominal fee charged for use of recreation area; campers/lodgers exempt when registered in camping/lodging facilities. Check out 1200. Call or write for operation hours, maps and information. Staffing is restricted Nov-Mar. No firearms allowed except unloaded hunting weapons.

SOUTH DAKOTA

ELLSWORTH FAM-CAMP (SD02R3)
Ellsworth Air Force Base, SD 57706-5000

TELEPHONE NUMBER INFORMATION: Main installation numbers: Comm: 605-385-1000, DSN: 312-675-1110. Police for fam-camp, Comm: 605-385-4001.

LOCATION: On base. N of I-90, 10 mi NE of Rapid City. Check in at fam-camp, inside and R of school gate entrance. USMRA: page 85 (B-5). NMC: Rapid City, 10 mi SW.

DESCRIPTION OF AREA: Located in the SW corner of SD. Black Hills National Forest, Mount Rushmore National Memorial and Badlands National Park are an easy drive away. Full range of support facilities available on base.

SEASON OF OPERATION: 15 May-15 Oct.

ELIGIBILITY: Active/Retired/NG/DoD and NAF Civilians.

RESERVATIONS: No adv resv. Address: Ellsworth Fam-Camp, Bldg 88421, 28 MWRS/MWRO, 2579 Quesada Dr. Ellsworth AFB, SD 57706-5000. Comm: 605-385-2995/2997, DSN: 312-675-2996/2997.

CAMP FACILITIES:	NO UNITS	HOOKUPS	FEE
Camper Spaces	14 Hardstand	W/E (110)	$10.00 dly
Tent Spaces	10 Open	None	5.00 dly

SPT FACILITIES:	Chapel	Grills	Laundry
	Picnic Areas	Playgrounds	Rec Equip Rntl
	Restrooms	Sewage Dmp Sta	Showers

ACTIVITIES:	Fishing/license	Hiking	Hunting/license
	Snow Skiing	Water Skiing	Whitewater Rafting

RESTRICTIONS: Pets allowed on leash. 7-day limit. No open fires. Firearms are prohibited and need to be turned in to Security Police Armory, Comm: 605-385-4055.

TENNESSEE

ARNOLD FAM-CAMP (TN03R2)
Arnold Air Force Base, TN 37389-5000

TELEPHONE NUMBER INFORMATION: Main installation numbers: Comm: 615-454-3000, DSN: 312-340-5011/3000. Security Police for fam-camp, Comm:615-454-5662, DSN: 312-340-5662.

LOCATION: On base. Take Arnold Engineering Development Center (AEDC) exit 117 from I-24; turn W, traveling toward Tullahoma, about 5 mi until passing gate 2; L on Pump Station Rd to flashing caution light; R to top of hill and another flashing light; turn L. Hobby Shop is first Bldg on R; fam-camp is to the L on Woods Reservoir. USMRA: page 41 (I-9). NMC: Chattanooga, 60 mi SE; Nashville, 60 mi NW.

DESCRIPTION OF AREA: Terrain is flat to rolling hills. Area offers a variety of recreational and historical sites within a 70-mi radius of the base. Tim's Ford State Park and Lake, and Old Stone Fort State Park are located within a 45-min drive. Jack Daniel's Distillery in Lynchburg and George Dickle Distillery in Tullahoma offer tours. Full range of support facilities available on base.

SEASON OF OPERATION: Mar - Oct.

ELIGIBILITY: Active/Retired/Arnold AFB Civilians/AEDC Camper Club.

RESERVATIONS: Required. Security dep req within 72 hrs of phone resv (M-F). Address: 656 SPTS/SVB (FAMCAMP), 100 Kindel Dr., Suite C319, Arnold AFB, TN 37389-5000. **Comm: 615-454-6084, DSN: 312-340-6084.**

CAMP FACILITIES:	NO UNITS	HOOKUPS	FEE
Camper Spaces	13 under 15 '	W/E (110)	$ 8.00 dly
	4 15-20 '	W/E (110)	8.00 dly
	5 20-25 '	W/E (110)	8.00 dly
Tent Spaces		None	5.00 dly

SPT FACILITIES:			
	Beach	Boat Rntl	Golf/9 holes
	Hobby Shop	Marina	Picnic Areas
	Playground	Racquet Sports	Rec Equip Rntl
	Restrooms	Showers	Snack Bar
	Sewage Dmp Sta	Swimming Area	Trails

ACTIVITIES:			
	Boating	Fishing/license	Hunting/license
	Softball	Swimming	Water Skiing

RESTRICTIONS: Pets allowed on leash. No pets in rec center. Firearms permitted, however **NO** discharge of weapons permitted within <u>SAFE</u> zone as posted.

TENNESSEE

NAVY LAKE RECREATION AREA (TN04R2)
Memphis Naval Air Station. Millington, TN 38054-5000

TELEPHONE NUMBER INFORMATION: Main installation numbers: Comm: 901-873-5111, DSN: 312-966-5111.

LOCATION: On base. From US-51 in Millington exit to Navy Road, E approx 5 mi to first gate on L and proceed to recreation area. R on Attu (first road inside gate) until you reach the Lakehouse (Also accessible from TN-14, I-40 & I-240.) USMRA: page 40 (B-9,10). NMC: Memphis, 20 mi SW.

DESCRIPTION OF AREA: Recreation area has 2 lakes and 14 picnic areas with cabanas and barbecue facilities. Lakes are stocked with bass, bream, catfish and crappie. Full range of support facilities on base.

SEASON OF OPERATION: Year round; tent camping best 1 Apr-1 Nov.

ELIGIBILITY: Active/Retired/Reserves/DoD Civilians.

RESERVATIONS: No adv resv. Address: MWR Dept, NAS Memphis, PO Box 54278, Bldg North 27, Millington, TN 38054-0278. Comm: 901-872-1573/873-5163, FAX: 901-873-5690, DSN: 312-966-5163.

CAMP FACILITIES:	NO UNITS	HOOKUPS	FEE
Camper Spaces	12 Paved	W/S/E (110/220 /30A)	$8.00 dly
Tent Spaces	Overflow/Gravel	None	5.00 dly

SPT FACILITIES:	Boat Rntl	Camp Equip Rntl	Ice
	Golf	Grills	Laundry
	Picnic Areas	Playgrounds	Rec Equip Rntl
	Restrooms	Sewage Dmp Sta*	Showers
	Softball Fields	Stables**	Vending Mach

*Rec area and at car wash on base.
**NAS riding stables by lake area; horses and stalls to rent.

ACTIVITIES:	Boating	Canoeing	Fishing
	Horseback Riding	Softball	Volleyball

RESTRICTIONS: Pets allowed on leash. Firearms must be checked in at Security; *they are not allowed in the Recreation area.*

TEXAS

BELTON LAKE RECREATION AREA (TX07R3)
Fort Hood, TX 76544-5000

TELEPHONE NUMBER INFORMATION: Main installation numbers: Comm: 817-287/288-1110, DSN: 312-737/738-1110. Police for rec area, Comm: 817-287-0309.

LOCATION: On post. 14 mi NE of main post area. From I-35 take Killeen/Ft Hood exit; W on US-190; R on TX-317 (Main St) and follow through Belton. L on TX-439, pass Frank's Lakeview exit; look for "Westcliff" sign on R and turn R onto Sparta Rd; follow for 6 mi, cross cattleguard and turn R at BLORA entrance (Cottage Rd). Check in after 1500. USMRA: page 87 (K-4). NMC: Austin, 60 mi S.

DESCRIPTION OF AREA: A very large area located along Belton Lake. Recreational opportunities include hiking in nearby wooded areas and a wide variety of water sports. Belton Lake is known for black and white bass and crappie. Full range of support facilities available on post.

SEASON OF OPERATION: Year round. Beach 15 Apr-15 Oct.

ELIGIBILITY: Active/Retired/DoD Civilians currently employed.

RESERVATIONS: Required for cottages with $15 deposit. Address: Community Recreation Division, AFZF-PA-CRD-OR-BLORA, Ft Hood, TX 765445056. **Comm:** 817-287-2523, DSN: 312-737-2523. Discounts available to holders of Golden Age, Golden Access and Golden Eagle Passports.

CAMP FACILITIES:	NO UNITS	HOOKUPS	FEE
Cottages, slp 4*	10		$20-25 dly/winter
			25-30 dly/sumr
Camper Spaces	11 Hardstand	W/S/E (30A)	8.00 dly
Camper Spaces	48 Hardstand	W/E (30A)	8.00 dly
Tent Spaces	5 Primitive	W/E (30A)	6.00 dly
Tent Spaces	36 Primitive	None	3.00 dly

*1 bdrm, A/C, TV; furn, except towels, soap.

SPT FACILITIES:	Bait Store	Beach	Boat Ramp
	Boat Rntl	Fishing Dock	Grills
	Horse Trails	Ice	Laundry
	Marina	Nature Trail	Paddle Boats
	Party Boat	Pavilions/resv	Picnic Areas
	Playground	Restrooms	Sewage Dmp Sta
	Showers	Snack Bar	Sports Fields
	RV/Trailer Rntl	Waterslides	
	Water Sports Equipment Rental		

ACTIVITIES:	Fishing/license	Jet Skiing	Rec Equip Avail
	Swimming	Water Skiing	Horse Rental

RESTRICTIONS: Pets must be on leash at all times; not allowed in cottages or in swimming area; owner must clean up after pets; owner will be assessed charges for any damage incurred by pets. No hunting in park. Swimming only at Sierra Beach while lifeguards are on duty. Nominal user fee for use of park (annual pass available). Ft Hood boating license required to rent boat with motor (tests on W-Su 0730-1530). Check out 0730-1000. Firearms are prohibited.

BLISS FAMILY CAMPGROUND (TX31R3)
Fort Bliss, TX 79916-6200

TELEPHONE NUMBER INFORMATION: Main installation numbers: Comm: 915-568-2121, DSN: 312-978-0831. Police for campground, Comm: 915-568-2115.

LOCATION: On post. From I-10 take US-54 E to Forrest Rd exit and enter Ft Bliss; L at 5th traffic light on Jeb Stuart Rd to Campgrounds. Check in at office. USMRA: page 86 (B,C-5,6). NMC: El Paso, adjacent.

TEXAS
BLISS FAMILY CAMPGROUND, continued

DESCRIPTION OF AREA: In west Texas near Rio Grande River. Carlsbad Caverns National Park, easy drive W. White Sands National Monument, 2-hr drive N. Ciudad Juarez, Mexico's largest border city, is a short distance across Rio Grande River. 4 museums on post. Full range of support facilities available on post.

SEASON OF OPERATION: Year round.

ELIGIBILITY: Active/Retired/DoD Civilians.

RESERVATIONS: No adv resv. Address: Commander, USAADACENFB, DCA/Family Campground, 1733 Pleasanton Rd., Fort Bliss, TX 79916-6816. Comm: 915-568-4693, DSN: 312-978-4693. Discount to holders of Golden Age and Golden Access Passports, and to AARP cardholders.

CAMP FACILITIES:	NO UNITS	HOOKUPS	FEE
Camper Spaces	40 Gravel	W/E (110)	$ 7.00 dly
Tent Spaces	50 Dirt	None	2.00 dly
Overflow	Limited	None	2.00 dly

SPT FACILITIES:			
	Chapel	Gas/24 hrs dly	Golf
	Grills	Laundry	Miniature Golf
	Pavilion	Picnic Area	Playground
	Restrooms	Sewage Dmp Sta	Showers
	Sports Fields		

ACTIVITIES:	Horseshoes	Rec Equip Avail	Swimming
	Ticket Office		

RESTRICTIONS: Pets allowed on leash only; owner must clean up after pets. 14-day limit; may be extended if space is available on scheduled date of departure. No open fires. Check out 1300.

BROOKS FAM-CAMP (TX17R3)
Brooks Air Force Base, TX 78235-5000

TELEPHONE NUMBER INFORMATION: Main installation numbers: Comm: 210-536-1110, DSN: 312-240-1110.

LOCATION: On base. Enter AFB at intersection of I-37 and Military Drive (Loop 13). Check in at Billeting Office, Bldg 214. USMRA: page 87 (J-6), 91 (C-4). NMC: San Antonio, 5 mi NW.

DESCRIPTION OF AREA: Located near a pond, and 3 mi from 2 lakes offering excellent fishing and boating. Local attractions include Sea World, the Alamo, and Riverwalk area. Full range of support facilities available on base.

SEASON OF OPERATION: Year round.

ELIGIBILITY: Active/Retired/DoD Civilians.

RESERVATIONS: No adv resv. Address: 648 SVS/SVMH, ATTN: Lodging Office/Innkeeper, 2804 5th St., Brooks AFB, TX 78235-5219. Comm: 210-536-1844, DSN: 312-240-1844.

CAMP FACILITIES:	NO UNITS	HOOKUPS	FEE
Camper Spaces	7 Hardstand	W/S/E (110)	$10.00 dly
Camper Spaces	8 Hardstand	W/E (110)	8.00 dly
Tent Spaces	Open	None	3.00 dly
Camper/Tent Spaces	Overflow	None	3.00 dly

SPT FACILITIES:	Grills	Laundry	Picnic Area
	Playground	Restrooms/hcp	Sewage Dmp Sta
	Showers		

ACTIVITIES:	Fishing	Rec Equip Avail

RESTRICTIONS: Pets allowed on leash. Firearm owners must inform security police after arriving on base.

CANYON LAKE ARMY RECREATION AREA (TX29R3)
Fort Sam Houston, TX 78234-5000

TELEPHONE NUMBER INFORMATION: Main installation numbers: Comm: 210-221-1110/1211, DSN: 312-471-1110/1211.

LOCATION: Off post. From I-35 N of San Antonio near New Braunfels, take FM-306 W for approx 15 mi to Jacobs Creek Park. Sign on R side on Jacobs Creek Park Rd. Check in at office 1600-2000. USMRA: page 87 (J-6). NMI: Randolph AFB, 35 mi S. NMC: San Antonio, 50 mi S.

DESCRIPTION OF AREA: Located in terrain that is characteristically hilly and rocky, with cedar and oak trees. Recreation area has 300 feet of sandy beach and a 1/4-acre marina. Full range of support facilities at Ft Sam Houston.

SEASON OF OPERATION: Year round. (Closed Christmas and New Year's Day.)

ELIGIBILITY: Active/Retired/Reserve/NG/DoD Civilians/Foreign Military.

RESERVATIONS: Required for mobile homes; *in person only for patrons in San Antonio area, by phone for others;* up to 28 days in adv for AD at Ft Sam Houston and up to 21 days in adv for all others. No adv resv for camping area. Address: ITR, Bldg 124, Stanley Rd, Ft Sam Houston, TX 78234-5000. **Comm: 210-221-0703/2333, DSN: 312-471-0703/2333,** 0800-1700 M-F, 0800-1600 Sa. "Snowbirds" welcome year round. Discounts available *for entrance fee only* to holders of Golden Age, Golden Access and Golden Eagle Passports.

CAMP FACILITIES:	NO UNITS	HOOKUPS	FEE
Mobile Homes, 3 bdrm furn, exc towels, soap	32		$20-30 dly*
Camper Spaces	32 Hardstand	W/E (110/30A)	8.00 dly
Tent Spaces	Open	None	5.00 dly

*Depending on rank. Monthly rates available.

SPT FACILITIES:	Beach	Boat Launch	Boat Rntl
	Boat Slip	Cabanas/fee	Fishing Pier
	Fishing Tackle	Grills	Laundry
	Marina	MWR	NAF Store
	Party Boat/	Pavillion	Picnic Areas*
	Pontoon	Playgrounds	Rec equip rntl
	Restrooms/hcp	Sewage Dmp Sta	Shelters/screened
	Showers/hcp	TV Room	TV/VCR rntl

* Group picnic area available by reservation.

TEXAS
CANYON LAKE ARMY RECREATION AREA, continued

ACTIVITIES: Boating   Fishing   Hiking
                      Swimming   Water Skiing

RESTRICTIONS: Pets allowed on leash. Check out 1400. Open fires in designated areas only. Nominal entrance fee into park ($2 per vehicle/annual permit $15). No firearms are allowed.

CARSWELL FAM-CAMP (TX04R3)
Carswell Fam-Camp is closed.

ELLIOTT LAKE RECREATION AREA (TX15R3)
Red River Army Depot, TX 75507-5000

TELEPHONE NUMBER INFORMATION: Main installation numbers: Comm: 903-334-2141, DSN: 312-829-4110. Police for recreation area, Comm:903-334-2911.

LOCATION: On post. Red River is W of Texarkana S of I-30 on US-82. Take Red River Army Depot exit to main gate. Follow signs from main post to lake area. USMRA: page 87 (N-2). NMC: Texarkana, 18 mi E.

DESCRIPTION OF AREA: Located in a wooded area on 183-acre Elliott Lake in NE corner of state. Excellent for overnight camping, vacationing, sightseeing and trips into scenic Arkansas mountains. Recreation area is a 210-acre reserve. Wide range of support facilities available on post.

SEASON OF OPERATION: Year round.

ELIGIBILITY: Active/Retired/Reserve/DoD Civilians.

RESERVATIONS: Required for cabins and shelters. Address: Community Recreation Branch, Bldg S-05, Red River Army Depot, ATTN: SDSRR-AN, Texarkana, TX 75507-5000. **Comm: 903-334-2254, DSN: 312-829-2254.**

CAMP FACILITIES:	NO UNITS	HOOKUPS	FEE
Cabins*	14 Gravel		$20.00 dly
Camper Spaces	23 Gravel	W/E (110/30A)	7.00 dly/35 wkly
Shelters	5 Gravel	Cots/Toilets	5.00 dly+15 dep
Tent Spaces	20 Gravel	None	2.00 dly

*2 bdrm, furn, PB, kit; no linens, TV or cookware. Equipped for handicapped.

SPT FACILITIES:	Beach	Boat Launch	Boat Rntl
	Canoes	Laundry	Marina
	Picnic Areas	Playground	Rec Equip Rntl
	Restrooms	Sewage Dmp Sta	Showers

ACTIVITIES:	Archery	Boating	Fishing/license
	Hiking	Hunting/license	Swimming

RESTRICTIONS: No pets allowed in cabins; can be kept outside on leash. Recreation permit required for all patrons. Key deposit ($25) required. No lifeguards: swim at your own risk. ATVs restricted.

GOODFELLOW RECREATION CAMP (TX32R3)
Goodfellow Air Force Base, TX 76908-5000

TELEPHONE NUMBER INFORMATION: Main installation numbers: Comm: 915-654-3231, DSN: 312-477-3217.

LOCATION: Off base. From US-87 on W side of San Angelo take Knickerbocker Rd S to Lake Nasworthy. *OR* from S of San Angelo, go E from US-67 (or W from US-277) on Knickerbocker Rd. USMRA: page 86 (H-7). NMI: Goodfellow AFB, 10 mi NE. NMC: San Angelo, 10 mi N.

DESCRIPTION OF AREA: Located on Lake Nasworthy in flat, open terrain with some trees and covered picnic areas. Full range of support facilities available on base.

SEASON OF OPERATION: Year round: Th-M.

ELIGIBILITY: Active/Retired/DoD Civilians.

RESERVATIONS: No adv resv. Address: Recreation Services, 17 SVS/SVSRO, Goodfellow AFB, TX 76908-5000. Comm: 915-944-1012, DSN: 312-477-3217 (ask operator to ring 944-1012).

TEXAS
GOODFELLOW RECREATION CAMP, *continued*

CAMP FACILITIES:	NO UNITS	HOOKUPS	FEE
Camper Spaces	19	W/E (110/30A)	$ 8.00 dly
Tent Spaces	Unlimited	None	3.00 dly

SPT FACILITIES:			
	Boat Launch	Boat Rntl	Fishing Pier
	Gas	Marina	Pavilion/hcp
	Picnic Area	Racquet Courts	Rec Equip Rntl
	Restrooms	Sewage Dmp Sta	Showers
	Snack Bar	Sports Fields	

ACTIVITIES:	Fishing	Sailing	Water Skiing

RESTRICTIONS: Pets allowed on leash; owner must clean up after pets. Campers already in the camping area on days when it is closed will not be required to leave. No open fires. Firearms are prohibited.

KELLY FAM-CAMP (TX33R3)
Kelly Air Force Base, TX 78241-5000

TELEPHONE NUMBER INFORMATION: Main installation numbers: Comm: 210-925-1110, DSN: 312-945-1110. Police for fam-camp, Comm: 512-925-6811.

LOCATION: On base. From US-90 go S on Cupples Rd for 2 mi (past the Kelly AFB main gate and over the overpass); L at the East Kelly AFB entrance. The fam-camp is on the first street to the right past the guard. Check in at Bldg 3503. USMRA: page 91 (B-3,4). NMC: San Antonio, 3 mi NE.

DESCRIPTION OF AREA: Located in the San Antonio metropolitan area which offers many sightseeing opportunities, e.g., the Alamo, Mission Concepcion (the oldest church in Texas), Institute of Texan Cultures, zoological gardens and aquarium, and Fiesta Week in April. Fam-camp is surrounded by pecan trees. Full range of support facilities available on base.

SEASON OF OPERATION: Year round.

ELIGIBILITY: Active/Retired.

RESERVATIONS: No adv resv. Address: MWR Office, 2851 ABG/MWRF, 3503 Offutt St., Kelly AFB, TX 78241-5000. Comm: 210-925-5725.

CAMP FACILITIES:	NO UNITS	HOOKUPS	FEE
Camper Spaces	32 Paved	W/S/E (110/30A)	$ 8.00 dly
Tent Spaces	Many Grass	None	3.00 dly
Overflow*			3.00 dly

*Patrons may use water, restrooms, showers and laundry available at fam-camp.

SPT FACILITIES:			
	Laundry/hcp	Picnic Area	Playground
	Restrooms/hcp	Sewage Dmp Sta	Showers/hcp

ACTIVITIES:	Rec Equip Avail	Sightseeing

RESTRICTIONS: 1 pet per family allowed. 15-day limit.

LACKLAND FAM-CAMP (TX49R3)
Lackland Air Force Base, TX 78236-5000

TELEPHONE NUMBER INFORMATION: Main installation numbers: Comm: 210-671-1110, DSN: 312-473-1110. Police for fam-camp, Comm: 210-671-2018; Crime Stop, Comm: 210-671-1100.

LOCATION: On base. From US-90 W of San Antonio take exit 17 (Lackland) S onto Military Drive. Enter Luke East Gate; straight ahead on Luke; L on Foster to fam-camp. Information desk at Wilford Hall has flyers and information. USMRA: page 87 (J-6,7). NMC: San Antonio, 16 mi NE.

DESCRIPTION OF AREA: Fam-camp is located on flat terrain. Pad for RV is 10'x35', for vehicle, 9'x19'. San Antonio offers many and varied opportunities for sightseeing. Conveniently located to a full range of support facilities available on base.

SEASON OF OPERATION: Year round.

ELIGIBILITY: Active/Retired. Sponsored visitors.

RESERVATIONS: No adv resv. Address: MWR Division, 37 MWRSS/MWRO, #2800, Foster Ave., Lackland AFB, TX 78236-5234. Comm: 210-671-3106, DSN: 312-473-3106 (M-F 0800-1700). *(Fam-Camp, Comm: 210-671-5179.)*

CAMP FACILITIES:	NO UNITS	HOOKUPS	FEE
Camper Spaces	24 Asphalt	W/S/E(110/30/50)	$10-12 dly*
*CTV $1 add dly.			

SPT FACILITIES:	Facilities currently under construction. On base:
	Gas Golf Laundry
	Stables

ACTIVITIES:	Sightseeing

RESTRICTIONS: Pets allowed on leash no longer than 10'; must have current immunizations; owner must clean up after pet. Manager at Site 14. No open fires. 15-day limit. Quiet hours 2200-0600. Check out 1200. Firearms to be checked in to the base armory.

LAGUNA SHORES (TX42R3)
Kelly Air Force Base, TX 78241-5000
(Note: Facility scheduled to close 1 October 1994)

TELEPHONE NUMBER INFORMATION: Main installation numbers: Comm: 210-925-1110, DSN: 312-945-1110. Police for rec area, Comm: 210-939-2480.

LOCATION: Off base. On Corpus Christi NAS. I-37 to exit 4A W of Corpus Christi; E on TX-358 approx 17 mi to NAS. Enter at South Gate. Go .3 mi and turn R just past the Reserve Center; go another .3 mi and turn onto Pelican. Follow Laguna Shores signs to office. Check in 1700-2200 (Sa by appointment only). USMRA: page 87 (K-8). NMC: Corpus Christi, in city limits.

DESCRIPTION OF AREA: The lodging facility is directly adjacent to Corpus Christi Bay and only moments away from Texas Gulf Coast and Padre Island National Seashore. Day trips can be made to the Rio Grande Valley, Mexico, San Antonio, Houston, Austin and the Texas Hill Country. Full range of support facilities available at Corpus Christi NAS.

TEXAS
LAGUNA SHORES, continued

SEASON OF OPERATION: Year round.

ELIGIBILITY: Active/Retired/DoD Civilians.

RESERVATIONS: Required, with payment in full (first month's payment for stays of 1 month or more). Resv may be made up to 31 days in adv for AD and DoD Civ at Kelly AFB and for "Winter Texans" (those staying a minimum of 1 mo between Dec and Feb); up to 24 days in adv for all others. Address: ITT, 651 MWRS/MWRT, Bldg 1780, Kelly AFB, TX 78251-5000. **Comm: 210-925-4585, DSN: 312-945-4585.** *Laguna Shores Office (information only)*, Comm: 512-939-7783.

LODGING: 38 2-bdrm apartments, PB, kit, LDR; completely furn except for towels and soaps. Renovated base housing.
      FEE: $26 dly for 2 pers; ea add pers $2; 6 pers max

SPT FACILITIES:	Boat Rntl*	Camp Eq Rntl*	Golf/base
	Marina*	Playground*	Rec Equip Rntl*
	Portable wheelchair ramp available upon request.		

*Nearby

ACTIVITIES: Fishing   Surfboarding   Swimming

RESTRICTIONS: No pets allowed. Sponsor must accompany guests. Check out by 1200.

LAKE AMISTAD RECREATION AREA (TX34R3)
Laughlin Air Force Base, TX 78843-5000

TELEPHONE NUMBER INFORMATION: Main installation numbers: Comm: 210-298-3511, DSN: 312-732-1110. Police for recreation area, Comm: 911.

LOCATION: Off base. From US-90 N of Del Rio, take Amistad Dam Rd (Spur 349) to Recreation area. Check in at Visitors Center 0700-1900 (15 Oct-31 Mar 0700-1500). USMRA: page 86 (H-9). NMI: Laughlin AFB, 22.5 mi SE. NMC: Del Rio, 12 mi SE.

DESCRIPTION OF AREA: Situated near Amistad Dam which serves as passageway to Mexico. Ideal fresh water recreation area and outstanding fishing. Many deer in the area. Good base for day trips into Mexico. Convenient to Ciudad Acuna, Mexico. Full range of support facilities at Laughlin AFB.

SEASON OF OPERATION: Year round; 16 Apr-15 Oct: Th-Sun, hol, 1000-2200; 16 Oct-15 Apr: Sa, Su, hol, 1100-1700.

ELIGIBILITY: Active/Retired/DoD and NAF Civilians/Others with Federal ID at discretion of commander.

RESERVATIONS: Required with payment in advance. Address: Outdoor Recreation, 47 MWRSS/MWRO, 416 Liberty Drive, Laughlin Air Force Base, TX 78843-5134. *Recreation Area*, Comm: 210-775-5971, FAX Comm: 210-298-5554.

CAMP FACILITIES:	NO UNITS	HOOKUPS	FEE*
Campers, 20 ', slp 4	4	W/E (110/30A)	$18.00 dly
Camper, 16 ', slp 2	2	W/E (110/30A)	18.00 dly
Camper/Tent Spaces	5 Concrete	W/E (110/30A)	8.00 dly

*Weekly and monthly winter rates available; TV hookups available.

TEXAS
LAKE AMISTAD RECREATION AREA, continued

SPT FACILITIES:	Boat Rntl	Cabanas/fee	Conv Store
	Grills	Laundry	Marina
	Picnic Areas	Restrooms/hcp	Showers/hcp
	Sewage Dmp Sta		

ACTIVITIES:	Boating	Fishing/license	Natural History
	Sailing	Sightseeing	Water Skiing

RESTRICTIONS: Pets allowed on leash. Check out 1300. Campers already registered on Tu will not be asked to leave. Generators are permitted. No firearms allowed.

LAKE MEDINA RECREATION CAMP (TX38R3)
Lackland Air Force Base, TX 78236-5000

TELEPHONE NUMBER INFORMATION: Main installation numbers: Comm: 210-671-1110, DSN: 312-473-1110. Police for rec camp, Comm: 210-671-1100.

LOCATION: Off base. From I-410 on SW side of San Antonio, take US-90 W to Loop 1604, N to TX FM-471 (Culebra Rd); W to TX FM-1283. Turn L at Hill Top Cafe; follow sign to camp near the dam. USMRA: page 87 (J-6). NMI: Lackland AFB, 30 mi SE. NMC: San Antonio, 30 mi SE.

DESCRIPTION OF AREA: Wooded area on beautiful, large, fresh-water Lake Medina. Boat certification is required for use of the large boats. For certification boaters must view a 15-minute film followed by written and driving tests at the camp. Full range of support facilities available at Lackland AFB.

SEASON OF OPERATION: Year round. Closed Tu-W in summer, M-F in winter.

ELIGIBILITY: Active/Retired/DoD Civilians.

RESERVATIONS: Accepted. Address: Lake Medina Recreation Camp, PO Box 6366, Mico, TX 78056. **Comm: 210-671-2366.**

CAMP FACILITIES:	NO UNITS	HOOKUPS	FEE
Campers, 22'**	7	W/E/AC (110)	$15.00 dly
Campers, 16'*	2	W/E/AC(110)	15.00 dly
RV Spaces	3 Gravel	W/E (110)	5.00 dly
Tent Spaces	12 Pads	None	3.00 dly
Tent Spaces	10 Primitive	None	None

*$35 weekly rate Oct-Mar.
**No linens or utensils provided.

SPT FACILITIES:	Beach	Boat Launch/fee	Boat Rntl
	Conv Store	Fishing Tackle	Grills
	Marina	Pavilions	Picnic Area
	Playground	Rec Center	Ski Equipment

ACTIVITIES:	Fishing	Horseshoes	Swimming
	Volleyball	Water Skiing	

RESTRICTIONS: Pets allowed on leash. No open fires. No motor vehicles allowed off blacktop roads. Nominal admission fee to camp. Attendance at boat safety class (Sa 0900) required for boat rental. No firearms allowed.

TEXAS

LAUGHLIN FAM-CAMP (TX13R3)
Laughlin Air Force Base, TX 78843-5000

TELEPHONE NUMBER INFORMATION: Main installation numbers: Comm: 210-298-3511, DSN: 312-732-1110. Police for recreation area, Comm: 911.

LOCATION: On base. Off US-90 E of Del Rio. Clearly marked. Report to Community Center, Bldg 235, just past gas station. USMRA: page 86 (H-9). NMC: Del Rio, 6 mi NW.

DESCRIPTION OF AREA: Situated near Texas/Mexico border and near Presa de la Amistad Reservoir and recreation area. Full range of support facilities on base.

SEASON OF OPERATION: Year round: 16 Apr-15 Oct: 1100-2200, closed W; 16 Oct-15 Apr: Sa, Su & hol 1100-1700, closed M-F.

ELIGIBILITY: Active/Retired/DoD Civilians.

RESERVATIONS: No adv resv accepted. Address: Recreation Services, 47 MWRSS/MWRO, 416 Liberty Dr, Laughlin AFB, TX 78843-5134. *For information,* Comm: 210-298-5474, DSN: 312-732-5224/5474.

CAMP FACILITIES:	NO UNITS	HOOKUPS	FEE
Camper Spaces	6	W/S/E (110/30A)	$ 6.00 dly
Camper Spaces	10	W/S/CTV/E(110/30A)	8.00 dly

SPT FACILITIES:	Grills	Picnic Area	Playgrounds
	PX/across street	Restrooms/hcp	

ACTIVITIES: Recreation Equipment Available

RESTRICTIONS: Pets allowed on leash. All firearms must be registered with security police.

RANDOLPH OFF-BASE RECREATION AREA (TX35R3)
415 B Street East
Randolph Air Force Base, TX 78150-5000

TELEPHONE NUMBER INFORMATION: Main installation numbers: Comm: 210-652/658-1110, DSN: 312-487-1110. Police for recreation area, Comm: 201-652-5500.

LOCATION: Off base. From I-35 N of San Antonio on N side of New Braunfels, FM-306 W to Canyon Lake Dam; R approx 2 1/2 mi to Jacobs Creek Rd; L to Rec Area. USMRA: page 87 (J,K-6). NMI: Randolph AFB, 43 mi SE. NMC: San Antonio, 50 mi S.

DESCRIPTION OF AREA: Located on NE end of Canyon Reservoir. Terrain is characteristically hilly and rocky with scatterings of cedar, live oak and Spanish oak trees. Campground located around cove. There is a majestic view of 8,240-acre lake and its 80-mi shoreline. Temperatures in summer make air conditioning desirable for enclosed trailers and recreational vehicles. Heat is needed only occasionally in winter. Variety of water-oriented activities. Full range of support facilities at Randolph AFB.

SEASON OF OPERATION: Year round; marina closed M-Tu.

ELIGIBILITY: AF Active/AF Retired/DoD Civilians at Randolph AFB. All others: space available.

RESERVATIONS: *Required for shelters only*; not accepted for camper or tent spaces. Address Outdoor Recreation Resource Center, 415 B Street East, Randolph AFB, TX 78150-5000. **Comm: 210-652-4125. Rec area, Comm: 210-964-3804.**

CAMP FACILITIES:	NO UNITS	HOOKUPS	FEE
Primitive Shelters*	11	E (110/220)	$18.00 dly
Camper Spaces	10 Hardstand	W/E	10.00 dly
Tent Spaces	45 Improved	None	7.00 dly**

*Reservation required.
**Shoreline Sites $4 daily.

SPT FACILITIES:	Boat Launch	Boat Rntl	Fishing Pier
	Gas/boats only	Grills	Marina
	Nature Trail	Picnic Areas	Playground
	Rec Equip Rntl	Restrooms	Sailboat/minifish
	Sewage Dmp Sta/	Showers(cold water only)	
	nearby	Snacks	Volleyball
	Sailing classes are offered seasonally		

ACTIVITIES:	Fishing	Sailing	Scuba Diving
	Water Skiing	Windsurfing	

RESTRICTIONS: Pets allowed on leash. Entry fee ($3) to rec area. No firearms allowed in park.

SHEPPARD AFB RECREATION ANNEX (TX16R3)
Sheppard Air Force Base, TX 76311-5000

TELEPHONE NUMBER INFORMATION: Main installation numbers: Comm: 817-676-2089, DSN: 312-736-2089. Police for rec annex, Comm: 903-893-4388.

LOCATION: Off base. From US-82 E of Gainesville, take US-377 N approx 11 mi (pass Gordonville exit) to TX FM-901 and turn L. (Just prior to this exit is a green SAFB Annex sign.) Go 2 mi; turn R at SAFB Annex. Follow signs approx 5 mi to recreation annex. Rec area is located on Texas side of Lake Texoma. Check in at main lodge, 1500. USMRA: page 87 (K-1,2). NMI: Dallas NAS, 95 mi S. NMC: Dallas, 95 mi S.

DESCRIPTION OF AREA: Located approx 120 mi E of base at Wichita Falls, near the Texas/Oklahoma line on one of the largest, most popular inland lakes in the area. Some of the best fishing is available as well as a variety of other water sports. Full range of support facilities available at Dallas NAS and Carswell AFB in Fort Worth.

SEASON OF OPERATION: Year round.

ELIGIBILITY: Active/Ret/Dependents/Guard/Reserve/Federal Civilian Employees.

RESERVATIONS: Accepted. Address: Sheppard Recreation Annex, Route 3, Box 151, Whitesboro, TX 76273. **Comm: 903-523-4613** (0800-1700 daily). Discounts available (RV areas only) to holders of Golden Age, Golden Access and Golden Eagle Passports.

TEXAS
SHEPPARD AFB RECREATION ANNEX, continued

CAMP FACILITIES:	NO UNITS	HOOKUPS	FEE
Cabin/VIP, 2 bdrm*	1		$40.00 dly
Cabin/VIP, slp 4*	1		40.00 dly
Mobile Home/VIP, slp 6*	1		40.00 dly
Cabins, slp 4-6*	41		25-30 dly
Camper Spaces	8 Gravel	W/S/E (110/30A)	10.00 dly**
Camper Spaces	16 Gravel	W/E (110/30A)	8.00 dly**
Tent Spaces	Many	None	None
Dry Boat Storage			18-25 mo
Day Act Slips	30	E	3.00 dly

*A/C, PB, TV; furn exc towels, personal items.
**Weekly and monthly rates available.

SPT FACILITIES:	Airstrip/grass	Bait	Beach
	Boat Launch	Boat Rntl	Boat Slips
	Conv Store	"Crappie" House/	Fitness Ctr
	Gas	heat	Grills
	Laundry	Movies	Multi-Purpose Ct
	Pavilions	Picnic Area	Playgrounds
	Rec Equip Rntl	Rec Room/TV	Restrooms
	Sewage Dmp Sta	Showers	Snack Bar
	Trails	Vending Mach	Video Rntl

ACTIVITIES:	Basketball	Fishing/monthly	Hiking
	Holiday Specials	contest	Horseshoes
	Volleyball	Water Skiing	Softball
	Golf Dr Rnge	Swimming	

RESTRICTIONS: No pets allowed in cabins; allowed on leash in other areas; proof of current rabies vaccination required. No fireworks. No firearms. Check out 1300. Hunting firearms only and must be registered at lodge.

SHIELDS PARK NAS RECREATION AREA (TX36R3)
Corpus Christi Naval Air Station, TX 78419-5000

TELEPHONE NUMBER INFORMATION: Main installation numbers: Comm: 512-939-2811, DSN: 312-861-1110. Police for rec area, Comm: 512-939-2480.

LOCATION: On base. From Corpus Christi take TX-358 E. Follow sign to NAS. Ask gate sentry for directions to marina and RV campground. USMRA: page 87 (K-8). NMC: Corpus Christi, 8 mi W.

DESCRIPTION OF AREA: Located on beautiful Corpus Christi Bay. The bay and gulf have many water sports and recreational opportunities. Corpus Christi offers a symphony, USS Lexington museum, historical homes, museum, and is the home of the Texas State Aquarium. Full range of support facilities available on base.

SEASON OF OPERATION: Year round; some activities are seasonal.

ELIGIBILITY: Active/Retired/Reserve/DoD Civilians.

RESERVATIONS: Accepted. Address: Outdoor Recreation, Ave D, Bldg 39, Naval Air Station, Corpus Christi, TX 78419-5000. **Comm: 512-937-5071.**

CAMP FACILITIES:	NO UNITS	HOOKUPS	FEE
Camper Spaces	24 Gravel	W/E (110/30A)	$ 7.00 dly
Tent Spaces	5	W	3.00 dly

SPT FACILITIES:			
	Beach	Boat Launch	Boat Rntl
	Camp Equip Rntl	Chapel	Fishing Piers/
	Gas	Golf	lighted
	Marina	Mini Mart	Pavilion
	Picnic Area	Racquet Sports	Sewage Dmp Sta
	Showers/gym	Skeet/Trap Rg	Sports Fields

ACTIVITIES:			
	Birding	Boating	Fishing
	Photography	Rec Equip Avail	Sailing
	Shelling	Swimming	

RESTRICTIONS: Pets allowed on leash. No open fires allowed. Firearms must be checked in with Security.

WEST FORT HOOD TRAVEL CAMP (TX08R3)
Fort Hood, TX 76544-5000

TELEPHONE NUMBER INFORMATION: Main installation numbers: Comm: 817-287/288-1110, DSN: 312-737/738-1110. Police for travel camp, Comm: 817-287-2176.

LOCATION: On post. 4 mi W of main post area. From I-35 take Killeen/Ft Hood exit; W on US-190; L on West Ft Hood turn-off. Travel Camp is on Clarke Rd, 1/4 mi on your right. Check in at office 0700-1745 M-F, 1000-1745 Sa, Su; closed Federal hol. Area marked. USMRA: page 87 (K-4). NMC: Austin, 60 mi S.

DESCRIPTION OF AREA: Ft Hood (largest military reservation in the world), is located in ranching and recreation country in central Texas. It's only a 30-min drive to Lake Belton and Lake Stillhouse, famous for recreation, black and white bass, and catfish. Travel camp boasts resident family of armadillos, summer night "fire-fly shows," and visits from the wild deer and rabbits. Full range of support facilities on post.

SEASON OF OPERATION: Year round.

ELIGIBILITY: Active/Retired/Reserve/NG/DoD Civilians.

RESERVATIONS: Required for groups with 20 to 60 units; accepted for others. Address: Community Recreation Division, Bldg 70004, Clarke Rd, AFZF-PA-CRD-WFHTC, Ft Hood, TX 76544-5056. **Comm: 817-288-9926; DSN: 312-738-9926.** Discount to holders of Golden Age and Golden Access Passports.

CAMP FACILITIES:	NO UNITS	HOOKUPS	FEE
Camper Spaces	64 Hardstand	W/S/E/CTV* (110/220/30A)	$ 9.00 dly/250 mo
Tent Spaces	20 Primitive	None	2.00 dly
RV/ Boat Storage**	116	Open Stand	15-20 mo

*Phone service available at 32 sites.
**Fenced, lighted, storage facility. Fees depend on size of vehicle.

TEXAS
WEST FORT HOOD TRAVEL CAMP, continued

SPT FACILITIES:

Cable TV	Chapel	Conv Store
Game Room	Gas	Golf
Grills	Laundry	Picnic Area
Playground	Restrooms	SewageDmp
Showers	Trails	Sta/fee

Equipment Checkout Center offers camping packages for rent from tents and motor homes to sleeping bags. Set-up available at travel camp.

ACTIVITIES:

Fishing/license	Hunting*/license	Jogging
Rec Equip Avail	Swimming	Water Skiing

*Annual deer harvest: Oct-Nov, bow and shotgun; Nov-Dec, rifle (guided hunt). Wild turkey hunt in Apr; dove and quail in Sep.

RESTRICTIONS: Pets allowed on leash. 24-hour hookup availability; register when office is open. Travel camp office 0700-1745 M-F, 1000-1745 Sa-Su; closed holidays. 14-day limit; exceptions up to 180 days available at office. Firearms not allowed in compound and must be registered with MPs on post.

UTAH

CARTER CREEK CAMP (UT01R4)
Hill Air Force Base, UT 84056-5000

TELEPHONE NUMBER INFORMATION: Main installation numbers: Comm: 801-777-7221, DSN: 312-458-1110. Police for camp, Comm: 801-777-3525.

LOCATION: Off base. From I-80 near Evanston WY, take WY/UT-150 S 34 mi to Bear River Service Station; .1 mi to E (left) on "Mill Creek RS-7." Approx 4 mi to camp on R side of road. Check in 1400-2000 with camp manager. USMRA: page 112 (F-3). NMI: Hill AFB, 105 mi W. NMC: Salt Lake City, 105 mi SW.

DESCRIPTION OF AREA: The surroundings of Carter Creek are typical of the Uintah Mountains with lodgepole pines and quaking aspen, a perfect combination of sight and sound. Rustic campsite in mountains reaching heights of 13,500 feet. Fishing lakes and ponds nearby. Full range of support facilities available at Hill AFB.

SEASON OF OPERATION: Weekend prior to 4 Jul-31 Oct.

ELIGIBILITY: Active/Retired/DoD Civilians at Hill AFB.

RESERVATIONS: Required. Address: Thornton Community Center, 2849 ABG/MWRO, Bldg 460, Hill Air Force Base, UT 84056-5000. **Comm: 801-777-3525/3661,** M-F 0900-1700.

CAMP FACILITIES:	NO UNITS	HOOKUPS	FEE
Cabins, 2-rm, slp 5*	6		$20-25 dly
Trailers	4		15.00 dly
Camper Spaces	4 Gravel	W/E (110)	8-10 dly
Tent Spaces	3 Wilderness	None	5.00 dly

*1 bdrm, refr, stove, sink w/cold running water, MW, heater, table w/5 chairs, 1 dbl bed, 1 sgl bed, 1 set bunk beds. Bring dishes, silverware, pots & pans, soap, towels, food, warm clothing, bedding, fishing gear, ice for personal coolers, & other recreational equipment. Limit of 5 pers.

SPT FACILITIES:	BBQ Fireplaces	Grills	Laundry
	Picnic Area	Playground	Restrooms
	Shower	Trails	

ACTIVITIES:	Fishing/license	Hiking	Horseshoes
	Hunting/license	Volleyball	

RESTRICTIONS: Pets allowed on leash; owner must clean up after pet. Check out 1300. No shooting in or near camp. Fires permitted in designated areas only. No phone available. *No provisions for drop-in patrons.* No firearms allowed in camp.

HILL FAM-CAMP (UT07R4)
Hill Air Force Base, UT 84056-5000

TELEPHONE NUMBER INFORMATION: Main installation numbers: Comm: 801-777-7221, DSN: 312-458-1110. Police for rec facilities: Comm: 911.

LOCATION: On base. Between Ogden and Salt Lake City. I-15 to exit 336; E on UT-193 2 mi to South Gate of base. Check in at Billeting Office, Mountain View Inn, Bldg 146. USMRA: page 112 (D-3). NMC: Ogden, 10 mi N.

DESCRIPTION OF AREA: Located near mountains at edge of urban area. Fam-camp convenient to recreation areas and points of interest around Great Salt Lake. Pineview Reservoir for boating and swimming, 25 mi E. Museum and aerospace park on base. Full range of support facilities available on base.

SEASON OF OPERATION: 1 Apr-31 Oct.

ELIGIBILITY: Active/Retired.

RESERVATIONS: *Confirmed resv only for AD on PCS or TDY orders*; others will be put on a waiting list. Address: Outdoor Recreation, 2849 ABG/MWRO, Hill AFB, UT 84056-5000. **Comm: 801-777-2601/1844, DSN: 312-458-2601/1844.**

CAMP FACILITIES:	NO UNITS	HOOKUPS	FEE
Camper Spaces	14 Paved	W/S/E (110/220)	$10.00 dly
Camper Spaces	14 Overflow	None	8.00 dly

SPT FACILITIES:	Boat Rntl	Chapel	Gas
	Golf	Grills	Laundry
	Picnic Area	Restrooms	Sewage Dmp Sta
	Sports Equip Rntl		

ACTIVITIES:	Jogging	Recreation Equipment Available

RESTRICTIONS: Pets allowed on leash only; must be walked in designated area; owner must clean up after pet. 10-day limit. No tent camping. No firearms allowed in camp.

UTAH

HILLHAUS LODGE (UT03R4)
Hill Air Force Base, UT 84056-5000

TELEPHONE NUMBER INFORMATION: Main installation numbers: Comm: 801-777-7221, DSN: 312-458-1110. Police for lodge, Comm: 801-777-3525.

LOCATION: Off base. I-15 to Ogden's 12th St exit; E to Ogden Canyon; pass Pineview Reservoir Dam. Proceed to Snowbasin Rd (UT-226); S approx 7 mi to Hillhaus sign. Check in 1300. USMRA: page 112 (D-2). NMI: Hill AFB, 30 mi SW. NMC: Ogden, 19 mi W.

SEASON OF OPERATION: Winter ski season: Nov-Apr.

DESCRIPTION OF AREA: Located high in mountains of Wasatch National Forest. Lodge is less than a mile from Snowbasin. Support facilities at Hill AFB.

ELIGIBILITY: Active/Retired/Reserve/DoD Civilians.

RESERVATIONS: Required with payment in full. Address: Outdoor Recreation, Thornton Community Center, Bldg 460, 2849 ABG/MWRO, Hill AFB, UT 84056-5000. **Comm: 801-777-3525, DSN: 312-458-3525.**

OVERNIGHT FACILITIES: Beautiful A-frame lodge, large sundeck, gas fireplace, snack bar, kitchen and dining area. Each unit has PB w/shower. Bedding, soap and towels provided. Prices include continental breakfast. Food service provided by staff. Contains sleeping areas below:

2 Suites, 4 pers limit	$55 dly (2 pers/$10 ea add pers)
1 Suite, 6 pers limit	50 dly (2 pers/$15 ea add pers)
1 Suite, 2 pers limit	50 dly
2 Rooms, 2 pers limit	45 dly
2 Room, 2 pers limit	40 dly
1 Loft (dormitory type), slp 7	75 dly

Groups may reserve the entire lodge *Monday through Wednesday only* at a cost of $350 which must be paid upon making the reservation (29-60 days in advance).

SPT FACILITIES:	Ice	Picnic Area	Restrooms
	Showers	Snack Bar	TV
ACTIVITIES:	Hiking	Horseshoes	Skiing/fee

RESTRICTIONS: No pets allowed. No smoking in suites or loft. Check out 1000. Bldg closes at 2000; no one admitted after that time. Patrons without overnight accommodations must also leave at this time. Patrons are not allowed to bring food or beverages into the lodge. Children under 12 will not be left unattended. Parents are responsible for their children & are liable for damage. No child care at Hillhaus Lodge. No firearms allowed.

OQUIRRH HILLS TRAVEL CAMP (UT06R4)
Tooele Army Depot, Tooele, UT 84074-5000

TELEPHONE NUMBER INFORMATION: Main installation numbers: Comm: 801-833-3211, DSN: 312-790-1110. Police for travel camp, Comm: 801-833-2314.

LOCATION: On post. From I-80 W of Salt Lake City, take UT-36 S approx 25 mi to main entrance. USMRA: page 112 (C-4). NMC: Salt Lake City, 35 mi NE.

DESCRIPTION OF AREA: View of largest open pit copper mine from top of Settlement Canyon. Enjoy sightseeing of canyons, mountains and desert. Wide range of support facilities on post, full range at Dugway Proving Ground 40 mi SW.

SEASON OF OPERATION: 1 May-30 Oct.

ELIGIBILITY: Active/Retired/DoD Civilians.

RESERVATIONS: Accepted 5 to 30 days in adv. Address: Community and Family Activities, Bldg 1011, Tooele Army Depot, Tooele, UT 84074-5001. **Comm: 801-833-3129, DSN: 312-790-3129.** Discounts for Golden Age & Golden Eagle Passports.

CAMP FACILITIES:	**NO UNITS**	**HOOKUPS**	**FEE**
Camper Spaces	14 Gravel	W/E (110)	$ 8 dly/50 wkly
Tent Spaces	8 Open Area	None	2.00 dly

SPT FACILITIES:			
	Archery	Boat Rntl	Bowling Alley
	Camp Equip Rntl	Camper Rntl	Chapel
	Golf Driv Range	Laundry	Playground
	PX/small	Racquetball	Restrooms
	Sewage Dmp Sta	Showers	Skeet/Trap Rg
	Sports Eq Rntl	Sports Fields	Stables
	Swim Pool/sumr		

ACTIVITIES:		
	Rec Equip Avail	Snow Skiing/1 hour away
	Fishing Reservoir	

RESTRICTIONS: Pets allowed on leash.

VIRGINIA

A. P. HILL RECREATION FACILITIES (VA39R1)
Fort A. P. Hill, Bowling Green, VA 22427-5000

TELEPHONE NUMBER INFORMATION: Main installation numbers: Comm: 804-633-5041, DSN: 312-934-8710. Police for rec facilities, Comm: 804-633-8425.

LOCATION: On post. *From N*, exit I-95 at Bowling Green/Fort A P Hill, (exit 126) US-17 (bypass); E to VA-2; S to Bowling Green; take US-301 NE to main gate. *From S*, I-95 to exit 104, VA-207; N to US-301 and main gate. 3 mi E of Bowling Green. Check in at Community Recreation Division, Bldg 106, 0800-2030 M-F (Sa 1 Sep-31 May). USMRA: page 47 (L,M-6,7). NMC: Fredericksburg, 14 mi NW.

DESCRIPTION OF AREA: The post is 77,000 acres of woodlands with lakes and ponds covering over 300 acres and offers abundant hunting and fishing opportunities in accordance with the laws of the state of Virginia. Some support facilities on post; full range available at Quantico MC Development Command, 45 mi NW and Naval Surface Warfare Center, VA, 25 mi NE.

SEASON OF OPERATION: Year round.

ELIGIBILITY: Active/Retired/Reserve/DoD Civilians.

RESERVATIONS: Accepted. Address: Commander, US Army Garrison, ATTN: Morale Support Activities Division, Fort A P Hill, Bowling Green, VA 22427- 5000. **Comm: 804-633-8219, DSN: 312-934-8219.** Discounts available to holders of Golden Age and Golden Access Passports.

VIRGINIA
A. P. HILL RECREATION FACILITIES, *continued*

LODGING:	FEE
The Lodge, overlooking a lake, has 9 bdrm units; max of 18 occupants in mixed group (gender), 20 in same group; DR, kit and lobby. *2 NIGHTS' STAY REQ DURING WEEKENDS.*	$ 25.00 pers dly/ 150.00 min dly
4 Log Cabins, **on Bullocks Pond,** 3 bdrm, LR, DR and kit. Sleep 6.	20.00 pers dly*

All units are fully furnished, including linens and kitchen utensils.
*Family rates available. $120 dly for groups, units or organizations.

CAMP FACILITIES:	NO UNITS	HOOKUPS	FEE
Camper spaces	48 Hardstand	W/S/E (110)	$ 10.00 dly

SPT FACILITIES:	Boat Rntl	Rec Center	Rec Equip Rntl
	Skeet Range	Swimming Pool	

ACTIVITIES:	Bicycling	Fishing	Hunting

RESTRICTIONS: No pets allowed in cabins or lodge; allowed on leash in camping area. no firearms allowed except those carried by bona-fide hunters.

BETHEL PARK RECREATION AREA (VA22R1)
Langley Air Force Base, VA 23665-5000

TELEPHONE NUMBER INFORMATION: Main installation numbers: Comm: 804-764-9990, DSN: 312-574-1110.

LOCATION: Off base. From I-64 take VA-134 N approx 4.5 mi to entrance to Bethel Manor Housing area. Stay on entry road (First Ave) to "T" intersection; L on Big Bethel Rd. Entrance to rec area is approx .25 mi on R. USMRA: page 47 (N-9) & page 52 (D-3). NMI: Langley AFB, 7 mi SE. NMC: Newport News, 10 mi S.

DESCRIPTION OF AREA: Situated along Big Bethel Reservoir in beautiful Virginia tidewater area offering activities such as boating, fishing and water sports. The rec area provides facilities for squadron-sponsored and family picnic activities and can accommodate approx 200 patrons. *This is a recreation area; no camping facilities are available. It is anticipated that 24 RV hookups will be completed in the fall of 1993.* Full range of support facilities available on base.

SEASON OF OPERATION: 1 Apr-31 Oct.

ELIGIBILITY: Active/Retired/DoD Civilians at Langley AFB.

RESERVATIONS: Required for **covered pavilions.** Address: Outdoor Recreation Office, 1 SVS/SVRO, Langley AFB, VA 23665-5534. **Comm: 804-764-7170, DSN: 312-574-7170.**

SPT FACILITIES:	Boat Launch	Boat Rntl	Fishing Pier
	Fishing Tackle	Golf/on base	Grills
	Marina/on base	Nature Trail	Pavilions/fee
	Picnic Area	Playground	Rec Equip Rntl
	Restrooms	Shoppette	Snack Bar
	Sports Fields	Tennis Courts	

ACTIVITIES: Badminton Boating Fishing
Horseshoes Volleyball

RESTRICTIONS: Pets allowed on leash. Off limits from sunset to sunrise. Swimming is not allowed in the reservoir.

CAPE HENRY TRAVEL CAMP (VA05R1)
Fort Story, VA 23459-5000

TELEPHONE NUMBER INFORMATION: Main installation numbers: Comm: 804-422-7305, DSN: 312-438-7305. Police for travel camp, Comm: 804-422-7601.

LOCATION: On post. *From S exit of Chesapeake Bay Bridge Tunnel* (US-13), take US-60 (Atlantic Ave) E to Ft Story. *From I-64* take US-60 E. *From VA-44* (Norfolk-VA Beach Expressway) exit US-58; L turn to N on Atlantic Ave (US-60) to 89th St to Ft Story. USMRA: page 47 (O-9). NMC: Virginia Beach, 3 mi S.

DESCRIPTION OF AREA: Ft Story, a sub-installation of Ft Eustis, is the site of the first stop of English settlers in the USA. The Cross at Cape Henry is located here. Old Cape Henry Lighthouse is the first lighthouse built by the federal government. The statue of Admiral Francois Joseph Paul de Grasse presented to the Virginia Beach Bicentennial Commission in 1976 is also located here. Full range of support facilities available on post.

SEASON OF OPERATION: Campground, Year Round; Mobile Homes, year round; Beach, Memorial Day-Labor Day.

ELIGIBILITY: Active/Retired/Reserve/DoD Civilians at Ft Story and Ft Eustis.

RESERVATIONS: Required. Address: Outdoor Recreation, ATTN: Travel Camp, Ft Story, VA 23459-5034. **Comm: 804-422-7601, DSN: 312-438-7601.** Discounts to holders of Golden Age and Golden Access Passports.

CAMP FACILITIES:	NO UNITS	HOOKUPS	FEE
Mobile Homes, 3 Bdrm	11		$40.00 dly*
Kamping Kabins, heat, A/C, 1 12x12 rm, slp 4	3	None	30.00 dly
Camper Spaces	24 Gravel	W/E (110)	14.00 dly

*Includes sponsor and spouse. $7 for each add pers over 6 years of age.

SPT FACILITIES: Beach Chapel Gas
Picnic Area Restrooms Sewage Dmp Sta
Showers Sports Fields Tennis Courts

ACTIVITIES: Rec Equip Avail Swimming

RESTRICTIONS: Pets allowed on leash; dogs in mobile homes must be under 20 pounds; for more details call "Reservations" numbers above. Ask about firearms restrictions.

VIRGINIA

CHEATHAM ANNEX RECREATION CABINS AND RV PARK (VA31R1)
Fleet and Industrial Supply Center, Cheatham Annex,
108 Sandra Ave.
Williamsburg, VA 23187-5000

TELEPHONE NUMBER INFORMATION: Main installation numbers: Comm: 804-887-4000, DSN: 312-953-4000. Police for RV park: Comm: 804-887-7222.

LOCATION: On base. From I-64 near Williamsburg, take exit 242B; E on VA-199 to main gate, check in MWR Check-in Center, Bldge 95, 1600. USMRA: page 47 (N-8). NMC: Newport News, 8 mi S.

DESCRIPTION OF AREA: Located in historical triangle of Jamestown, Colonial Williamsburg and Yorktown. Convenient to Busch Gardens, Pottery Factory, and College of William and Mary. Limited support facilities on base; full range at Yorktown Naval Weapons Station, 7 mi S.

SEASON OF OPERATION: Year round.

ELIGIBILITY: Active/Retired/Reserve.

RESERVATIONS: Accepted by phone only, 0800-0930 on M, up to 90 days in adv with non-refundable dep. Address: MWR, FISC, Cheatham Annex, 108 Sanda Ave, Williamsburg, VA 23187-8792. **Comm: 804-887-7224, DSN: 312-953-7224.**

FACILITIES AT RECREATION CABINS located along Cheatham Lake:

	FEE:
12 Cabins, sleep 4-10, furn, color CTV, phone, refr, kit utensils, dishes, linens; and a boat (with motor, battery, battery charger, paddles, cushions), 11 cabins located in wooded area on Cheatham Lake. All cabins have A/C and central heat, woodburning stove or fireplace (wood furn). 1 cabin equipped for handicapped.	$35-51 dly*/ 210-306 wkly*
	33-48 dly**/ 198-288 wkly**

*Summer rates; depending on cabin.
**Winter rates; depending on cabin.

FACILITIES AT RV PARK overlooking York River and Kings Creek:

	FEE
19 Camper Spaces with W/CTV/E (110/220)	$9 dly/54 wkly
Play-Mor Campers, 12' & 16'	15-20 dly
(off-base deposit required)	
Pop-up Campers	15 dly

SPT FACILITIES:

Boat Rntl	Camp Equip Rntl	Fishing Pier/hcp
Golf	Grills	Grocery/limited
Gymnasium	Laundry	Nature Trails
Pavilion	Pay Telephone	Picnic Area
Playground	Racquetball Ct	Restrooms
Sewage Dmp Sta	Showers	Sports Field
Swimming pools	Tennis Courts	Weight Room
Youth Pier*		

*Pier and shore fishing on Lascara Laguna for children under 15 yrs.

ACTIVITIES:

Bicycling	Boating	Crabbing
Fishing	Horseshoes	Rec Equip Avail
Swimming		

RESTRICTIONS: No pets allowed in cabins. Guests responsible for cleanliness of facility upon departure. No refunds for early departure. Check out 1200. No campfires, firearms, bow & arrows pellet guns or BB guns.

"THE COLONIES" TRAVEL PARK (VA32R1)
Fuller Lane
Fort Monroe, VA 23651-5000

TELEPHONE NUMBER INFORMATION: Main installation numbers: Comm: 804-727-2111, DSN: 312-680-2111. Police for travel park, Comm: 804-727-2238.

LOCATION: On post. From I-64 at Hampton, take exit 69. Follow historic sign markers to Fortress Monroe. USMRA: page 47 (N-9), page 52 (F-4). NMC: Hampton, adjacent to post.

DESCRIPTION OF AREA: Quiet, serene campsite named after the Thirteen Colonies. Each site has a state sign showing the state bird, flower, tree, and date it joined the Union. Post is located at the hub of many historical and recreational areas, e.g., Williamsburg, Jamestown, Yorktown, Busch Gardens, Virginia Beach. Full range of support facilities on post.

SEASON OF OPERATION: Year round.

ELIGIBILITY: Active/Retired/Reserve/DoD Civilians working at Fort Monroe.

RESERVATIONS: Accepted with one night's deposit. Address: Community Recreation, Fuller Lane, Attn: RERC PO Box 51106, Ft Monroe, VA 23651-6144. **Comm: 804-727-2384, DSN: 312-680-2384.** Discounts to holders of Golden Age, Golden Access and Golden Eagle Passports.

CAMP FACILITIES:	NO UNITS	HOOKUPS	FEE
Camper Spaces, 35 '	13 Gravel	W/S/E (110/220)	$14.00 dly

SPT FACILITIES:			
	Archery	Beach/fee	Bicycle Rntl
	Boat Rntl	Camp Equip Rntl	Camper Rntl
	Chapel	Fitness Center	Gas
	Grills	Laundry	Playground
	Picnic Area	Port-a-Potties/hcp	Racquetball
	Rec Equip Rntl	Restrooms/nearby	Sewage Dmp Sta
	Showers	Swim Pool/sumr	Tennis Courts

ACTIVITIES:			
	Bicycling	Boat Tours	Crabbing
	Fishing	Jogging	Windsurfing

RESTRICTIONS: Pets allowed on leash no longer than 6'; proof of rabies vaccination required; owner must clean up after pet. No open fires. No firearms allowed. No metal detectors or digging permitted.

LITTLE CREEK MWR RV PARK (VA38R1)
1432 Hewitt Drive
Little Creek Naval Amphibious Base, Norfolk, VA 23521-5007

TELEPHONE NUMBER INFORMATION: Main installation numbers: Comm: 804-464-7000, DSN: 312-680-7000. Police for RV park, Comm: 804-363-4444.

LOCATION: From I-64 take Northampton Blvd exit (US-13) N to Amphibious Base exit; N on Independence Blvd (VA-225) to Gate 5. *OR* from Bay Bridge Tunnel (US-13), take US-60 W to Gate 5. Go RV park is locatednear Gate 4 on Amphibious Dr. USMRA: page 47 (O-9). NMC: Norfolk, 6 mi W.

VIRGINIA
LITTLE CREEK MWR RV PARK, continued

DESCRIPTION OF AREA: The Naval Amphibious Base is nestled among many lakes and other bodies of water in a wooded area near the Chesapeake Bay. Full range of support facilities available on base and conveniently located.

SEASON OF OPERATION: Year round.

ELIGIBILITY: Active/Retired/Reserve on orders.

RESERVATIONS: Accepted. Address: MWR, Naval Amphibious Base Little Creek, Norfolk, VA 23521-2522. **Comm: 804-464-7516, DSN: 312-680-7516** (0800-1630 M-F).

CAMP FACILITIES:	NO UNITS	HOOKUPS	FEE
RV Spaces	45 Gravel	W/E (110/30&50A)	$10.00 dly*
Tent Spaces	6 Grass	None	5.00 dly

* $60.00 wkly, $ 240.00 mnthly

SPT FACILITIES:			
Archery*	Beaches	Boat Rntl*
Camper Rntl*	Chapel	Fitness Trail
Gas*	Golf	Grills
Jogging Trail	Marina	Miniature Golf*
Pay Telephones	Picnic Area	Playground
Restrooms	Sewage Dmp Sta/	Showers
Vending Mach	fee	

*Nearby

ACTIVITIES:		
Boating	Hiking	Fishing/license
Jogging	Swimming	

RESTRICTIONS: Pets allowed on leash. Fishing license may be obtained at the Navy Exchange. No fires.

LUNGA PARK (VA35R1)
Marine Corps Combat Development Command
Quantico, VA 22134-5001

TELEPHONE NUMBER INFORMATION: Main installation numbers: Comm: 703-640-2121, DSN: 312-278-2121. Police for campground, Comm: 703-640-2251.

LOCATION: On base. From N on I-95 take exit 148 (MCCDC Quantico). W on MCB-4 approx 7.5 mi to Lunga Reservoir office (1.5 mi past FBI Academy). USMRA: page 47 (L-5,6). NMC: Washington DC, 30 mi N.

DESCRIPTION OF AREA: Campgrounds situated along the Lunga Reservoir in a wooded park. The reservoir's name comes from the river on the Guadalcanal where the "Battle of Bloody Ridge" was fought. Area is within driving distance of Fredericksburg, Manassas, Mount Vernon and Washington DC. Recent addition is a 1.5 mi nature/fitness trail extending from one end of the park to the other. Full range of support facilities available on base, approx 13 mi from campgrounds. Field archery range developed in 1993.

SEASON OF OPERATION: Year round.

ELIGIBILITY: Active/Retired.

RESERVATIONS: No adv resv. Address: Lunga Park, c/o Recreation Branch, PO Box 186, Marine Corps Combat Development Command, Quantico, VA 22134-0186. Comm: 703-640-5270, DSN: 312-278-5270.

CAMP FACILITIES:	NO UNITS	HOOKUPS	FEE
Camper Spaces	5 Gravel	W/S/E (110/20A)	$12.00 dly
Camper Spaces	6 Gravel	S/E (110/20A)	12.00 dly
Camper Spaces	2 Gravel	W/E (110/20A)	10.00 dly
Camper Spaces	6 Gravel	E (110/20A)	10.00 dly
Camper/Tent Spaces	8 Wilderness	None	6.00 dly

SPT FACILITIES:			
	Archery Range	Boat Launch/fee	Boat Rntl/15Apr-15Oct
	Chapel/on base	Golf/on base	Grills
	Marina/Potomac	Nature/Fitness	Pavilions/fee
	Picnic Area	Trail	Playground
	Port-a-Potties	Sewage Dmp Sta	Stables/on base

Facilities are accessible to handicapped. General Store scheduled to open in '94.

ACTIVITIES: Boating Eq Avail Fishing/license

RESTRICTIONS: Pets allowed on leash. No swimming in the reservoir. Boat rentals available 15 Apr-15 Oct. Firearms must be registered on base.

PICKETT TRAVEL CAMP (VA33R1)
Fort Pickett, Blackstone, VA 23824-5000

TELEPHONE NUMBER INFORMATION: Main installation numbers: Comm: 804-292-8621, DSN: 312-438-8621. Police for travel camp, Comm: 804-292-8444.

LOCATION: On post. From US-460 W of Petersburg, take Ft Pickett exit; follow the signs to Ft Pickett. USMRA: page 47 (K-9). NMC: Petersburg, 40 mi NE.

DESCRIPTION OF AREA: 9 lakes and ponds available within installation boundaries. Travel camp is in wooded area adjacent to main post. Petersburg and Richmond have many museums, dinner theaters and historical sights. Wide range of support facilities available on post.

SEASON OF OPERATION: Year round.

ELIGIBILITY: Active/Retired.

RESERVATIONS: Required. Address: Commander, US Army Garrison, ATTN: AFZA-FP-PW-H, Fort Pickett, Blackstone, VA 23824-5000. **Comm: 804-292-8309/2443, DSN: 312-438-8309/2443.** Check in Billeting Office, Bldg 469, 0730-1600 daily, other hours M.P. Station Bldg 471

CAMP FACILITIES:	NO UNITS	HOOKUPS	FEE
Pegram Camper Spaces	27 Hardstand	W/S/E (110)	$ 9.00 dly
Tent Spaces	8	None	5.00 dly

SPT FACILITIES:			
	Bicycle Rntl	Boat Rntl	Camp Equip Rntl
	Chapel	Gas	Laundry
	Restrooms	Sewage Dmp Sta	Showers
	Sports Fields	Tennis Courts	

VIRGINIA
PICKETT TRAVEL CAMP, continued

ACTIVITIES: Boating   Fishing/license   Hunting/license
                Rec Equip Avail

RESTRICTIONS: Pets allowed on leash. Boating permits required ($10 annually).
Firearms allowed subject to Federal, VA, and county laws.

STEWART CAMPGROUND (VA04R1)
Naval Security Group Activity Northwest
Chesapeake, VA 23322-5000

TELEPHONE NUMBER INFORMATION: Main installation numbers: Comm:
804-421-8000, DSN: 312-564-1336. Police for campground, Comm: 804-421-8561.

LOCATION: On base. At NC/VA border, between Hickory VA. and Moyock NC.
From I-64 S of Norfolk, take VA-168 (Battlefield Blvd) S approx 16 mi to traffic
light at Ballahack Rd; R approx 3 mi to Relay Rd. L through gate; L on Olympic
Ave. Check in at Rec Services, Bldg 281 (duty hours), or main gate (after hours).
USMRA: page 47 (O-10). NMC: Norfolk VA, 35 mi N.

DESCRIPTION OF AREA: Located 75 mi N of Outer Banks NC. Region noted
as vacationer's and sportsman's paradise. Civil War cemetery on base with graves
of both Union and Confederate soldiers. Campground is in a wooded area secluded
from installation operations area. 6 mi from Northwest River Park (NWRP), a
boating and fishing area. Limited support facilities on base; full range at Norfolk
NS, 30 mi N.

SEASON OF OPERATION: 1 May until 1 Dec.

ELIGIBILITY: Active/Retired/Reserve/DoD Civilians.

RESERVATIONS: Accepted with deposit. Address: Recreation Services, MOU #1
Box 697, NSGA Northwest, Chesapeake, VA 23322-5000. **Comm: 804-421-8262,
FAX: 804-421-8785, DSN: 312-564-1336-EX-262.**

CAMP FACILITIES:	NO UNITS	HOOKUPS	FEE
Camper Spaces	18 Dirt	E (110/30A)	$ 8.00 dly

SPT FACILITIES:	Boat Rental	Camper Rental	Grills
	Pavilion/screened	Picnic Area	Playground
	Restrooms	Showers	Softball Field

ACTIVITIES: Rec Equip Avail   Softball

RESTRICTIONS: Pets allowed on leash. No open fires on ground. No all-terrain
vehicles. Water available at comfort station for filling only. No firearms allowed.

YORKTOWN CG CAMPGROUND (VA37R1)
Yorktown Coast Guard Reserve Training Center, VA 23690-9761

TELEPHONE NUMBER INFORMATION: Main installation numbers: Comm
and FTS 804-898-3500. Police for campground, Comm: 804-898-2314.

LOCATION: On base. I-64 to Yorktown exit; NE on US-17 through Yorktown,
approx 8 mi. Reserve Training Center is 2 mi NE of town. Check in at Gymnasium, Bldg 53, after 1200. USMRA: page 47 (N-8). NMC: Newport News, 15 mi SE.

DESCRIPTION OF AREA: Situated in a wooded area along the York River. Historic and recreational areas of Yorktown, Jamestown, Williamsburg, Bunch Gardens and Water Country USA are nearby. Fresh-water fishing in the lake behind the campground (bass, crappie, catfish and blue gill); also salt-water fishing (flounder, trout, croker, spots and more). Limited support facilities on base; full range available at Yorktown Naval Weapons Station, 5 mi N.

SEASON OF OPERATION: Year round; no water Oct-Apr.

ELIGIBILITY: Active/Ret/Reserve on AD/DoD, DoT and NAFA Civ Employees.

RESERVATIONS: Required for camper spaces, at least 1 week in adv, with non-refundable $10.00 deposit if no-show. Address: Morale, Welfare & Recreation, Coast Guard Reserve Training Center, Yorktown, VA 23690-9761. **Comm and FTS: 804-898-2127.**

CAMP FACILITIES:	NO UNITS	HOOKUPS	FEE
Camper Spaces	10 Gravel	W/E (110/30A)	$10.00 dly
Tent Spaces	5 Gravel	None	5.00 dly

SPT FACILITIES:			
	Bicycle Rntl	Boat Rntl	Camp Equip Rntl
	Chapel	Fishing Gear	Fitness Trail
	Gas	Grills	Gymnasium
	Ice	Laundry	Picnic Area
	Rec Equip Avail	Restrooms	Sewage Dmp Sta
	Showers	Snack Bar	Sports Fields

ACTIVITIES:			
	Boating	Fishing/license	Racquetball
	Softball	Swimming	Tennis

RESTRICTIONS: Pets allowed on leash; owner must clean up after pets daily. Prior to pitching tent, check in with Gym Watch, Bldg 53, for approval of location. 2-week limit. No vehicles permitted in tent areas. No open fires. Trash cans and bags are provided for daily clean-up, which is the responsibility of campers. Check out 1200.

WASHINGTON

CAMP MURRAY BEACH (WA21R4)
Camp Murray, Tacoma, WA 98430-5000

TELEPHONE NUMBER INFORMATION: Main installation numbers: Comm: 206-581-1950, DSN: 312-355-7110. Police for camp, Comm: 206-581-8939.

LOCATION: On post. From I-5 S of Tacoma, take exit 122 W across railroad tracks; L through Camp Murray gate and follow signs to beach. Check in at office 1200-1830. USMRA: page 101 (C-5). NMC: Tacoma, 10 mi N.

DESCRIPTION OF AREA: Camp Murray is located on the southern end of Puget Sound in the Olympia Mountain region. Quiet, wooded site along American Lake. Winter temperature range 35-45°, summer 65-80°. No support facilities on post; full range available at Ft Lewis, 2 mi S.

SEASON OF OPERATION: Year round.

WASHINGTON
CAMP MURRAY BEACH, continued

ELIGIBILITY: Active/Retired/Reserve/NG.

RESERVATIONS: Advised; accepted up to 30 days in adv. Address: Camp Murray Beach, Tacoma, WA 98430-5004. **Comm: 206-581-8950, DSN: 312-355-7950.**

CAMP FACILITIES:	NO UNITS	HOOKUPS	FEE
Camper Spaces	24 Gravel	W/S/E (110/30A)	$10.00 dly/65 wkly
Tent Spaces	Open	None	5.00 dly/35 wkly
SPT FACILITIES:	Beach	Boat Rntl	Laundromat
	Marina	Picnic Area	Playground
	Propane	Restrooms	Showers
ACTIVITIES:	Basketball	Boating	Fishing/license
	Horseshoes	Jogging	Laundry
	Propane	Snorkeling	Swimming
	Volleyball	Water Skiing	

RESTRICTIONS: Pets allowed on leash; must be walked in designated areas only. No off-road vehicles. Quiet hours 2200-0800. Check out 1200. No firearms allowed.

CLEAR LAKE RECREATION AREA (WA01R4)
Fairchild Air Force Base, WA 99011-5000

TELEPHONE NUMBER INFORMATION: Main installation numbers: Comm: 509-247-1212, DSN: 312-657-1110. Police for rec area, Comm: 911.

LOCATION: Off base. From I-90 take exit 264 N on Salnave Rd; R on Clear Lake Rd .5 mi to area. USMRA: page 101 (I-4). NMI: Fairchild AFB, 13 mi N. NMC: Spokane, 12 mi NE.

DESCRIPTION OF AREA: Located on Clear Lake in a state where natural wildlife is a challenge and recreational adventure for the naturalist, photographer, artist, birdwatcher, fisherman and camper. This 34-acre resort is the perfect place for camping, water skiing, fishing and boating. Full range of support facilities available on base.

SEASON OF OPERATION: Mid-Apr to mid-Jun: 0700-1900; mid-Jun to 30 Sep Th-M 0900-2100, Tu-W 1100-1900—subject to change after Labor Day.

ELIGIBILITY: Active/Retired/Reserve on AD/NG/Civilians at Fairchild AFB.

RESERVATIONS: Accepted with deposit. Address: Clear Lake Recreation Area, S 14824 Clear Lake Rd, Cheney, WA 99004. **Comm: 509-299-5129.** (*For information off season*, Comm: 509-247-5366, DSN: 312-657-5366.)

CAMP FACILITIES:	NO UNITS	HOOKUPS	FEE
Cabins, kit, shower	1		$16 dly/80 wkly
Cabins, kit, no shower	2		12 dly/60 wkly
Campers. A/C, 18 '	4		14 dly/70 wkly
Camper Spaces	18 Paved	W/E (110/30A)	7 dly/42 wkly
Tent Spaces	10	Some with water	3 dly/18 wkly
Overflow	Open	None	5.00 dly

SPT FACILITIES:	Beach	Boat Launch/hcp	Boat Rntl
	Camp Equip Rntl	Fishing Pier/hcp	Gas/regular
	Grills	Picnic Areas	Playground
	Sewage Dmp Sta	Showers	Snack Bar
	Tackle Shop	Vending Mach	Video Game Rm

ACTIVITIES:	Boating	Fishing/license	Rec Equip Avail
	Sailing	Swimming	Water Skiing

RESTRICTIONS: Pets allowed on leash. Swimming is permitted inside marked area only. Open fires in designated areas only; trees must not be cut down for use as firewood. Boating safety briefing required for ski boat rental; briefing given Wednesday at 1000, MWR Equipment Checkout, Bldg 2249C, or at rec area. Check out 1200. No firearms in rec area.

CLIFFSIDE RV PARK (WA12R4)
Whidbey Island Naval Air Station, WA 98278-5000

TELEPHONE NUMBER INFORMATION: Main installation numbers: Comm: 206-257-2211, DSN: 312-820-0111. Police for RV park, Comm: 206-257-3122.

LOCATION: On base. Off WA-20, 4 mi NW of Oak Harbor. From WA-20 turn onto Ault Field Rd; R at Langley Blvd, thru Main Gate of NAS to 4-way stop; L onto 5th St to stop sign, then R onto Saratoga St; L onto 8th St which will become a dirt road leading into Cliffside Park. Check in at Outdoor Rec Center, Bldg 117. USMRA: page 101 (C-2,3). NMC: Seattle, 60 mi SE.

DESCRIPTION OF AREA: Beautiful scenic area with salt-water beach and marina nearby offering many water sports. Full range of support facilities available on base.

SEASON OF OPERATION: Year round.

ELIGIBILITY: Active/Retired/Reserve/DoD Civilians with MWR User Card.

RESERVATIONS: Accepted with Deposit: up to 90 days in adv for AD, up to 60 days for others. Address: Outdoor Recreation Center, Bldg 117, Naval Air Station, Whidbey Island, Oak Harbor, WA 98278-2100. **Comm: 206-257-2434, DSN: 312-820-2434.**

CAMP FACILITIES:	NO UNITS	HOOKUPS	FEE
Camper Spaces	18 Gravel	W/E (110)	$ 6.50 dly/39 wkly
Camper Spaces, 40 '	2 Gravel	W/E (110)	6.50 dly/39 wkly
Tent Spaces	6 Gravel/Grass	None	3.00 dly/18 wkly

SPT FACILITIES:	Boat Launch	Boat Rntl	Grills
	Marina	Picnic Area	Rec Equip Rntl
	Restrooms	Sewage Dmp Sta	Showers

ACTIVITIES:	Boating	Fishing	Water Sports

RESTRICTIONS: House pets allowed on leash; must not be left unattended outside; owner must clean up after pet. 2-week limit during Jul and Aug. Maximum of 8 pers and 2 vehicles per site. No open fires on ground or beach. Quiet hours 2300-0800. Check out 1100. No firearms allowed.

WASHINGTON

HOLIDAY PARK FAM-CAMP (WA03R4)
McChord Air Force Base, WA 98438-5000

TELEPHONE NUMBER INFORMATION: Main installation numbers: Comm: 206-984-1910, DSN: 312-984-1110. Police for fam-camp, Comm: 206-984-5777.

LOCATION: On base. From I-5 S of Tacoma, take exit 125 E. Follow signs to McChord AFB and thru main gate; R on A St, L on Outer Dr; R at Holiday Park. Check in at office, 24 hrs dly. USMRA: page 101 (C-5) & page 103 (B-7). NMC: Tacoma, 8 mi NE.

DESCRIPTION OF AREA: Located in western area of state at base of Puget Sound. Fam-camp offers a base for prime sightseeing and recreational opportunities on numerous waterways and lakes in Puget Sound area and nearby national parks: Mt Ranier, Olympic and North Cascades. Camp area is surrounded by giant firs and pines. Full range of support facilities on base.

SEASON OF OPERATION: Year round.

ELIGIBILITY: Active/Retired/Reserve/DoD Civilians.

RESERVATIONS: No advance reservations. Address: Holiday Park Fam-Camp, 735 Fifth St, PO Box 5000, McChord AFB, WA 98438-5000. Comm: 206-984-5488.

CAMP FACILITIES:	NO UNITS	HOOKUPS	FEE*
Camper Spaces	18 Hardstand	W/S/E (110/30A)	$11.00 dly/65 wkly
Camper Spaces	18 Hardstand	W/E (110/30A)	10.00 dly/60 wkly
Camper Spaces	20	None	5.00 dly32.50 wkly
Tent Spaces	20	None	3.00 dly/18 wkly

SPT FACILITIES:	Grills	Pavilion	Pay phones
	Picnic Areas	Playground	Restrooms/hcp
	Sewage Dmp Sta	Shelters	Showers
	Sports Fields		

ACTIVITIES:	Hiking	Horseshoes	Sightseeing
	Softball	Volleyball	

RESTRICTIONS: Pets allowed on leash; *must* have certificate and tag for current rabies vaccination. 2-week limit May-Sep. Check out 1100. Firearms must be cleared at Security Gate.

JIM CREEK REGIONAL OUTDOOR RECREATION AREA (WA07R4)
21027 Jim Creek Road
Jim Creek Naval Radio Station (T), Arlington, WA 98223-8599

TELEPHONE NUMBER INFORMATION: Main installation numbers: Comm: 206-435-2161, DSN: 312-891-1220. Police for recreation area, Comm: 206-435-2161-EX-335.

LOCATION: On base. From I-5, take exit 208; E on WA-530 for approx 10 mi, thru Arlington; cross bridge, pass Trafton store on L; take first R on Jim Creek Rd (266th St NE) 6 mi to end. USMRA: page 101 (D-3). NMC: Seattle, 60 mi SW.

DESCRIPTION OF AREA: Jim Creek borders the Mt Baker-Snoqualmie National Forest and the Boulder River Wilderness Area. Located in the foothills of the North Cascades about one hour north of Seattle, Jim Creek has over 5,000 acres—most of it wilderness, with a wide variety of recreational opportunities. In addition to Twin Lakes (famous for great fishing, canoeing and wildlife viewing) there are 3 small lakes and beaver ponds accessible by hiking. No support facilities on base; full range available at Whidbey Island NAS, 60 mi W.

SEASON OF OPERATION: Year round.

ELIGIBILITY: Active/Retired/DoD Civilians.

RESERVATIONS: Accepted. Address: NRS (T) Jim Creek, Outdoor Recreation Area, Arlington, WA 98223-8599. **Comm: 206-435-7335, 800-734-1123** *(good only in area code 206)*; DSN: 312-891-1220.

CAMP FACILITIES:	NO UNITS	HOOKUPS	FEE
Camper Spaces	2 Concrete	W/E (110)	$8.00 dly
Camper/Tent Spaces	23 Gravel/Dirt	None	6.00 dly
Day Camp			
Group Camping for Scouts, Campfire Girls, etc.			None

SPT FACILITIES:	Boat Launch	Boat Rntl	Conference Center
	Gym/Showers	Hiking Trails	Picnic Area
	Playground	Rec Equip Rntl	Restrooms/hcp
	Softball Field	Tennis Court	

ACTIVITIES:	Boating	Fishing/license	Hiking
	Deer Hunting	Mountain Biking	River rafting*
	in season	Rock Climbing*	Snow Skiing(XC)*

* Activities nearby base.

RESTRICTIONS: Pets allowed on leash. No unlicensed off-road vehicles and no swimming allowed. Cameras allowed in unrestricted areas only. *Level of radio frequency is considered a potential hazard to people employing electronic life aid/support systems.* Smoking and open fires only in designated areas. Check out 1200 hrs. OIC permission is required for the admission of all firearms.

LEWIS TRAVEL CAMP (WA13R4)
Fort Lewis, WA 98433-5000

TELEPHONE NUMBER INFORMATION: Main installation numbers: Comm: 206-967-1110, DSN: 312-357-1110. Police for travel camp, Comm: 206-967-3107.

LOCATION: On post. From I-5 take exit 120. Follow signs to N Fort Lewis. Take first R after guard shack. USMRA: page 101 (C-5). NMC: Tacoma, 15 mi N.

DESCRIPTION OF AREA: Located at southern end of Puget Sound in unique, snow-topped Olympia Mountain region. Tranquil, wooded site along American Lake. Winter temperature range 35-45° and those in summer, 65-80°. Enjoy the beautiful weather in Washington; if you don't — wait 5 minutes and it will change! Full range of support facilities available on post.

SEASON OF OPERATION: Year round.

WASHINGTON
LEWIS TRAVEL CAMP, continued

ELIGIBILITY: Active/Retired/Reserve/NG/DoD and NAF Civilians.

RESERVATIONS: Advised; accepted up to 60 days in adv. Address: Ft Lewis Travel Camp, Community Recreation Division, Outdoor Recreation Br, NCO Beach Rd, Bldg 8069, Ft Lewis, WA 98433-5000. **Comm: 206-967-7744, DSN: 312-357-7744.**

CAMP FACILITIES:	NO UNITS	HOOKUPS	FEE
Camper Spaces	24 Gravel	W/CTV/E(110/30A)	$10.00 dly*
Camper Spaces	6 Overflow	E (110/30A)	8.00 dly
Tent Spaces	5 Wilderness	None	5.50 dly*

*Weekly, monthly and off-season rates available.

In addition, there are 120 rustic camper and tent spaces available at Chambers Lake, Lewis Lake and Nisqually River. These sites have no hookups and are free.

SPT FACILITIES:		
Beach	Boat Rntl	Camp Equip Rntl
Chapel	Fishing Dock	Game Room/TV
Gas	Golf	Laundry
Lounge/TV	Marina	Pavilion
Pay Telephones	Picnic Areas	Playground
Restrooms/hcp	Sewage Dmp Sta	Showers/hcp
Snack Bar	Sports Eq Rntl	

Travel trailers may be rented from Outdoor Equipment Resource Center.

ACTIVITIES: Fishing/license Hunting Snow Skiing

RESTRICTIONS: Pets allowed on leash; owner must clean up after pets. No open fires or wood fires. 30-day limit. Quiet hours after 2200. Check out 1200.

PACIFIC BEACH CENTER (WA16R4)
200 West Memorial Drive
Everett Naval Station, WA 98207-1700

TELEPHONE NUMBER INFORMATION: Main installation numbers: Comm: 206-304-3000, DSN: 312-727-3000. Police for center, Comm: 911.

LOCATION: Off base. From I-5 at Olympia, take exit 104 (Aberdeen/Port Angeles); W on US-8 and US-12 through Aberdeen to Hoquiam. Follow US-101 N approx 4 mi to sign indicating Ocean Beaches; turn L and continue on Ocean Beach Rd through Copalis Crossing, Carlisle and Aloha to Pacific Beach. Follow Main St to entrance to Pacific Beach Recreation and Conference Center. Watch for signs to office; check in 1600-2000. USMRA: page 101 (A-4,5). NMI: Ft Lewis, 115 mi NE. NMC: Aberdeen, 25 mi SE.

DESCRIPTION OF AREA: Situated on Olympic Peninsula, overlooking Pacific Ocean, providing starting point for exploring the Peninsula with its spectacular rain forest, Quinalt Indian Reservation and Ocean Shores area. It also offers steelhead and salmon fishing. Limited support facilities on base; full range available at Ft Lewis.

SEASON OF OPERATION: Year round.

ELIGIBILITY: Active/Retired/Reserve/NG/DoD Civilians/100% DAV.

RESERVATIONS: Recommended for RV park, studios and motel units; required for cabins and suites; with deposit: up to 90 days in adv for AD, up to 60 days in adv for Retired and Reserve, up to 30 days in adv for all others. Address: Pacific Beach Center, 108 First St, PO Box O, Pacific Beach, WA 98571-5000. (Make checks payable to "Pacific Beach.") **Comm: 1-800-626-4414, 206-276-4414, FAX: 206-276-4615** (M-F 1000-1600, Sa-Su 1000-1600). (*For information*, Comm: 206-526-3579, DSN: 312-941-7461.)

CAMP FACILITIES:	NO UNITS	HOOKUPS	FEE*
Beach Houses, 3 bdrm**	23		$45-70 dly
Beach Houses, 4 bdrm**	5		50-75 dly
Suites (adults only)**	4		45-50 dly
Studios**	15		20-40 dly
Family Units**	12		25-45 dly
RV Spaces	43 Hardstand	W/E(110/30A)	7-11 dly
Camper/Tent Spaces	100	None	5.00 dly

*Depending on rank, days of week, and season. Oceanview with fireplace, $10 add dly. $5 add dly for units with wood stoves. Cribs (no linens), $5 per visit. $1 add dly for 33 RV spaces with CTV; wkly and mo rates avail.
**Cabins slp 2 pers ea bdrm; suites and studios slp 2 adults; family units slp 2 adults and 2 children. All fully equipped.

SPT FACILITIES:

Basketball/1 on 1	Bowling	Cable TV
Conference Fac	Exercise Room	Hot Tubs/Spa
Laundry	Lounge	Meeting Rooms
Pay Telephones	Restaurant	Restrooms/hcp
Sewage Dmp Sta	Showers	Social Room
Weight Room		

Most bathrooms and buildings handicapped accessible.

ACTIVITIES:

Beachcombing	Bingo	Card Tournament
Clamming	Crabbing	Dancing
Fishing	Group Activities	Hiking
Hunting	Kiddie Bingo	Weekly Events

Scheduled activities for all ages.

RESTRICTIONS: Pets allowed on leash and must be registered; owner must clean up after pet. No open fires except in covered picnic area, in grills and camp stoves; must not be left unattended at any time. 2-night min; 3-night min on hol wknds (F-M); 14-day limit. No cooking in studios and family units; no children, pets nor smoking in suites. Any excess cleaning/repair will be billed to patron. Sponsor must accompany guest during stay. Quiet hours 1000-0700. Check out 1100 (1300 for RV/tent spaces). No RV/camper parking at beach houses. Hunting rifles must be declared, no other firearms are allowed.

ROCKY POINT RV PARK (WA22R4)
Whidbey Island Naval Air Station, WA 98278-5000

TELEPHONE NUMBER INFORMATION: Main installation numbers: Comm: 206-257-2211, DSN: 312-820-0111. Police for RV park, Comm: 206-257-3122.

LOCATION: Off base. Off WA-20, 4 mi NW of Oak Harbor. From WA-20 turn onto Ault Field Rd; R at Langley Blvd to Main Gate of NAS. Check in at Outdoor Rec Center, Bldg 117, and obtain directions to RV park which is approx 3 mi from Outdoor Rec Center. USMRA: page 101 (C-2,3). NMC: Seattle, 60 mi SE.

WASHINGTON
ROCKY POINT RV PARK, continued

DESCRIPTION OF AREA: RV park located within walking distance of local Gallery Golf Course. Sites with water view, and salt-water beach and picnic area nearby. Full range of support facilities available on base 3 mi away.

SEASON OF OPERATION: Year round.

ELIGIBILITY: Active/Retired/Reserve/DoD Civilians with MWR User Card.

RESERVATIONS: Accepted with deposit: up to 90 days in adv for AD, up to 60 days for others. Address: Outdoor Recreation Center, Bldg 117, Naval Air Station, Whidbey Island, Oak Harbor, WA 98278-2100. **Comm: 206-257-2434, DSN: 312-820-2434.**

CAMP FACILITIES:	NO UNITS	HOOKUPS	FEE
RV Spaces, self-cont	23	None	$4 dly/24 wkly

SPT FACILITIES:	Boat Launch	Boat Rntl	Grills
	Marina	Picnic Area	Rec Equip Rntl
	Restrooms	Sewage Dmp Sta	Showers

ACTIVITIES:	Boating	Fishing	Golf
	Water Sports		

RESTRICTIONS: House pets allowed on leash; must not be left unattended outside; owner must clean up after pet. Maximum of 8 pers and 2 vehicles per site. No open fires on ground or beach. Quiet hours 2300-0800. Check out 1100. No firearms allowed.

WESTPORT RECREATION PARK (WA14R4)
Ocean Avenue
Grays Harbor Coast Guard Station, Westport, WA 98595-0568

TELEPHONE NUMBER INFORMATION: Main installation numbers: Comm: 206-268-0121, FTS: 396-9307. Police for rec park, Comm: 911.

LOCATION: On base. At Grays Harbor Light. US-12 to Aberdeen; SW on WA-105 to Westport. Take 1st exit into Westport; approx 3 mi to R turn, following signs to US Coast Guard Station. Check in with OOD at front desk 1100-2200. USMRA: page 101 (A-5). NMC: Olympia, 50 mi E.

DESCRIPTION OF AREA: Salmon capital of the world with 18 mi of sandy beach and excellent clam digging. Great salmon fishing from charter boats. Full range of support facilities available at Ft Lewis, 85 mi E.

SEASON OF OPERATION: 1 Mar-31 Oct.

ELIGIBILITY: Active/Retired/Reserve/DoD Civilians.

RESERVATIONS: Required, *in writing* with payment, as early as possible but no later than 2 wks in adv. (Make checks payable to "Thirteenth Coast Guard District Morale Fund.") Address: Commanding Officer, Ocean Ave, USCG Station Grays Harbor, Westport, WA 98595-0568. **Comm: 206-268-0121, FTS: 420-9307.**

CAMP FACILITIES:	NO UNITS	HOOKUPS	FEE
Camper Spaces	6 (1 paved)	W/E (110)	$ 4.00 dly
Tent Spaces	6 Dirt/Grass	None	2.50 dly

WASHINGTON
WESTPORT RECREATION PARK, continued

SPT FACILITIES:	Beach	Charter Boats	Grills
	Grocery/nearby	Laundry/nearby	Marina/nearby
	Nature Trails	Picnic Area	Playground
	Restrooms	Sewage Dmp Sta	Showers
	Tennis Courts		

ACTIVITIES:	Baseball	Fishing	Hiking
	Surfing	Surf Fishing	Swimming

RESTRICTIONS: Pets allowed on leash no longer than 6 feet; owner must clean up after pets. 7-day limit, to include only 1 weekend. No motorcycles. No firearms allowed.

WEST VIRGINIA

SUGAR GROVE CABIN (WV06R1)
Sugar Grove Naval Radio Station (R), WV 28615-5000

TELEPHONE NUMBER INFORMATION: Main installation numbers: Comm: 304-249-6303, DSN: 312-564-7276. Police for cabin area: Comm: 304-249-6312/6310.

LOCATION: On base. Take US-33 W from Harrisonburg VA to Brandywine WV. Approx 5 mi to Sugar Grove Rd; L to Naval Radio Station. Signs at Brandywine direct you to the station. Check in at MWR Office (located in same bldg as Hobby Shop) M-F 0730-1600; at Quarterdeck after duty hours. USMRA: page 47 (I-6). NMC: Harrisonburg VA, 34 mi SE.

DESCRIPTION OF AREA: Located in the mountain section of West Virginia, the Station is bisected by US-33. It is an area of quiet beauty with hills and mountains, beautiful valleys, and deep gorges where streams have carved their way through the mountains. Limited support facilities available on base; full range available at Quantico Marine Corps Combat Development Command (in Virginia), approx 3.5-hour drive east.

SEASON OF OPERATION: Year round.

ELIGIBILITY: Active/Retired/Reserve/NG/DOD Civilians.

RESERVATIONS: Required. Address: MWR, Naval Radio Station (R), Sugar Grove, WV 26815-5000. **Comm: 304-249-6360, DSN: 312-564-7276.**

CAMP FACILITIES: Rustic 1-room Log Cabin, sleeps up to 12, furnished, electricity, refrigerator, kerosene heat, stove. Running water, electric heat, and indoor toilets facilities. Bring linens, pillows, towels, kitchen utensils, etc.
FEE: $20.00 daily

SPT FACILITIES:	Boat Motors	Boat Rntl	Camp Equip Rntl
	Camper Rental	Port-a-Pottie	Rec Equip Rntl
	Tent Rental	EM Club/walking distance	

WEST VIRGINIA
SUGAR GROVE CABIN, *continued*

ACTIVITIES:	Bowling	Fishing	Hiking
	Hunting	Picnicking	

RESTRICTIONS: Pets allowed on leash. No pit bulls. The cabin is frequently used by sports teams who are traveling. No firearms allowed. Must be secured by Security Police.

WISCONSIN

PINE VIEW RECREATION AREA (WI01R2)
Fort McCoy, Sparta, WI 54656-5141

TELEPHONE NUMBER INFORMATION: Main installation numbers: Comm: 608-388-2222, DSN: 312-280-1110.

LOCATION: On post. Exit I-90 at Sparta to WI-21; 8 mi NE to main gate. Well marked. Rec area off W Headquarters Rd, 1 mi W of Post Headquarters. USMRA: page 68 (C,D-7). NMC: LaCrosse, 35 mi W.

DESCRIPTION OF AREA: Beautiful wooded area bounded by Squaw Lake and LaCrosse River. 13 ponds and small lakes on post are ideal for fishing activities. Squaw Lake is well stocked with rainbow trout and large mouth bass. Wide range of support facilities available on post.

SEASON OF OPERATION: 1 May-1 Dec.

ELIGIBILITY: Active/Retired/Reserve/NG/DoD and NAF Civilians.

RESERVATIONS: Accepted. Priority system for reservations based on status of sponsor; call for information. Address: Community Recreation Div, 1439 South "M" St, ATTN: Pine View Recreation Area, Ft McCoy, WI 54656-5141. **Comm: 608-388-3517/3841, DSN: 312-280-3517/3841.** Discounts to holders of Golden Age Passports.

CAMP FACILITIES:	NO UNITS	HOOKUPS	FEE*
Duplex, 1 bdrm	2		$30-35 dly
Campers, in place, 21/23 '	2	E (110)	25-30 dly
Campers, in place, 16 '	1	E (110)	20-25 dly
Camper Spaces	105 Gravel	E (110)	9-10 dly
Camper/Tent Spaces	12	None	7-8 dly

*Depending on status of sponsor.

SPT FACILITIES:	Bicycle Rntl	Boat Rntl	GrillsH i k i n g
	Trail	Laundry/nearby	Miniature Golf
	Pavilion/fee	Picnic Area	Playground
	Restrooms	RV Storage	Sewage Dmp Sta
	Showers	Snack Bar	

ACTIVITIES:

| Bicycling | Boating | Fishing/license |
| Hunting/license | Swimming | Winter Sports |

Whitetail Ridge Recreation Area, catering to all levels of skiers, Dec-Mar, depending on the weather. Facilities include: 4 lighted ski slopes with snowmaking capability, downhill and 5 mi cross-country skiing, 185' vertical and 1300' long runs, 2 ski lifts, tubing slope with rope tow, equipment rental, chalet and snack bar. Groomed snowmobile trail network also passes through the Whitetail Ridge area. For info call Comm: 608-388-4498, DSN: 312-280-4498. No firearms allowed.

RESTRICTIONS: Pets allowed on leash. 14-day limit.

RAWLEY POINT COTTAGE (WI04R2)
2420 S. Lincoln Memorial Drive
Milwaukee Coast Guard Group, WI 53207-1997

TELEPHONE NUMBER INFORMATION: Main installation numbers: Comm and FTS: 414-747-7100 (0700-1500). Police for cottages, Comm: 911.

LOCATION: Off base. From I-43 near Two Rivers take exit 79; N on WI-42 into the city. R on 17th St; cross drawbridge; R on East St 4 blocks to Two Rivers CG Station at 13 East St. Check in with OOD 1200-2100 to obtain keys. Cottage is located 5 mi N of CG Sta: Take 17th St to R on WI-42 (22nd St). Go straight on CR "O" which curves to L (NG Armory on corner). Stay on "O" 4 mi; watch for sign at entrance to Point Beach State Park. Turn R into park and stop at Ranger gate. Tell ranger you are going to lighthouse; go through gate and turn R into lighthouse parking lot. USMRA: page 68 (G-7). NMI: Two Rivers CG Sta, 4 mi S. NMC: Manitowoc, 10 mi S.

DESCRIPTION OF AREA: Historical 115-year-old lighthouse overlooking Lake Michigan. Cottage is situated within 2800-acre Point Beach State Park. Twin cities of Two Rivers/Manitowoc are rich in festivals, fishing derbies and maritime events. Charter boats provide offshore fishing for lake trout and salmon. Limited support facilities at Twin Rivers CG Station; full range at Ft McCoy, 175 mi W.

SEASON OF OPERATION: Year round.

ELIGIBILITY: Active/Retired/Reserve/DoT Civilians/CG Auxiliary.

RESERVATIONS: Required, *by phone*: up to 60 days in adv for AD CG; 40 days in adv for all other AD and Ret; 15 days in adv for Reserve and Auxiliary. Full payment required 7 working days prior to check-in. Address: Commander, USCG Group Morale Fund, 2420 S Lincoln Memorial Dr, Milwaukee, WI 53207-1997. **Comm and FTS: 414-747-7185.**

LODGING: 1 townhouse with 2 apartments, each has 2 bdrms and sleeps 8 adults. PB, kit, MW, TV, VCR, W/D, dishes, pots and pans; furn. Bring linens (queen, full and twin), blankets, towels and toilet items.
      FEE: $25.00 dly

SPT FACILITIES:

| Beach | Bicycles | Grills |
| Picnic Area | | |

Nearby park and commercial facilities offer:

Camping	Chapel	Golf
Grocery	Laundry	Marina
Rec Center	Tours	Trails

Free Tour of Nuclear Power Generating Plant (off base)

WISCONSIN
RAWLEY POINT COTTAGE, continued

ACTIVITIES:	Fishing	Hiking	Hunting
	Swimming	Snow Skiing (XC)	

RESTRICTIONS: Pets allowed on leash; owner responsible for any damages; must clean up after pet daily. 2-night to 1-week limit. Check out by 1200. Use and possession of firearms must be in accordance with Federal, State, and local laws.

SHERWOOD POINT COTTAGE (WI03R2)
Milwaukee Coast Guard Group, WI 53207-1997

TELEPHONE NUMBER INFORMATION: Main installation numbers: Comm and FTS: 414-747-7100 (0700-1500).

LOCATION: Off base. From US-41 at Green Bay, take WI-57 N to Sturgeon Bay; check in at Coast Guard Station, 2501 Canal Rd, 1200-2100. To get to cottage take WI-42/57 S to County 'S'; turn R on Duluth St; L on Elm St to County 'M'; R to Potawatomi State Park; turn L just before Fishing Hole Tavern. This is access road to CG lighthouse. Approx 9 mi from Elm and County 'M'. USMRA: page 68 (H-5). NMI: Ft McCoy, 190 mi SW. NMC: Green Bay, 45 mi SW.

DESCRIPTION OF AREA: Lighthouse situated on western shores of Lake Michigan. Beautiful cottage overlooking bay and wooded area. Near winter ski area. Wide range of support facilities available at Ft McCoy, 190 mi SW.

SEASON OF OPERATION: Year round.

ELIGIBILITY: Active/Retired/Reserve/DoT Civilians/CG Auxiliary.

RESERVATIONS: Required, *by telephone only*: up to 60 days in adv for AD CG; up to 40 days in adv for other AD and Retired; up to 15 days in adv for Reserve and Auxiliary. Full payment required 7 working days prior to check-in. Address: Commander, Coast Guard Group Morale Fund, 2420 S Lincoln Memorial Dr, Milwaukee, WI 53207-1997. **Comm and FTS: 414-747-7185.**

LODGING: 1 cottage, 3 bdrm, sleeps 8 adults; furn, except bed linens, blankets, towels and toilet items; comm kit, MW, color TV, VCR.
FEE: $25.00 dly.

SPT FACILITIES:	Bicycles	Picnic Area	Telephone
ACTIVITIES:	Bicycling	Boating	Fishing
	Hiking	Hunting	

RESTRICTIONS: Pets allowed on leash; owners responsible for any damages; must clean up after pets daily. 2-night to 1-week limit. Check out by 1200. Use and possession of firearms must be in accordance with Federal, State, and local laws.

WYOMING

GRANT'S VILLAGE, YELLOWSTONE NATIONAL PARK (WY06R3)
Idaho Falls Naval Administrative Unit, ID 84302-1613

TELEPHONE NUMBER INFORMATION: Main installation numbers: Comm: 208-522-0767, FTS: 208-526-5994.

LOCATION: Off base. Located in Wyoming S of the junction of US-20 and US-89/287 in Yellowstone National Park. Pick up keys and instructions/directions at Idaho Falls ID Naval Administrative Unit (Morale, Welfare and Recreation) M-F 0930-2230, Sa 0930-1200: I-15 to exit 119 N of Idaho Falls; L on Grand View to Skyline Dr; R to 1575 N Skyline Dr. USMRA: page 102 (A,B-2). NMI: Malmstrom AFB MT, 245 mi N. NMC: Idaho Falls ID, 154 mi SW.

DESCRIPTION OF AREA: Located in the heart of Yellowstone National Park, less than 1 mi from Yellowstone Lake which has a marina with boat launching facilities; fishing is also allowed (obtain permit when entering park). There is abundant wild life in the area. Located conveniently for visits to Old Faithful Geyser, Grand Canyon of Yellowstone, Mammoth Hot Springs, Teton National Park, Jackson Hole, and many other attractions. Bring lots of film for your camera. Full range of support facilities available at Malmstrom AFB MT.

SEASON OF OPERATION: 15 May-15 Sep.

ELIGIBILITY: Active/Retired/Reserve (must have commissary card).

RESERVATIONS: Required; may be made up to 30 days in adv. Address: Navy MWR, 1575 North Skyline Dr, Idaho Falls, ID 83402-1613. **Comm: 208-522-0767.**

CAMP FACILITIES:	NO UNITS	HOOKUPS	FEE
Travel Trailers, 24 '	6	W/S/E	$17.50 dly
Self-contained/slp 8 (6 adults and 2 children)			

SPT FACILITIES:	Picnic Area (a bear area)		Trails

ACTIVITIES:	Bicycling	Boating	Fishing/license
	Hiking	Sightseeing	

RESTRICTIONS: No pets allowed.

WARREN FAM-CAMP (WY02R3)
70103 Randall Avenue
Francis E. Warren Air Force Base, WY 82005-5000

TELEPHONE NUMBER INFORMATION: Main installation numbers: Comm: 307-775-1110, DSN: 312-481-1110. Police for fam-camp, Comm: 307-775-3501.

LOCATION: On base. Off I-25, 2 mi N of I-80. Clearly marked. Stop at Main Gate. Check in at Recreation Supply, Bldg 328, M-F 0730-1700, Sa-Su 0800-1200. After registering, use south entrance off Missile Dr if camper is over 10 'in height. USMRA: page 102 (I-8). NMC: Cheyenne, adjacent.

DESCRIPTION OF AREA: Located in open, rolling country in SE corner of state. Laramie and Medicine Bow National Forest are short distances W. Full range of support facilities available on base.

WYOMING
WARREN FAM-CAMP, continued

SEASON OF OPERATION: May-Sep. Oct-Apr: Electric only.

ELIGIBILITY: Active/Retired/DoD Civilians.

RESERVATIONS: Recommended. Address: Recreation Supply, Bldg 328, 90 MWRSS/MWRO, Francis E Warren AFB, WY 82005-5000. **Comm: 307-775-2988/ 2169, DSN: 312-481-2988.**

CAMP FACILITIES:	NO UNITS	HOOKUPS	FEE
Camper Spaces	25 Gravel	W/E (110/220/30A)	$10.50 dly
Camper Spaces	12 Gravel	W	7.00 dly
Camper Spaces	15	None	5.00 dly
Camper/Tent Spaces	10+ Open	None	5.00 dly

SPT FACILITIES:		
Laundry	Picnic Area	Playground
Rec Equip Rntl	Restrooms	Sewage Dmp Sta
Showers		
PX and Commissary within walking distance.		

ACTIVITIES:		
Fishing	Hiking	Hunting

RESTRICTIONS: Pets allowed. **CAUTION:** Access off Randall Ave has low clearance of 11'6" under railroad trestle.

NOTES

UNITED STATES POSSESSIONS

GUAM

GUAM USA AND MARIANAS ISLANDS (GU04R8)
FPO AP 96540-5000

TELEPHONE NUMBER INFORMATION: Main installation numbers: Comm: 011-671-564-1110, DSN: 315-322-1110. Police for rec areas, Comm: 911.

LOCATION: Consolidated Recreation is comprised of 3 recreation districts. **District I** is Naval Sta; **District II** is located between Agana and Tamuning on NAS; and **District III** is located between Tamuning and Dededo on back road to Andersen AFB. Marine Drive, the only main road on Guam, goes completely around the 37-mile-long island. USMRA: page 130 (C-2,3).

DESCRIPTION OF AREA: Guam has a tropical climate and warm humid weather. Attractions vary considerably and include secluded beaches, cooling waterfalls, historic villages, caves and mountains. Many are accessible only by hiking. Hikers and swimmers should be aware of unusual terrain, jagged limestone, slippery red mud, hidden gullies, changing weather, tide and surf conditions. It is recommended that tourists do not hike or swim alone, but in groups of 3 or more. Full range of support facilities available at NS, NAS and AFB.

SEASON OF OPERATION: Year round.

ELIGIBILITY: Active/Retired/NG/Reserve/DoD Civilians.

RESERVATIONS: Not required. Address: Naval Station Guam, PSG-455, Box 169, FPO AP 96540-5000. Comm: 011-671-564-4153, DSN: 315-339-4153, FAX Comm: 011-671-564-1853.

CAMP FACILITIES: Camping is allowed on all beaches on Guam with no hookups and no fees.

SPT FACILITIES:		
Archery/III	Beaches	Boat Rntl
Cabanas	Chapels	Gas
Golf/III	Marinas/I	Picnic Areas
Racquet Sports	Rec Equip Rntl	Sports Fields

ACTIVITIES:		
Bicycling	Fishing	Hiking
Hunting/III	Scuba Diving	Swimming

RESTRICTIONS: Beach areas where pets are not allowed are marked. No firearms allowed.

NOTE: We have been informed that "Consolidated Recreation" no longer exists but that each District handles inquiries pertaining to its own facilities.

PUERTO RICO

BORINQUEN RECREATION AREA (PR08R1)
Borinquen US Coast Guard Air Station
Aquadilla, PR 00604-5000

TELEPHONE NUMBER INFORMATION: Main installation numbers: Comm: 809-882-3500 EX-1701, FTS: 498-3500 EX-1701.

LOCATION: Off base. At the old Ramey AFB, N of Aguadilla. Take PR-2 W from San Juan or N from Mayaguez to PR-110 N to CGAS. USMRA: page 130 (B,C-2). NMC: San Juan, 65 mi E.

DESCRIPTION OF AREA: The recreation area is located in western Puerto Rico on a high cliff overlooking the Caribbean—the perfect setting for beautiful sunsets. The converted lighthouse has 2 apartments which reflect the tropical flavor of the area. Temperatures range from 70-80° and humidity is usually low. Limited support facilities available on base approx 2 mi from the lighthouse.

SEASON OF OPERATION: Year round.

ELIGIBILITY: Active/Retired/Reserve/NG/DOD Civilians.

RESERVATIONS: Required; up to 45 days in adv for AD, up to 30 days for all others. Address: Commanding Officer, US Coast Guard Air Station Borinquen, Attn: Lighthouse Reservations, Aquadilla, Puerto Rico 00604-5000. **Comm: 809-890-3127 (ask for the lighthouse).** Ask for information regarding car rentals when making your reservations.

LODGING: 2 apartments, overlooking the ocean, 2 bdrm; fully furn, A/C, CTV, MW. Cribs available.

FEE: $35.00-$45.00 daily

SPT FACILITIES:	Grills	Laundry	Pavilion
	Picnic Area	Rec Equip Rntl	
ACTIVITIES:	Fishing	Scuba Diving	Sightseeing
	Snorkeling	Sunbathing	Surfing
	Swimming		

RESTRICTIONS: No pets allowed.

FOREIGN COUNTRIES

CANADA

NORTH EAST ARM CAMP (CN01R1)
Argentia US Naval Facility, FPO AE 09730-5000

TELEPHONE NUMBER INFORMATION: Main installation numbers: Comm: 709-227-8555/8556, DSN: 312-568-8555/8556. Police for camp, Comm: 709-227-8777.

LOCATION: Off base. Argentia is reached by car or by ferry from N Sydney, Nova Scotia. The nearest airport is at St John's. The camp is located at ocean terminus of Argentia access to Trans-Canadian Highway (TCH-1). RM: p-117, G/24. NMI: Argentia USN Facility, 7 mi E. NMC: St John's, 75 mi NE.

DESCRIPTION OF AREA: Wild, beautiful country with abundant fishing and hunting. The naval facility is a small command with most support facilities available.

SEASON OF OPERATION: Year round; availability may be limited during winter months for maintenance.

ELIGIBILITY: Active/Retired/DoD Civilians.

RESERVATIONS: Required at least 30 days in adv. Address: MWR Director, PO Box 12, US Naval Facility, Argentia, FPO AE 09597-5000. **Comm: 709-227-8709/2017, DSN: 312-227-8709.**

LODGING: 8 Cabins, slp up to 9 pers. 1 room with bath/shower, fireplace, cooking utensils, dishes, bunk beds. No bedding.
     FEE: $23.00 dly for any 1-night stay
               18.00 dly, F-Su, for more than 1 night
               13.00 dly, M-Th, for more than 1 night

SPT FACILITIES:

BBQ Pits	Boat Launch	Boat Rntl
Camper Rntl	Canoe Rntl	Picnic Area
Playground	Rec Lodge*	Sailboats

*May be rented for $25 dly.

ACTIVITIES:

Fishing	Hiking	Swimming

RESTRICTIONS: 7-day limit per month. Pets, except Alaskan Huskies, allowed on leashes; must have International Health Certificate no more than 1 week old; must have Import Certificate from Province of Newfoundland.

GERMANY

BAUMHOLDER ROLLING HILLS TRAVEL CAMP
(GE55R7)
Baumholder Community Recreation Area, APO AE 09034-5000

TELEPHONE NUMBER INFORMATION: Main installation numbers: Comm: (US) 011-49-6783-6-1700, DSN: 314-485-1700, (GE) ETS 485-113. Police for campground, ETS: 114.

LOCATION: Off post. Camp is in the Baumholder Community Recreation Area. From Autobahn 6 W of Kaiserslautern, take Trier/Birkenfeld exit (Autobahn 62) NW 20 km to Freisen/Baumholder/Idar-Oberstein exit, N 10 km towards Baumholder. L after gold course (before high shcool); L at fork; L at next corner to Recreation Center and Fam-camp. HE: map 39, G/1. NMI: Ramstein AB, 25 mi. NMC: Kaiserslautern, 35 mi SE.

DESCRIPTION OF AREA: Gem city of Idar-Oberstein, famous for its precious-stone industry and diamond factory, is nearby. Area has castles, Palatinate Forest, Mosel River, and vineyards. **Bosen Lake, 19 mi from post, offers swimming, fishing and windsurfing.** Recreation area has most support facilities.

SEASON OF OPERATION: Year round.

ELIGIBILITY: Active/Retired/DoD Civilians/Local Nationals.

RESERVATIONS: Accepted. Address: CRD, Outdoor Recreation, 222 Base Support Battalion, APO AE 09034-5000. *Travel Camp,* Comm: (US) 011-49-6783-6-7182, (GE) ETS: 485-7182.

CAMP FACILITIES:	NO UNITS	HOOKUPS	FEE
Camper Spaces	30 Hardstand	E (220)	$ 8.00 dly
Camper/Tent Spaces	10	None	5.00 dly
Camping/groups of 20+	Primitive	None	30.00 dly/group

SPT FACILITIES:			
	Fitness Ctr	Foodland Store	Golf/9 holes
	Grills	Indoor Climbing	Pavilions
	Picnic Areas	Center on post	Playgrounds
	Rec Equip Rntl	Restrooms	Showers
	Swimming Pool	Tennis Courts	

ACTIVITIES:			
	Hiking	Kayaking	Rafting
	Rock Climbing	Sightseeing	Snow Ski/DH&XC
	Windsurfing		

RESTRICTIONS: Pets allowed on leash. No water Nov-Apr. Check with camp management for policy on firearms.

BERCHTESGADEN AFRC (GE07R7)
APO AE 09029-5000
(NOTE: This facility will close 30 September 1995.)

TELEPHONE NUMBER INFORMATION: Main installation numbers: Comm: (US); 011-49-8652-61057, (GE) 08652-61057, ETS-441-5623/5823.

LOCATION: Exit Munich-Salzburg Autobahn E-11 at Bad Reichenhall, S on GE-20, 11 mi to Berchtesgaden. HE: map 94, D/4. NMC: Munich, 100 mi NW.

DESCRIPTION OF AREA: Nestled in the heart of the Bavarian Alps, just 8 miles from the Austrian border, Berchtesgaden is a 1,200-year old storybook village with church spires framed by scenic mountains rising to nearly 9,000 feet. Breathtaking scenery and a wide variety of sporting and tourist opportunities await visitors to this popular all-season recreation spot. Skiers will love the great ski facility, with ski packages for beginners and experts in cross country and downhill. There are also the four tennis courts, kayaking, white water rafting, and the Skytop Golf Course.

There are tours to the Salzburg, Austria Home of the "Sound of Music" or a visit to the world-class bobsled run, where the brave can try their luck at controlling a racing luge; or dress in traditional miners clothes and explore vast open rooms carved out of a salt mountain on the Salt Mine Tour; or take the Berchtesgaden Town Tour and see the Royal Castle, visit a cuckoo clock factory and much more.

AFRC Berchtesgaden has lodging for more than 700 guests in the historic General Walker Hotel, The Evergreen Lodge and Haus Chancellor.

SEASON OF OPERATION: Year round.

ELIGIBILITY: AD/Retired/DOD civilian assigned overseas.

RESERVATIONS: Accepted up to six months in advance (through May 1994). One year for groups of 25 or more. Deposits required within 30 days after booking. Write to: AFRC Berchtesgaden Reservations Office, Unit 24401, APO AE 09029 or Salzbergerstr. 45, 83471 Berchtesgaden. Comm: (USA) **011-49-8652-61057**, (GE) 08652-61057, ETS-441-5623/5823, FAX-(USA) 011-49-8652-62768, (GE) 08652-62768. Note: Call early morning - 6 hours ahead of United States Eastern Standard Time.

FACILITIES: APO, Green Machine(ATM), beauty/barber shop, commissary, chapel, library, sports shop, gym, Bavarian Shop, class VI (Package Store), Foodland, PX, Stars & Stripes Bookstore, child care center, hotel restaurants & bars, TV room and much more.

General Walker Hotel			
		E1 - E5	**E-6+**
Double	W/O Bath	$40.00	$44-48.00
Double	W/ Bath	$50.00	$54-58.00
Evergreen Lodge			
Single	W/ Bath	$35.00	$41.00
Double	W/O Bath	$45.00	$51.00
Suite/2		$75.00	$75.00
Suite/3		$75.00	$75.00
Haus Chancellor			
Apt/2		$110.00	$110.00
Apt/3		$ 65.00	$ 65.00

GERMANY Berchtesgaden AFRC, continued			
Apt/5		$ 75.00	$ 75.00
Apt/6		$125.00	$125.00

* All room rates are based on double occupancy.
* For single occupancy deduct $3.00 from the double occupancy rate.
* Children under 16 years are free in the room on available bed space.
* Cots $6.00 - Cribs $3.00.

The following credit cards are accepted by AFRC: Diners Club, Carte Blanche, American Express, MasterCard, DISCOVER and VISA. Personal checks are accepted in all areas.

RESTRICTIONS: No pets allowed.

CHIEMSEE ARMED FORCES RECREATION CENTER (GE08R7)
APO AE 09098-5000

TELEPHONE NUMBER INFORMATION: Main installation numbers: Comm: 011-49-8051-803-172, ETS: 441-2355/396.

LOCATION: Located directly off Munich-Salzburg Autobahn A-8 SE of Munich. Busses use Felden exit; automobiles continue for 800 meters and exit at the sign for AFRC Chiemsee. HE: map 94, B/3. NMC: Munich, 50 mi NW.

DESCRIPTION OF AREA: Situated along the shores of Chiemsee Lake, Germany's largest lake. Enjoy a variety of water sports or take advantage of the nearby Chiemgauer Alps offering scenic panoramas and opportunities for skiing, hiking and hang gliding. Limited support facilities at AFRC; full range at McGraw Kaserne in Munich.

SEASON OF OPERATION: Year round.

ELIGIBILITY: Active/Retired/DoD Civilians assigned overseas.

RESERVATIONS: Accepted up to 180 days in adv with deposit. Address: Chiemsee, Reservations, Unit 24504, APO AE 09098-5000. **Comm: 011-49-8051-803-172, ETS: 441-2355/396, FAX: 011-49-8051-803-158, Telex: 592-417 AFRC BD**; M-F 0800-1900, Sa 0900-1700. Some rooms specially fitted for handicapped.

SPT FACILITIES:	Activity Center Boat Rntl Game Room Miniature Golf Restaurant	Beach Conv Store Laundry Picnic Area Snack Bar	Boat Launch Fitness Center Library Playground Tennis Courts
ACTIVITIES:	Archery Fishing Paddle Boats Sailing Tours	Bicycling Hang Gliding Paragliding Snow Skiing Windsurfing	Catamarans Jogging Rec Equip Avail Swimming

HOTEL ROOM RATES

Rates: E1-E5, deluxe double w/bath $43*, E6+ $49 (Park Hotel); E1-E5* deluxe double w/bath $49, E6+ $56 (Lake Hotel). Single occupancy deduct $3 from double rate, more than two adult occupants, add $9 to double rate. Cribs $3/night, children under 16 free on available bed space - if cot or sofabed is needed, $6 per night. Group information rates and prices of larger rooms available on request. Special Sports packages and Romantic Getaway Packages available. VISA, MasterCard and American Express accepted.

RESTRICTIONS: No pets allowed.

CHIEMSEE AFRC TRAVEL CAMP (GE57R7)
Armed Forces Recreation Center, APO AE 09098-5000

TELEPHONE NUMBER INFORMATION: Main installation numbers: Comm: (US) 011-49-8051-803-172, (GE) ETS: 441-2355/396.

LOCATION: Located directly off Munich-Salzburg Autobahn A-8 SE of Munich. Exit 800 meters beyond Felden exit when you see the sign for AFRC Chiemsee. HE: map 94, B/3. NMC: Munich, 50 mi NW.

DESCRIPTION OF AREA: Situated on southern shores of Chiemsee Lake, Germany's largest inland lake. King Ludwig's Herrenchiemsee Castle is located on an island in the middle of the lake. Berchtesgaden and Hitler's Eagles Nest are nearby. Completely renovated in 1988. Limited support facilities at AFRC; additional facilities at Bad Aibling Kaserne.

SEASON OF OPERATION: Year round.

ELIGIBILITY: Active/Retired/DOD Civilians assigned overseas.

RESERVATIONS: Required: Accepted up to 6 mo in adv with deposit. Address: Chiemsee AFRC Campground, APO AE 09098-5000. **Comm: (US) 011-49-8051-803-613, (GE) ETS: 441-2719.** Special rates for groups.

CAMP FACILITIES:	NO UNITS	HOOKUPS	FEE*
RV Spaces	22 Hardstand	W/S/E (220)	$14.00 dly
Camper Spaces	17	W/S/E (220)	14.00 dly
Camper Spaces	74	W/S	12.00 dly
Camper/Tent Spaces	120 Grassy	None	10.00 dly
Group, Scouts and Youths only (min of 20)			2.00 pers dly

*Includes up to 4 persons; $2.00 ea add adult. Seasonal and monthly rates available.

SPT FACILITIES:			
	Boat Rntl	Camp Equip Rntl	Dishwashing Fac
	Game Room	Grills	Ice
	Laundry	Picnic Area	Playground
	Restrooms	Shoppette	Showers/hot
	Snack Bar	TV Room/Video	

GERMANY
CHIEMSEE AFRC TRAVEL CAMP, continued

ACTIVITIES:

Bicycling	Boating	Fishing
Hang Gliding	Hiking	Rec Equip Avail
Sailing	Snow Skiing	Swimming
Touring	Windsurfing	

RESTRICTIONS: Pets allowed on leash; must be kept quiet.

GARMISCH ARMED FORCES RECREATION CENTER
(GE10R7)
APO AE 09053-5000

TELEPHONE NUMBER INFORMATION: Main installation numbers: Comm: (USA) 011-49-8821-750-712/847, ETS: 440-2712/2847.

LOCATION: Take Autobahn E-6 S from Munich to Garmisch-Partenkirchen. From Austria take national roads numbered 2 or 187. HE: map 92, F/3. NMC: Munich, 60 mi N.

DESCRIPTION OF AREA: Located at foot of Zugspitze, Germany's highest mountain. Unforgettable Alpine scenery and wide variety of sports activities at AFRC vacation area. Garmisch is one of the most popular Alpine resorts in Germany. AFRC offers two hotels and a modern travel camp with accommodations for approx 540 guests. Full range of support facilities at AFRC.

SEASON OF OPERATION: Year round.

ELIGIBILITY: Active/Retired/DoD Civilians stationed in USEUCOM.

RESERVATIONS: Accepted up to 180 days in adv with deposit. Address: AFRC Garmisch Reservations Office, Unit 24501, APO AE 09053-5000. **Comm: (USA) 011-49-8821-750-575, FAX: 011-49-8821-3942, (GE) 08821-79081, ETS: 440-2575, Telex: 592-417 AFRC BD**; M-F 0800-2000, Sa 0900-1700.

SPT FACILITIES:

Activity Center	Bank	Chapel
Commissary	Conv Store	Fitness Center
Game Room	Golf/9 holes	Laundry
Library	Medical Clinic	Picnic Area
Playground	PX	Racquetball
Restaurants	Ski Lodge*	Sports Fields
Tennis Courts	Tours	

*Hausberg Lodge, nestled in the beautiful Bavarian Alps, features a huge restaurant, kitchen and classrooms. It provides a reception area for AFRC skiers, with ski equipment/storage points, ski repair shop, and locker rooms connected to a central heating/ventilation system to dry equipment. It also offers ski equipment rental, the AFRC Ski School, and lift tickets for all ski areas in Garmisch.

GERMANY
GARMISCH ARMED FORCES RECREATION CENTER, continued

ACTIVITIES:

Bicycling	Canoeing	Children's Program
Climbing	Hiking	Ice Skating
Jogging	Kayaking	MountainBicycling
Rec Equip Avail	Skiing	Swimming
Tours	Whitewater Rafting	

HOTEL ROOM RATES

With Private Bath	**E1-E5/Others***
Single Occupancy	$46.00/50.00
Double Occupancy	49.00/53.00
Family Suites	Ask for rates.

*E1-E5 room rate is $30 for individual travelers not involved in group travel or conference.

Children under 16 staying in parent's room on existing beds, free; if cot is required, add $6 daily. For more than 2 adults, add $9 per person daily. Cribs are $3 daily. Special group rates and prices of larger rooms are available on request. The above rates became effective in winter 1994 and are subject to change without notice. Prices normally change as each new fiscal year begins on 1 Oct. VISA, MasterCard, Diners Club and American Express accepted.

RESTRICTIONS: No pets allowed.

GARMISCH AFRC TRAVEL CAMP (GE58R7)
Armed Forces Recreation Center, APO AE 09053-5000

TELEPHONE NUMBER INFORMATION: Main installation numbers: Comm: 011-49-8821-750-714, ETS: 440-2714. Military Police, ETS: 440-2801.

LOCATION: Take Autobahn E-6 from Munich to Garmisch. From Austria take national roads numbered 2 or 187. Camp is adjacent to Breitenau Housing Area. Check in 0730-2200 (winter), 0700-2215 (summer); no restrictions on arrival time. HE: map 92, F/3. NMC: Munich, 60 mi N.

DESCRIPTION OF AREA: Located at the foot of Zugspitze, Germany's tallest mountain. Oberammergau, famous for wood carving and for its Passion Play, is 13 mi away. Garmisch is one of the most popular Alpine resorts in Germany. A wide variety of sports and a full range of support facilities available at AFRC.

SEASON OF OPERATION: Year round.

ELIGIBILITY: Active/Retired/DoD Civilians stationed in USEUCOM.

RESERVATIONS: Up to 90 days in adv w/deposit. Address: Garmisch AFRC Travel Camp, Unit 24501, APO AE 09053-5000. **Comm: 011-49-8821-750-848, ETS: 440-2848.** VISA, MasterCard, Diners Club and American Express accepted.

GERMANY
GARMISCH AFRC TRAVEL CAMP, continued

CAMP FACILITIES:	NO UNITS	HOOKUPS	FEE
Trailer (5 berth)	On Site		$40.00 dly
Trailer (4 berth)	On Site		32.00 dly
Camper Spaces	92 Gravel*	W/E (220)	14.00 dly/4 pers**
Van/Tent Spaces	12 Landscaped	W	9.00 dly/2 pers**
Tent Area	Open/Grass	W	7.00 dly/2 pers**

*Number varies with season.
**$2 dly each add adult; $1.50 add child (age 6-16). Monthly and seasonal rates available.

SPT FACILITIES:	Conv Store	Dishwashing Fac	Laundry
	Playground	Restaurant	Restrooms
	Sewage Dmp Sta	Showers/hot	Trailer Rntl

ACTIVITIES:	Bicycling	Fishing/license	Hiking
	Ice Climbing	Kayaking	Mountaineering
	Snow Skiing	Tours	Whitewater Rafting

RESTRICTIONS: Pets allowed on leash; must be kept quiet.

KUHBERG COMMUNITY PARK AND TRAVEL CAMP (GE56R7)
53rd ASG, CMR 438, 410th, BSB Bad Kreuznach, APO AE 09111-5000

TELEPHONE NUMBER INFORMATION: Main installation numbers: Comm: (US) 011-49-671-609-113, DSN: 314-490-1110, (GE) 0671-609-113, ETS: 490-113. Police for travel camp, ETS: 114 or 490-6366/7357/7327. Medical/fire emergencies ETS: 490-117.

LOCATION: Off post. Approx 60 mi SW of Frankfurt. Camping area is located 2.8 mi SW of Rose Barracks. Traveling W on B-420 in Hackenheim, turn L at 2nd traffic light ("US Army Recreation & Training Area," "Jugenherberge" and Tierheim" signs). Drive 2.4 km through vineyards; go L at fork in road. L after 400 meters, into parking area (Rheingrafenstein Community Park & Travel Camp). Check in at Kuhberg Site, Bldg 5414. HE: map 40, A/1. NMI: Rose Barracks, BSB Bad Kreuznach, 2 mi N. NMC: Bad Kreuznach, 3 mi N.

DESCRIPTION OF AREA: Located above the scenic Nahe Valley, the travel camp boasts a variety of outdoor activities and a helpful staff to provide information and directions to numerous local attractions such as Germany's oldest radium spa. Beautiful parks and forest areas. Area along the Rhein River has many castles and vineyards. Full range of support facilities at Rose Barracks, BSB Bad Kreuznach.

SEASON OF OPERATION: Year round; minimal operational support in winter.

ELIGIBILITY: Active/Retired/DoD Civilians/NATO Forces.

RESERVATIONS: Recommended; 1 night's fee (VISA and MasterCard accepted) and personal data required. (Checks should be made payable to: BK CMWRF.) Address: Bad Kreuznach Outdoor Recreation (Attn: Kuhberg), 53rd ASG, 410th BSB-BK, CMR 438, APO AE 09111-5000. **Comm: (US) 011-49-671-609-6498/6496, FAX: 011-49-671-74797, DSN: 314-490-6498.**

CAMP FACILITIES:	NO UNITS	HOOKUPS	FEE*
Campers. slp 4	Limited # in place		$25.00 dly
Camper/Tent Spaces	26 Hardstand	E (220)	10.00 dly/50 wkly
		None	7.00 dly/35 wkly
Tent Spaces	55 Grass	None	5.00 dly/25 wkly

*Fees are for 4 pers at camper spaces and 2 pers at tent spaces; $1 for each add pers. Special rates for groups of 50 or more. Seasonal rates available. Weekend rates available in tent camping areas. Prices are likely to be lower due to new policy mandates.

SPT FACILITIES:

Archery Range	Basketball Courts	Camp Supply Resale
Dishwashing Area	Fitness Course	Gas
Grills	Horseshoe Pits	Ice
Laundry	Miniature Golf	Multi-purpose Rm
Pavilions	Picnic Areas/hcp	Playgrounds
Rec Equip Rntl	Recylce Station	Restrooms/hcp
Sewage Dmp Sta	Showers/hot	Snack Bar
Sports Fields	Tennis Courts	Volleyball/Sand Cts

Group picnic/party facilities (i.e. pavilions, super grills, rotisserie) available.

ACTIVITIES:

Badminton	Basketball	Castle Hikes
Field Sports	Jogging	Kite Flying
Mountain Biking	Ping Pong	Rafting Tours
Rock Climbing	Ski Tours	Softball
Volksmarching		

RESTRICTIONS: Pets allowed on leash. Only charcoal grill and stove fires permitted. Trash separation/recycling required by law. Check with travel camp management regarding policy on firearms.

RHEIN-MAIN
RECREATION AREA/CAMPGROUND (GE09R7)
Rhein-Main Air Base, APO AE 09097-5000

TELEPHONE NUMBER INFORMATION: Main installation numbers: Comm: (US) 011-49-069-699-0 or -1, DSN: 314-330-1110, (GE) ETS: 330-1110. Police for campground, ETS: 114.

LOCATION: On base. From Autobahn E-5 take Zeppelinheim/Rhein-Main AB exit. Check in at campground (24 hrs dly) across the Autobahn from AB main gate. HE: map 40, B/1. NMC: Frankfurt, 10 mi N.

DESCRIPTION OF AREA: Cosmopolitan Frankfurt has a zoo, fairgrounds and convention center. Wiesbaden, with spas and gambling casinos, is nearby. Many vineyards and castles in the area. Campground is a well-preserved and maintained site. Full range of support facilities on base.

SEASON OF OPERATION: Year round.

ELIGIBILITY: Active/Retired/DoD and NAF Civilians.

GERMANY
RHEIN-MAIN CAMPGROUND, continued

RESERVATIONS: Accepted. Address: 435 SVS/SVRO, ATTN: Outdoor Recreation, Rhein-Main AB, APO AE 09097-5000. **Comm: 011-49-69-699-7274, DSN: 314-330-7274, M-F 1000-1630.**

CAMP FACILITIES:	NO UNITS	HOOKUPS	FEE
Camper Spaces	10 Grass	E (220)	$ 6.00 dly
Camper/Tent Spaces	64 Grass	None	6.00 dly
Camper Rental, slp 3			25.00 dly*

*Weekly and monthly rates available.

SPT FACILITIES:	Grills	Rec Equip Rntl	Restrooms
	Showers		

ACTIVITIES:	Bicycling	Jogging	Swimming

RESTRICTIONS: Pets allowed on leash. Check out 1300. No hunting. No open fires. Check with campground management regarding policy on firearms.

ALL NEW!!!
VILSECK, GERMANY REC AREA
APO AE 09112-5420

Year-round luxury lodging is offered at the *Big Mike Travel Camp* at Vilseck, Germany. It is located in the beautiful Oberpfalz about a 45-minute drive from Nürnberg or Czechoslovakia. (ITR at Vilseck offers trips to that country as well as nearby porcelain/crystal factories so popular with those who like to save money.)

Outdoor Recreation runs the Big Mike Travel Camp and offers a full program of year-round outdoor adventures.

The camp has tent camping and RV spaces (with water and electric hookups) in addition to apartments. There are 2 sets each of 2- and 3- bedroom apartments attractively furnished and including a living room and full kitchen with silverware and dishes. Linens are provided. Rates run $55 daily for 2-bedroom units and $65 daily for 3-bedroom units. Weekly rates are $275 and $325, respectively.

Tent camping is available at $7 for 2 persons plus $2 for each additional person over 13 years of age. The fee for RV spaces is $10 daily.

To reach Vilseck, follow posted signs to Rose Barracks. Once on the post, follow the signs to "Travel Camp." Outdoor Rec is located at Bldg 2236; address: 281 BSB, APO AE 09112-5000. From the USA, phone is Comm: 011-49-966-283-2563; in Germany 0966-283-2563.

Thanks to SFC & Mrs. Donald Beck, we have this new listing. They even included an attractive brochure! Readers helping each other—what a great network we have!

GREECE
IRAKLION CAMPGROUND (GR03R9)
Iraklion Air Station, APO AE 09846-5000
(This base closed in June 1994.)

ITALY

ADMIRAL CARNEY PARK (IT03R7)
Via Campiglione Pozzuola
Naples Naval Support Activity, FPO AE 09619-5000

TELEPHONE NUMBER INFORMATION: Main installation numbers: Comm: 011-39-81-724-1110, DSN: 314-625-1110. Police for park DSN: 625-4195.

LOCATION: Off Base. On the west coast of Italy in Admiral Carney Park. HE: map 51, E/6. NMI: Naval Support Activity Naples, 6 mi NE. NMC: Naples, 7 mi NE.

DESCRIPTION OF AREA: Active port city of Naples. The Roman cities of Herculanum and Pompeii and active volcano Vesuvius are nearby. The beautiful island of Capri is 22 mi away by boat or helicopter. Carney Park, with its large grassy fields and paved roads, is a 96-acre recreation facility located in the crater of an extinct 13th-century volcano. It has 5 festivals annually. Full range of support facilities available at NSA Naples.

SEASON OF OPERATION: Year round.

ELIGIBILITY: Active/Retired; DoD Civilians assigned overseas.

RESERVATIONS: Required. Address: Morale, Welfare and Recreation, PSC 810, Box 13, FPO AE 09619-1013. **Comm: 011-39-81-526-1579, FAX: 011-39-81-526-4913.** Deposit required for 1st day; check payable to "MWR 10120"; include your address and DSN number (if available) for confirmation.

CAMP FACILITIES:	NO UNITS	HOOKUPS	FEE
Cabins, furnished	26		$30-45 dly*
Camper Spaces	3 Hardstand	W/S/E (220)	15.00 dly
Tent Spaces	30 Grassy Area		10.00 dly

*Weekly rates available.

SPT FACILITIES:			
	Chapel/NSA	Camp Equip Rntl	Conv Store
	Golf/NATO Base	Grills	Laundry
	Miniature Golf	Picnic Area	Playground
	Restrooms/flush	Showers/hot	Snack Bar
	Sports Fields	Swim Pool/olym	Tennis Courts
	Handicapped Toilets		

Camp Volcano summer day camp program (ages 5-12). Register by day or week.

ACTIVITIES:			
	Baseball	Basketball	Football
	Soccer	Softball	Volleyball

RESTRICTIONS: No pets allowed. No firearms allowed.

ITALY

AVIANO FAM-CAMP (IT09R7)
Aviano Air Base, APO AE 09601-5000

TELEPHONE NUMBER INFORMATION: Main installation numbers: Comm: 011-39-434-66-7520, DSN: 314-632-1110.

LOCATION: On base. In NE Italy near Austrian border. Exit A-28 at Pordenone; N on IT-159 8 mi to Aviano AB. HE: map 93, C/4. NMC: Pordenone, 9 mi S.

DESCRIPTION OF AREA: Located at the base of the Alps in beautiful surroundings. Many beach resorts along the Adriatic Coast, 50 mi S; snow skiing resorts, 30 mi N. Venice is 1 hour away. There are many historical sights to see. Full range of support facilities available on base.

SEASON OF OPERATION: May-Oct.

ELIGIBILITY: Active/Retired; DoD Civilians assigned overseas.

RESERVATIONS: Required. Address: MWR Rental Supply, 40 CSG/MWRO, Aviano Air Base, APO AE 09601-5000. **DSN: 314-632-7633.**

CAMP FACILITIES:	NO UNITS	HOOKUPS	FEE
Camper Spaces	6 Paved	E (110/220)	$ 5.00 dly
Camper Spaces	2 Paved	None	5.00 dly

SPT FACILITIES:			
	Chapel	Golf/9 holes	Laundry
	Picnic Areas	Rec Center	Rec Equip Rntl
	Restrooms	Showers	Snack Bar
ACTIVITIES:	Hiking	Sightseeing	Snow Skiing

RESTRICTIONS: Visitors must show ID card at gate. Sign in and pay in Bldg 106A, Area A1, before going to fam-camp located at flight line.

SEA PINES CAMP AND LODGE (IT02R7)
219 BSB CMR 426, APO AE 09613-5000

TELEPHONE NUMBER INFORMATION: Main installation numbers: Comm: 011-39-50-54-7111, DSN: 314-633-7225, ETS 633-7225. Police ETS: 633-7575.

LOCATION: On post. Located midway between Livorno and Pisa. From Autostrada A-1 take Pisa Sud exit. *Turn L and continue to end of road; L 1 block to Stop sign, then R onto Via Aurelia (SS 1); R to S Piero A Grado. This small road will take you over a drawbridge. Follow Camp Darby signs.* Check in at Sea Pines Lodge 24 hours daily in summer (0700-2100 in winter). HE: map 50, A/3. NMC: Pisa, 6 mi N.

DESCRIPTION OF AREA: Situated in the midst of a beautiful Umbrella Pine forest halfway between Pisa and Livorno. Famous Leaning Tower of Pisa is 6 mi away; the walled city of Lucca, 20 mi; Florence, 75 mi.

ITALY
SEA PINES CAMP AND LODGE, continued

The site is just a few kilometers from the American Beach on the Tyrrhenian Sea where safe swimming is available (minimal fee). The many support facilities available on post are within easy walking distance.

SEASON OF OPERATION: Year round.

ELIGIBILITY: Active/Retired/NATO Forces/DoD Civilians.

RESERVATIONS: Required. May be made up to 1 year in adv, with deposit for resv made 30 days or more in adv. Payment of balance is upon arrival and in US dollars only. Address: Sea Pines Camp and Lodge, HQ, 219th Support Battalion (Base), 31314, Box 20, APO AE 09613-5000. **Comm: 011-39-50-54-7225, ETS: 633-7225 (0700-2100 daily, 24 hours daily in summer).**

SEA PINES LODGE: A 24-room American-style motel. Each room has its own entrance, windows on 2 walls, PB, refr, color TV and VCR, and sleeps 4. No cooking. Also avail are a comm kit, social room with TV/VCR, slot machines, and the Camp Darby Telephone Office.

> **FEE:** $35 dly for 1 pers/40 dly for 2 pers
> 50 dly for 3 pers/55 dly for 4 pers
> 5 add dly for cot/3 add dly for crib/3.50 dly for pet

CAMP FACILITIES:	NO UNITS	HOOKUPS	FEE
Cabins, 2 bdrm	20		$45.00 dly*
Camper Spaces/2 hcp	125	W/E (220)	10-14 dly
Camper Spaces		W only	8-12 dly
Group Sites	(10 pers+)		2 dly ea pers

*Heated, 1 dbl bed, 1 bunk bed, table and chairs; no linens. Occupants must use shower building. Two handicapped sites on campground.

SPT FACILITIES:	Beach/sumr	Camp Equip Rntl	Chapel
	Conv Store	Gas	Grills
	Italian Ice Crm	Laundry	Miniature Golf
	Picnic Area	Playground	Racquet Courts
	Rec Center	Rec Equip Rntl	Restrooms/hcp
	Sewage Dmp Sta	Showers/hot/hcp	Shuttle Bus
	Snack Bars	Trailer Rntl	

ACTIVITIES:	Boating	Scuba Diving	Swimming
	Tennis	Tours	Windsurfing

RESTRICTIONS: Pets allowed on leash; must not be left unattended; must have valid health certificate and vaccination record; in Lodge rooms: $3.50 dly, $50 damage deposit. 12-day limit in season for lodge only. Quiet hours 2200-0800. Check out 1000. No ground fires. *No hunting.* Check with management for firearms policies.

ITALY

VICENZA TRAVEL CAMP (IT08R7)
Viale Della Pace
Caserma Carlo Ederle, Vicenza, Italy, APO AE 09630-5000

TELEPHONE NUMBER INFORMATION: Main installation numbers: Comm: 011-39-634-51-7111, DSN: 634-1110/7301. Police for camp DSN: 634-7626.

LOCATION: On post. Take Vicenza E exit from Venice/Milan Autostrada A-4. Follow signs to Caserma Carlo Ederle. Camp is at SE corner of post. HE: map 91, H/6. NMC: Vicenza, adjacent.

DESCRIPTION OF AREA: Great sightseeing opportunities: Venice, the canal city; Lido and Jesolo beaches on the Adriatic; and Romeo and Juliet's city, Verona. Full range of support facilities available on post. Convenient to BX, Comm, Burger King, Gym, Swimming Pool.

SEASON OF OPERATION: Year round.

ELIGIBILITY: Active/Retired; DoD Civilians assigned overseas.

RESERVATIONS: No adv resv. Address: CRD, Outdoor Recreation, CMR 427, HQ 22d ASG/USMCAV, APO AE 09630-5000. Comm: 011-39-634-51-7094, DSN: 634-7094.

CAMP FACILITIES:	NO UNITS	HOOKUPS	FEE
Camping Spaces	7 Hardstand	W/E (110/220)	$12.50 dly
Tent Spaces	8 Open Grass	None	7.00 dly

SPT FACILITIES:			
	Chapel	Conv Store	Grills
	Laundry/post	Picnic Area	Rec Equip Rntl
	Restrooms	Showers/hot	Snack Bar

ACTIVITIES:			
	Snow Skiing/nearby		Swimming/sumr

RESTRICTIONS: Pets allowed on leash. No open fires. Noise control after 2300. No firearms allowed.

JAPAN

NEW SANNO U.S. FORCES CENTER (JA01R8)
APO AP 96337-0110

TELEPHONE NUMBER INFORMATION: Main installation numbers: Comm: 011-81-3-3440-7871, DSN: 315-229-8111. Police call Hotel Operator.

LOCATION: At 4-12-20 Minami Azabu, Minato-ku, Tokyo 106; a 5-minute walk from nearest subway station, Hiroo (Hibiya Line). NMI: Tokyo Administrative Facility/Hardy Barracks, 10 mi. NMC: Tokyo, in city limits.

DESCRIPTION: Located in quiet residential area not far from downtown Tokyo, the New Sanno opened in 1983 and offers its guests commercial hotel quality accommodations and food service at affordable prices. Each of 149 guest rooms features modern furnishings and private bath or shower, central heat and air conditioning. Rental video movies are available. 2 traditional Japanese-style suites allow guests to enjoy the full flavor of the Orient.

The facility includes a family dining room, a Japanese-style restaurant, an elegant Continental-style restaurant, a lounge, and snack bar. Entertainment and special events are scheduled in the ballroom which accommodates up to 350 guests. Banquet and conference facilities are available and include audio-video equipment.

Guests can enjoy the outdoor rooftop pool (seasonally), the exercise room, the video game room. First- and second-floor arcades feature the Navy Exchange, Stars & Stripes bookstore, convenience store, and several local concessionaires. There are also an APO, military banking facility, pack & wrap service, barber shop, beauty salon, flower shop and many other American-style conveniences, including laundry and dry cleaning. Public restrooms on the lobby level are configured for the handicapped.

Information and Tours Desk personnel can make all necessary arrangements for touring local attractions or booking tickets for theater, concerts or sports events. They can also book airline and steamship reservations. Call Comm: 81-3-3440-7871-EX-7200/1, DSN: 229-7200/1.

If you are arriving at Tokyo's Narita International Airport, an economical airport express bus is available into the city and to New Sanno's front door. Daily buses also run to and from Yokota Air Base (schedule available at AMC terminal).

The New Sanno is a Joint Services, all-grades, all-ranks facility managed by the US Navy as Executive Agent.

SEASON OF OPERATION: Year round.

ELIGIBILITY: Active/Retired (Retiree Dependents must have sponsor with them while staying at the New Sanno)/US Embassy Tokyo/UN Command (Rear)/Reserve on AD/DoD and other Federal Civilian Employees on official orders to or through Japan.

RESERVATIONS: Recommended at least 45 days in adv with 1 night's deposit for each room reserved. Deposits may be made by check or money order or charged to American Express, Diners Club, MasterCard or VISA. Address: The New Sanno Hotel, Unit 45003, APO AP 96337-0110, Attn: Reservations. **Comm: 011-81-3-3440-7871-EX-7121, DSN: 315-229-7121; FAX: Comm: 011-81-3-440-7824, DSN: 315-229-7102.**

ROOM RATES FOR THE NEW SANNO U.S. FORCES CENTER

Room Type	No.	I*	II*	III*	IV*
Single (queen bed)	43	$25.00	$32.00	$38.00	$52.00
Double (queen+single bed)	78	35.00	41.00	48.00	65.00
King Suite (king+parlor)	17	50.00	54.00	58.00	76.00
Twin Suite (2 twins+parlor)	3	50.00	54.00	58.00	76.00
Family Room (sgl rm+bunk room)	2	50.00	61.00	72.00	90.00
Family Suite (twin suite w/2 twins, 2 bunks+sleeper sofa)	1	50.00	61.00	72.00	90.00

JAPAN
NEW SANNO U.S. FORCES CENTER, continued

Japanese Suite	2	63.00	68.00	74.00	94.00

*I: E1-E5; **II:** E6-O3, WO1-WO4; **III:** O4-O10; **IV:** Retired/Non-DoD. **I, II & III** include comparable DoD Civilian grades. **II** includes, Unremarried Widows, and Orphans (all with DD1173). All rates subject to change.

RESTRICTIONS: No pets allowed. No firearms.

OKUMA BEACH RESORT—OKINAWA (JA09R8)
Kadena Air Base, APO AP 96368-5000

TELEPHONE NUMBER INFORMATION: Main installation numbers: Comm: 011-81-098-041-5164, DSN: 315-634-4601.

LOCATION: Off base. On Okinawa, take Hwy 58 N from Kadena AB approx 50 mi. Turn L just before Hentona. Check in 1500 at Okuma main office. NMI: Kadena AB, 50 mi S. NMC: Naha JA, 62 mi S.

DESCRIPTION OF AREA: This 120-acre recreational complex is a beautiful, quiet getaway on a peninsula with snow-white beaches on both the Pacific Ocean and East China Sea. Picturesque drive takes you through pineapple fields and acres of sugar cane. Full range of support and outdoor recreational facilities available.

SEASON OF OPERATION: Year round. Closed M-Tu: 1 Nov-31 Mar.

ELIGIBILITY: Active/Retired/DoD Civilians assigned overseas.

RESERVATIONS: Required up to 90 days in adv. Address: Leisure Resource Center, Schilling Rec Center, 18 MWRS/MWMR, APO AP 96368-5000. **Comm: 011-81-611-734-4322, DSN: 315-634-4322.**

CAMP FACILITIES:	NO UNITS	FEE*
7 Cabanas/hcp	30 rooms/2 dbl beds/shared bath	$22.50 dly
	10 rooms/2 dbl beds/PB	30.00 dly
	12 rooms/1 dbl, 1 sgl bed/PB	30.00 dly
	9 suites/2 rms/4 dbl beds/PB	37.50 dly
	1 VIP suite	37.50 dly
Campsite #1	Families only, South Beach	6.00/tent dly
Campsite #2	Singles and groups, West Beach #2	6.00/tent dly

*Reduced rates in winter.

SPT FACILITIES:			
	Beach	Bicycle Rntl	Chapel
	Conference Rm	Conv Store	Dispensary
	Golf/9 holes	Laundry	Library
	Lounge	Miniature Golf	Movies
	Multi-Purpose Ct	Nature Trails	Picnic Area
	Rec Center	Restaurant	Restrooms/hcp
	Showers/hcp	Tennis Courts	Theater
	Water Sports Eq		

ACTIVITIES:			
	Bicycling	Boating	Croquet
	Fishing	Hiking	Horseshoes
	Sailing	Scuba Diving	Skin Diving

Snorkeling	Swimming	Tours
Water Skiing	Windsurfing	

Glass bottom boat tours and water instructional classes are available.

RESTRICTIONS: No pets allowed. Check out 1100. In order to rent sailboat and windsurfing equipment, certification by a sanctioned organization (or the passing of a qualification test given by the chief instructor) is required. Certification is also required for use of any diving equipment and/or service.

NOTE: As of press time, we have been unable to confirm this information.

TAMA HILLS RECREATION AREA (JA10R8)
Yokota Air Base, APO AP 96328-5000

TELEPHONE NUMBER INFORMATION: Main installation numbers: Comm: 011-81-423-77-7009, DSN: 315-224-3421/3422.

LOCATION: Off base. 15 miles SE of Yokota AB. NMC: Tokyo, outskirts.

DESCRIPTION OF AREA: A 500-acre retreat west of Tokyo, Tama was originally built by the Japanese Imperial Army in 1938 as a munitions storage area. After extensive repairs and renovations the center was reopened in 1983. The lodge and cabins all have private baths. Hot tubs are available year round. It is a quiet, wooded getaway offering a large range of facilities.

SEASON OF OPERATION: Year round.

ELIGIBILITY: Active/Retired/DoD Civilians.

RESERVATIONS: Required up to 3 months in adv. Address: Tama Recreation Center, 475 ABW/MWRL, Yokota Air Base, APO AP 96328-5000. **Comm: 011-81-423-77- 7009, DSN: 315-224-3421/3422.**

CAMP FACILITIES:	NO UNITS	HOOKUPS	FEE
Lodge	19 Rooms		$20.00 dly
Lodge	4 Suites		35.00 dly
Cabins, dbl & sgl	14 Gravel		25-50 dly
Camp/Tent Spaces	21 Gravel	W	1.00 dly

SPT FACILITIES:			
	Archery/fee	Camp Equip Rntl	Golf/18 holes
	Grills/fee	Laundry	Miniature Golf
	Picnic Area/fee	Playground	PX/small
	Rec Equip Rntl	Restaurants	Restrooms
	Showers	Stables	Swim Pool/sumr
	Tennis Cts/fee	Trails	Trap Range

ACTIVITIES:			
	Bicycling	Horseback Riding	Jogging
	Trap Shooting		

RESTRICTIONS: Pets allowed only in cabins.

JAPAN

WHITE BEACH RECREATION SERVICES (JA13R8)
CFAO MWR PSC 480 Rec. Svc.
Okinawa Commander Fleet Activities, FPO AP 96370-1100

TELEPHONE NUMBER INFORMATION: Main installation numbers: Comm: 011-81-631-2264/2266, OPER: 098-892-5111. Police for rec area, Comm: 011-81-642-2200/2300.

LOCATION: Off base. On the Pacific Island of Okinawa, S of Japan. On east side of the island on Katsuren Peninsula in Buckner Bay. From Hwy 24, N of Okinawa City, turn E on Hwy 329 to Hwy 8 to White Beach. NMI: Kadena AB, 8 mi W. NMC: Naha, 12 mi S.

DESCRIPTION OF AREA: Beautiful beach, many recreational activities, and Port-O-Call Club at White Beach. The club is open to all ranks and provides a full-menu dining room, amusement center, ballroom, casual bar. Full range of support facilities available at Kadena AB.

SEASON OF OPERATION: Year round.

ELIGIBILITY: Active/Retired/DoD Civilians.

RESERVATIONS: Required (30 days in adv for cabins) with full payment 72 hrs in adv. Address: White Beach Recreation Services, CFAO, PCS-480, MWR/Rec Svc W/B, FPO AP 96370-0057. Comm: 011-81-631-2264/2266, FTS: 098-892-1111.

CAMP FACILITIES:	NO UNITS	HOOKUPS	FEE
Cabins/Snuggler's Cove*	8		$30.00 dly
Campers	20	W/E (110)	20.00 dly
slp 4 adults/2 children			
Camper Spaces	5	W	4.00 dly
Camping on beach and in picnic areas		E/picnic areas	None

*Fully furn, PB, Kit; TV, VCR, queen size bed, towels. Getaway Special (for 2) includes cabin, dinner and breakfast for 2: $40-45.

SPT FACILITIES:			
	Barber Shop	Beach	Camp Equip Rntl
	Cliff Dining Rm	Fishing Piers	Grills
	Marina	Pavilions	Picnic Areas
	Post Office	Racquetball Court	Rec Equip Rntl
	Rec Hall	Restrooms/hcp	Shoppette
	Showers	Snack Bars	Sports Fields
	Swim Pool/sumr	Tennis Courts	Weight Room

ACTIVITIES:			
	Bicycling	Canoeing	Croquet
	Fishing	Horseshoes	Sailing
	Snorkeling	Swimming	Volleyball

RESTRICTIONS: No pets allowed. No firearms allowed.

KOREA

DRAGON HILL LODGE (RK09R8)
UNIT 15335, APO AP 96205-0427

TELEPHONE NUMBER INFORMATION: Main installation number: Comm: 011-82-2-790-0016. Police for lodge, Comm: 011-82-2-790-0016-EX-6900. FAX: 011-82-2-790-0036.

LOCATION: Located on South Post, Yongsan, in Seoul. From Kimpo International Airport, enter Olympics Stadium Expressway 88 for approx 15 mi, then take Panpo Bridge exit and cross bridge. Look for Capital Hotel on R as you come off bridge. Stay on R side of road and do not go underground where road splits. Go to the major intersection and turn L (1 mi from bridge), enter 2nd gate on L (gate 10) and proceed to Lodge. NMC: Seoul, in city limits.

DESCRIPTION OF AREA: Conveniently located for shopping at Itaewon, where you can find bargains ranging from Antiques to Zippers. This new Lodge opened in the spring of 1990. It has 299 rooms/suites and a variety of dining facilities which include a Mexican restaurant, full-service dining, fine dining, pizza parlor; and two cocktail lounges with dancing. Meeting rooms and private catering facilities for groups up to 200 are also available. Other facilities include family hair care, post exchange, tennis courts, health and fitness club, full-service bank, arcade, tailor and retail stores. Community Center in the middle of Yongsan Post is a "home away from home." (Yongsan means Dragon Hill.) Full range of support facilities available on South Post.

SEASON OF OPERATION: Year round.

ELIGIBILITY: Active/Retired/DOD Civilians.

RESERVATIONS: The lodge is booked solid months in advance; reservations may be made up to 1 year in advance by AD military; by DoD civilians on PCS, or on TDY orders to Korea; and by visiting relatives and guests of patients in military clinics or military patients in local hospitals. All others may make reservations up to 6 months in advance. Priority sequence: personnel on (1) TLA status, (2) leave/vacation status, (3) TDY status. The lodge maintains a same-day wait list. Address: Dragon Hill Lodge, Unit 15335, APO AP 96205-0427. **Comm: 011-82-2-790-0016, FAX: 011-82-2-792-1576.**

LODGING: 267 1-bdrm units with PB, equipped kit, color TV, VCR, clock radio, and telephone.

> FEE: $38-58 dly for personnel on leave/vacation status
> 78 dly for personnel on PCS/TDY orders

10 2-bdrm suites, for large families of 5 or more in long-term PCS status; master bdrm/living room w/queen size sofa bed and equipped kit + a bdrm with 2 dbl beds and PB; each of the rooms has color TV, VCR, clock radio, and telephone.

> FEE: $146.00 dly

Rooms equipped for handicapped, and non-smoking rooms are available.

ACTIVITIES: Sightseeing   Shopping   Tennis

RESTRICTIONS: No pets allowed. Pets may be boarded at the Vet Clinic by Gate 17 on South Post. Call clinic M-F 1000-1900 or Sa 1000-1730 for appointment. No firearms allowed.

(NC13R1) Fort Fisher U.S. Air Force Recreation Area, Pleasure Island, North Carolina.

(SC02R1) U.S. Navy Short Stay rec area, located at Lake Moultrie, about 35 miles from U.S. Naval Station, Charleston, South Carolina.

Photos courtesy U.S. Armed Forces.

(CA05R4) U.S. Marine Corps Big Bear Recreation Facility, Big Bear Lake, California.

APPENDIX A

General Abbreviations
This appendix contains general abbreviations used in this book. Commonly understood abbreviations (e.g. M-F for Monday through Friday) and standard abbreviations found in addresses have not been included in order to save space.

A
AAF - Army Air Field
AB - Air Base
A/C - Air Conditioning
Activ - Activities
AD - Active Duty
Add - Additional
Adv - Advance
AF - Air Force
AFAF - Air Force Auxiliary Field
AFB - Air Force Base
AFR - Air Force Range
AFRC - Armed Forces Recreation Center
AFS - Air Force Station
Approx - Approximately
APO - Army Post Office
Apt - Apartment(s)
Avail - Available

B
Bdrm - Bedroom
Biwkly - Biweekly
Bldg - Building
Bltg - Billeting
Br - Branch
BX/PX - Base Exchange

C
CG - Coast Guard
CGAS - Coast Guard Air Station
Civ - Civilian
Comm - Community/Commercial
Cont - Contained
Conv - Convenience
CR - County Road
Crm - Cream
CSS - Coastal Systems Station
Ct - Court
Ctr - Center
CTV - Cable Television

D
DAV - Disabled American Veteran
DBL - Double
Dept - Department
Dev - Development
DH - Downhill
Div - Division
Dly - Daily
Dmp - Dump
DoD - Department of Defense
DoT - Department of Transportation

DSN - Defense Switching Network
DST - Daylight Savings Time
DW - Dishwasher

E
E - East
E - Electric
Eff - Efficiency
Eq/Eqip - Equipment
ETS - European Telephone System
EX - Telephone Extension
Exec - Executive

F
Fac - Facility
Fam - Family
FPO - Fleet Post Office
Frzr - Freezer
Ft - Fort
FTS - Federal Telephone System
Furn - Furniture/Furnished

G
Govt - Government
Gp - Group

H
Hcp - Handicapped
HE: p - Hallwag Europe Road Atlas: page
Hol - Holiday
Hq - Headquarters

I
Info - Information
IT - Italy
ITR - Information, Ticketing and Reservation Office
ITT - Information, Tour and Travel

J
JPAO - Joint Public Affairs Office

K
Kit - Kitchen(ette)
Km - Kilometer

L
L - Left
LDR - Living/Dining Room
LI - Location Identifier
LR - Living Room
Ltd - Limited

APPENDIX A, continued

M
Mach - Machine
Max - Maximum
MC - Marine Corps
MCAS - Marine Corps Air Station
MCB - Marine Corps Base
Mi - Mile(s)
Mil - Military
Min - Minimum
Mo - Monthly
MW - Microwave Oven
MWR - Morale, Welfare and Recreation

N
N - North
NAEC - Naval Air Engineering Center
NAF - Non-appropriated Fund
NAF - Naval Air Facility
NAS - Naval Air Station
Nat - National
NAWC - Naval Air Warfare Center
NAWS - Naval Air Weapons Station
NB - Naval Base
NCU - Naval Communication Unit
NG - National Guard
NMC - Nearest Major City
NMI - Nearest Military Installation
NS - Naval Station
NSA - Naval Support Activity
NSGA - Naval Security Group Activity
NSWC - Naval Surface Weapons Center
NTC - Naval Training Center
NWC - Naval Weapons Center
NWS - Naval Weapons Station

O
OD/ODD - Officer of the Day
Olym - Olympic
Outdr - Outdoor

P
PB - Private bath
PCS - Permanent Change of Station
Pers - Personnel/Person(s)
Pkg - Package
PO - Post Office
Prog - Program
PX - Post Exchange

R
R - Right
Rec - Recreation
Refr - Refrigerator
Req - Required
Res - Reserve
Resv - Reservation
Ret - Retired
Rg - Range

RK - Republic of Korea
Rm - Room
Rmps - Ramps
Rntl - Rental
RV - Recreational Vehicle

S
S - South
S - Sewer
SB - Shared Bath
Self-cont - Self-Contained
Sgl - Single
Slp - Sleep(s)
Spt - Support
Sta - Station
Sumr - Summer
Svc - Service

T
TAD - Temporary Attached Duty
TDY - Temporary Duty
Tourn - Tournament

U
USA - United States Army
USAF - United States Air Force
USCG - United States Coast Guard
USMRA - United States Military Road Atlas
USMC - United States Marine Corps
USN - United States Navy

V
VCR - Video Cassette Player
Veh - Vehicle

W
W - Water
W - West
Wntr - Winter
W/ - With
W/D - Washer/Dryer
W/S/E - Water/Sewer/Electricity
Wk - Week(ly)
Wknd - Weekend

X
XC - Cross Country

APPENDIX B

Camping on Other Federal Property

Thousands of campsites are available to the public on various types of Federal reserves around the country. These sites are located in national parks, national forests, game and wildlife refuges, Federal water reservoir reserves, Tennessee Valley Authority dam sites, U.S. Army Corps of Engineers Recreation Facilities, and other federal areas.

Many of these sites are near or on routes to military installations to which you may be traveling. A wealth of information is available from a variety of sources concerning these camp sites and adjacent recreation areas.

If a military installation is not conveniently located along your route, maybe one of the public areas will be. Or, if you cannot get space at a military area, perhaps you can get space at a nearby public recreation area.

Listed below are addresses of federal agencies from which information about camping on federal lands other than military installations can be obtained. Also listed are titles and descriptions of some of the available material.

Superintendent of Documents, US Government Printing Office (GPO), Washington, DC 20402. Tel: (202) 783-3238. (Orders and inquiries)

GPO prints many items for all the government agencies. You may write for these materials or you may order them by telephone using your credit card.

National Park System Map & Guide, 312-248/40/1-1992.

The National Parks: Camping Guide 1991, 024-005-01080-7 ($4.00). This 113-page booklet contains descriptions and basic information in chart form on the facilities and recreational opportunities available to the users of National Park Service camping areas.

National Parks Index, 024-005-01094-7—1993 ($3.75).

The National Parks: Lesser-Known Areas, 024-005-00911-5—1991 ($1.50). Listings, by state, of more than 170 national parks, their accommodations, locations and historical significance.

National Trails System Map & Guide, 342-398/60062-1993.

Washington, DC (Official National Park Guidebook), 024-005-01034-3—1989[pending a reprint] ($5.00). This 175-page booklet contains travelers tips, information and maps for various tourist attractions in and around Washington, DC.

National Wildlife Refuges, 024-010-00690-1—1991 ($1.00). This is a fold-out map showing locations of 300 wildlife refuges. Facilities, best viewing seasons at each refuge, and addresses for more information are listed.

Department of Interior, Bureau of Land Management (BLM), Rm 5600, 1849 C St NW, Washington, DC 20240. Tel: (202) 208-5717.

Recreation Guide to BLM Public Lands, 1991 (Free). Color map listing facilities and services in areas maintained by the BLM.

For Other Free Camping Information From BLM call 1-800-47-SUNNY.

US Department of Agriculture, Forest Service, Washington, DC. Tel: (202) 447-3957.

APPENDIX B, continued

Information concerning camping sites in National Forests is supplied by regional offices of the Forest Service rather than the Washington, DC, headquarters office. Write to Regional Forester, Forest Service, Dept of Agriculture, in one of the following cities: Milwaukee (WI), Atlanta (GA), Denver (CO), Albuquerque (NM), San Francisco (CA), Portland (OR), Ogden (UT), Missoula (MT) or Juneau (AK).

US Army Corps of Engineers, Publications Depot, 2803 52nd Avenue, Hyattsville, MD 20781-1102. Tel: (301) 436-2063.

Lakeside Recreation Series, Nos. EP 1130-2-419 through 428 (August 1992) are offered free of charge. These very nice pamphlets are directories of lakeside recreational opportunities at Corps projects. They have color maps, facilities charts and written descriptions of each project, divided into regions of the US: New England, Mid-Atlantic States, Southeast, Great Lakes States, Upper Mississippi Basin, Central States, South Central States, Great Plains, Northwest, Southwest, Midwest and West. They also have brochures on facilities at individual lakes.

Tennessee Valley Authority, Program Support & Information Services, Division of Land & Forest Resources, Forestry Building, Norris, TN 37828. Tel: (615) 494-9800.

Recreation on TVA Lakes A brochure which includes information on camping and other recreation facilities in the TVA region. It is offered free of charge with a note or phone call to the TVA - 1992 - TVA/LR/OM/PU/1 . Pamphlets are also published by some of the TVA states.

Golden Eagle, Golden Age, Golden Access Passports

Golden Eagle Passport. An annual entrance permit to national parks, monuments, and recreation areas that charge entrance fees and are managed by the Federal government. It admits the permit holder and a carload of accompanying people. It does not cover user fees, such as fees for camping. It may be purchased for $25 in person or by mail. Address: National Park Service, Washington, DC 20240. To obtain in person, ask at any area of the National Park System where entrance fees are charged. A Golden Eagle Passport is good for one calendar year.

Golden Age Passport. A free lifetime entrance permit to those national parks, monuments, and recreation areas that charge entrance fees and are managed by the Federal government. **It is available to persons 62 and older.** The Passport also provides a 50 percent discount on user fees charged for facilities and services, such as camping, boat launching and parking. The Golden Age passport does not cover fees charged by private concessionaires even though they may be located on Federal property. Those eligible may obtain Golden Age Passports in person at most Federally-operated recreation areas where they can be used; therefore, it may not be necessary to obtain the passport in advance of a vacation trip. The Golden Age Passport cannot be obtained by mail.

Golden Access Passport. A free lifetime-entrance permit, similar to the Golden Age Passport, for persons who have been medically determined to be blind or permanently disabled. It must be picked up in person at Federally-operated recreation areas.

Computer Reservations for Camping Facilities on Federal Property

Advance reservations in more than 800 *national forest campgrounds* can also be made by calling a central toll-fee number. There is a $6 charge, however, for making the booking. This is in addition to the regular daily use fee for the campsite, which ranges from $4 to $12 depending on the campground. Credit cards are accepted. The reservation service, operated by **MISTIX**, is available daily from 8 a.m. to 5 p.m. Pacific time at 1-800-283-CAMP (1-800-283-2267).

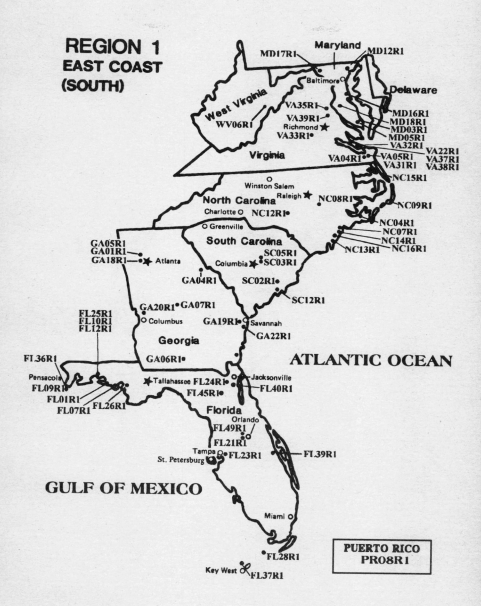

REGION 1
EAST COAST
(SOUTH)

Maryland

MD17R1 MD12R1

Baltimore

Delaware

West Virginia

VA35R1
VA39R1
Richmond
VA33R1

MD16R1
MD18R1
MD03R1
MD05R1
VA32R1
VA22R1
VA37R1
VA05R1
VA31R1 VA38R1

WV06R1

Virginia

VA04R1

NC15R1

Winston Salem

Raleigh
North Carolina

NC08R1

Charlotte

NC12R1

NC09R1

Greenville

South Carolina

NC04R1
NC07R1
NC14R1
NC13R1 NC16R1

GA05R1
GA01R1
GA18R1

Atlanta

Columbia

SC05R1
SC03R1

GA04R1

SC02R1

SC12R1

GA20R1 GA07R1

FL25R1
FL10R1
FL12R1

Columbus

GA19R1 Savannah

GA22R1

Georgia

GA06R1

ATLANTIC OCEAN

FL36R1

Pensacola
FL09R1
FL01R1
FL07R1 FL26R1

Tallahassee FL24R1

Jacksonville

FL40R1

FL45R1

Florida
Orlando
FL49R1
FL21R1
Tampa
St. Petersburg FL23R1

FL39R1

GULF OF MEXICO

Miami

FL28R1

Key West
FL37R1

**PUERTO RICO
PR08R1**

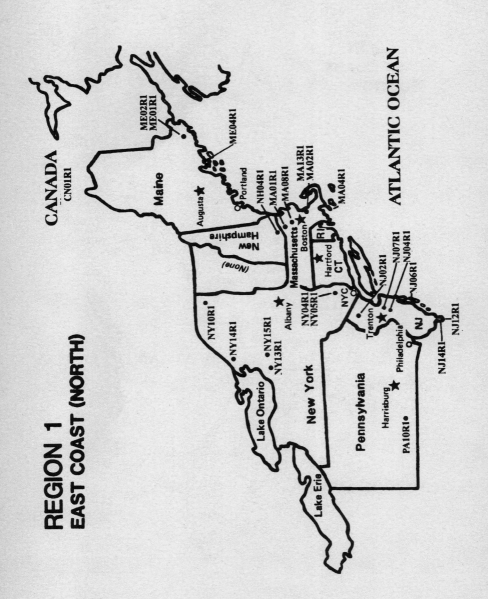

REGION 1
EAST COAST (NORTH)

REGION 2
CENTRAL (NORTH)

REGION 2
CENTRAL (SOUTH)

Cincinnati ○

Missouri

○ Kansas City   St. Louis ○

KY03R2   ★ Frankfurt
            ○ Louisville
            ○ Lexington

★ Jefferson City

● MO01R2

Kentucky

KY04R2

Nashville ★   Knoxville ○

○ Fort Smith   ● TN04R2   **Tennessee**   ● TN03R2
● AR06R2   ○ Memphis

Huntsville ○
AL12R2 ●
        ● AL09R2

Arkansas
● AR05R2

Birmingham ○

★

Tuscaloosa ○

Mississippi

Alabama   ● AL05R2

LA09R2
○ ●
Shreveport

Louisiana   ★ Jackson   ○ Meridian   AL11R2 ● ★
                                              Montgomery

                                              AL10R2 ●
● ●LA14R2   MS12R2 ●   ● AL14R2
LA04R2   Mobile ○
            MS05R2 ●

Baton Rouge ● ★   AL07R2

New Orleans ○

○ LA03R2
LA08R2

GULF OF MEXICO

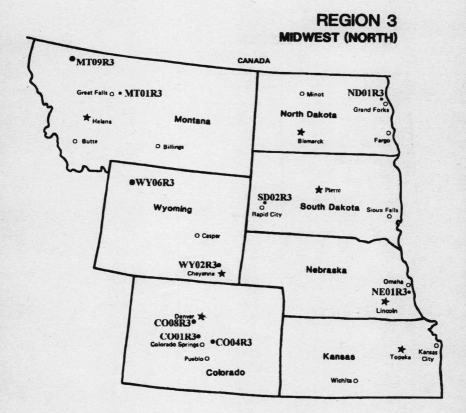

REGION 3
MIDWEST (NORTH)

CANADA

•MT09R3

Great Falls ○ • MT01R3

★ Helena   Montana

○ Butte   ○ Billings

○ Minot   ND01R3
North Dakota Grand Forks
★ Bismarck   ○ Fargo

•WY06R3

Wyoming

○ Casper

★ Pierre
SD02R3
○   South Dakota   Sioux Falls
Rapid City   ○

WY02R3•
Cheyenne ★

Nebraska

Omaha
NE01R3•
★
Lincoln

Denver ★
CO08R3•
CO01R3• •CO04R3
Colorado Springs ○

Pueblo ○

Colorado

Kansas

★ Topeka Kansas
City

Wichita ○

REGION 3
MIDWEST (SOUTH)

CANADA

REGION 4
WEST COAST

WA12R4
WA07R4
●WA22R4
●Seattle
WA16R4●
Olympia ★
●Tacoma
WA13R4/WA21R4
WA14R4●
WA03R4
Washington

Spokane
○
WA01R4

Portland
○

★ Salem

○
Eugene

Oregon
(NONE)

Idaho

★ Boise

●ID05R4

Idaho Falls
○

●ID03R4
●ID02R4

○
Pocatello

UT03R4
UT07R4●

○ Ogden

●UT01R4

UT06R4●
★ Salt Lake City

○ Provo

CA17R4
CA49R4
CA24R4

CA60R4●
●CA69R4

○ Reno

CA68R4●
★
Sacramento

●NV05R4

★
Carson City

Nevada

CA66R4●

●CA63R4

○ Oakland
●CA72R4

San Francisco

California

Utah

●CA82R4
●CA78R4

CA67R4●
●CA62R4
●CA88R4

Las NV04R4●
Vegas○

●CA05R4

AZ11R4●
○ Flagstaff

Arizona

CA11R4●
○ Los Angeles

CA81R4●

AZ15R4● ★
Phoenix

CA31R4●
CA76R4

CA07R4●
●CA65R4
CA64R4●
○San Diego
CA87R4●
CA03R4

○ Yuma
●AZ12R4

Tucson ○ ●AZ14R4
AZ21R4
●AZ10R4

PACIFIC OCEAN

MEXICO

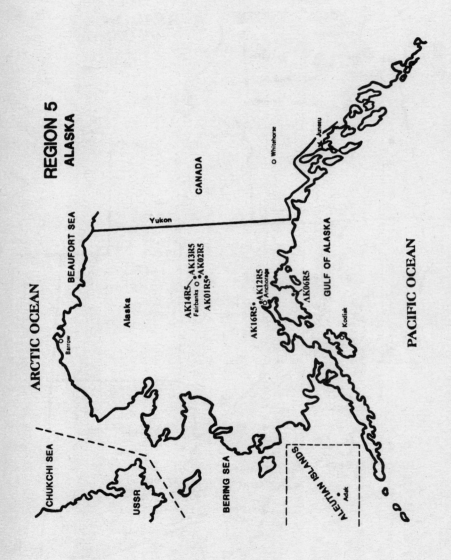

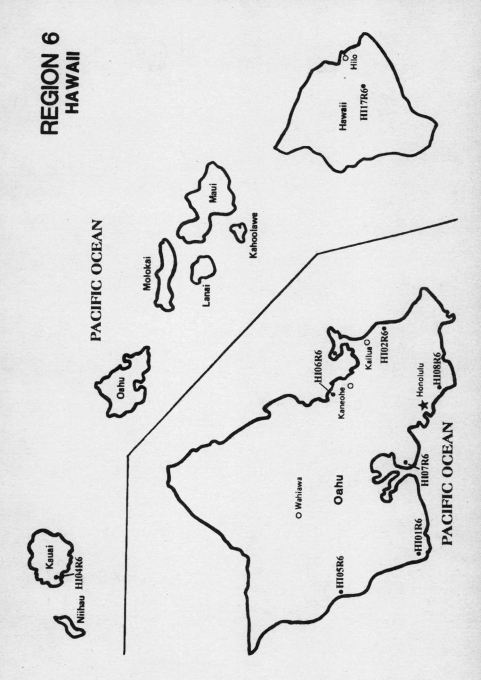

REGION 6
HAWAII

PACIFIC OCEAN

Hilo
Hawaii
HI17R6●

Maui
Kahoolawe
Molokai
Lanai

Oahu

Kailua○
HI06R6
Kaneohe○
HI02R6●
Honolulu★
HI08R6
HI07R6
O Wahiawa
Oahu
HI01R6●
PACIFIC OCEAN
HI05R6●

Kauai
HI04R6
Niihau

REGION 7
EAST EUROPE

West Germany

★ Bonn

• GE56R7

• GE55R7

GE09R7 GE57R7
        GE08R7•   Austria

                GE10R7
Switzerland GE58R7•
         IT09R7•
   IT08R7• •

Italy   Yugoslavia

   Florence○   ★
                        Belgrade
      •IT02R7

Corsica Rome ★   ADRIATIC SEA

              •IT03R7

Sardinia

                    REGION
                      9

        Sicily   GREECE
                    GR03R9

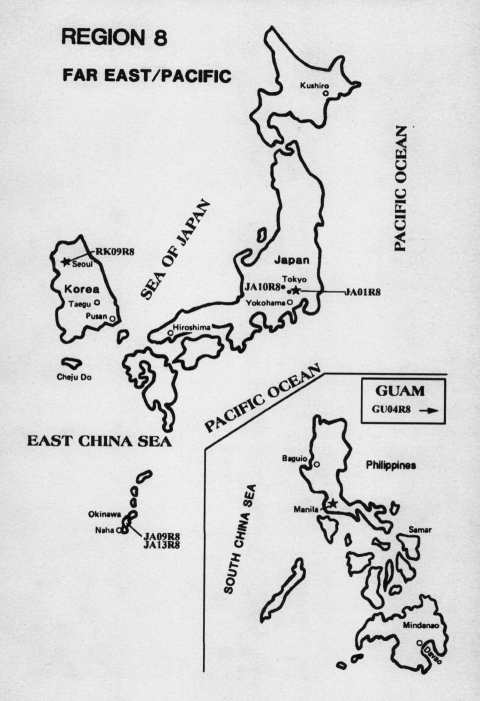

REGION 8

FAR EAST/PACIFIC

Kushiro

PACIFIC OCEAN

SEA OF JAPAN

RK09R8

Seoul

Korea

Taegu

Pusan

Japan

Tokyo

JA10R8   JA01R8

Yokohama

Hiroshima

Cheju Do

EAST CHINA SEA

PACIFIC OCEAN

GUAM
GU04R8 →

Baguio   Philippines

SOUTH CHINA SEA

Manila

Samar

Okinawa

Naha   JA09R8
JA13R8

Mindanao

Davao

Top three photos courtesy U.S. Armed Forces.

(MD03R1) Family fun is available at the U.S. Navy's Goose Creek/West Basin Recreation Area, Patuxent River Naval Air Warfare Center, Maryland.

(MD05R1) U.S. Navy's Solomons Navy Recreation Center, Solomons, Maryland.

(MD05R1) Solomons Navy Rec Area Fishing Pier, Solomons, Maryland.

(FL28R1) U.S. Coast Guard Marathon Recreation Cottages located in the Florida Keys on Vaca Key. *Photo courtesy U.S. Coast Guard.*

MASSACHUSETTS - U.S. Air Force Fourth Cliff Family Recreation Area

(MA02R1) U.S. Air Force Fourth Cliff Family Recreation Area, about 30 miles from Boston, Massachusetts.

All photos courtesy U.S. Air Force.

(UT03R4) U.S. Air Force Hillhaus Lodge is located about 30 miles from Hill Air Force Base, Utah.

(WA16R4) U.S. Navy Pacific Beach Military Ocean Getaway, Pacific Beach, Washington.

(RK09R8) Dragon Hill Lodge, U.S. Army South Post, Yongsan, South Korea.

(VA35R1) U.S. Marine Corps Lunga Park, Quantico, Virginia.

All photos courtesy U.S. Armed Forces

CENTRAL ORDER COUPON

Military Living Publications
P.O. Box 2347, Falls Church VA 22042-0347
TEL: (703) 237-0203 • FAX: (703) 237-2233

Publications	QTY
R&R Space-A Report®. *The worldwide travel newsletter.* 6 issues per year. 5 yrs/$47.00 - 2 yrs/$22.00 - 3 yrs/$30.00 - 1 yr/$14.00	
Military Space-A Air Basic Training. $11.00	
Military Space-A Air Opportunities Air Route Map. (Folded) $10.00	
Military Space-A Air Opportunities Around the World. $15.95	
Temporary Military Lodging Around the World. $13.95	
Military RV, Camping & Rec Areas Around the World. $11.95	
U.S. Forces Travel and Transfer Guide, USA and Caribbean Areas. $11.95	
U.S. Military Museums, Historic Sites & Exhibits. (Soft Cover) $16.95 - (Hard Cover) $26.95	
United States Military Road Atlas $16.95	
U.S.Military Installation Road Map. (Folded) $6.50	
United States Military Medical Facilities Map (Folded) $6.95	
COLLECTOR'S ITEM! Desert Shield Commemorative Maps. (Folded) $7.00 (2 unfolded wall maps in a hard tube) $16.00	
Assignment Washington: Military Road Atlas. Maps & Charts of Washington Area Military Installations. $8.95	
California State Military Road Map ALL NEW 1994! - (Folded) $4.95 Florida State Military Road Map ALL NEW 1994! - (Folded) $4.95 Mid-Atlantic States Military Road Map ALL NEW 1994! - (Folded) $4.95 Texas State Military Road Map ALL NEW 1994! - (Folded) $4.95	
Military Living Magazine, Camaraderie Washington. *Local Area magazine.* 1 year (12 issues) 1st Class Mailing $10.00	
Virginia Addresses add 4.5% sales tax (Books, Maps, & Atlases only) TOTAL $	

*If you are an R&R Space-A Report® subscriber, you may deduct $1.00 per book. (No discount on the R&R Report itself or on the maps or atlases.) For 1st Class Mail, add $1.00 per book or map. Mail Order Prices are for U.S. APO & FPO addresses. Please consult publisher for International Mail Price. Sorry, no billing.
GREAT FUND RAISERS! Please write for wholesale rates.
We're as close as your telephone...by using our Telephone Ordering Service. We honor VISA, MasterCard, and American Express. Call us at **703-237-0203 (Voice Mail after hours)** or Fax 703-237-2233 and order today! Sorry, no collect calls. Or...fill out and mail the order coupon below. Thank You!

NAME:

STREET:

CITY/STATE/ZIP:

PHONE: SIGNATURE:

RANK (or rank of sponsor):____ Branch Of Service:

Active Duty:_Retired:_Widow/er:_100% Disabled Veteran:_Guard:_Reservist:_Other:__

Card #_____ Card Expiration Date:____

Mail check/money order to Military Living Publications, P.O. Box 2347, Falls Church, VA 22042-0347 - **Tel: 703-237-0203** - FAX: 703-237-2233.

Prices subject to change. Please check here if we may ship and bill difference.☐

NOTES

CENTRAL ORDER COUPON

Military Living Publications
P.O. Box 2347, Falls Church VA 22042-0347
TEL: (703) 237-0203 • FAX: (703) 237-2233

Publications	QTY
R&R Space-A Report®. *The worldwide travel newsletter.* 6 issues per year. 5 yrs/$47.00 - 2 yrs/$22.00 - 3 yrs/$30.00 - 1 yr/$14.00	
Military Space-A Air Basic Training. $11.00	
Military Space-A Air Opportunities Air Route Map. (Folded) $10.00	
Military Space-A Air Opportunities Around the World. $15.95	
Temporary Military Lodging Around the World. $13.95	
Military RV, Camping & Rec Areas Around the World. $11.95	
U.S. Forces Travel and Transfer Guide, USA and Caribbean Areas. $11.95	
U.S. Military Museums, Historic Sites & Exhibits. (Soft Cover) $16.95 - (Hard Cover) $26.95	
United States Military Road Atlas $16.95	
U.S.Military Installation Road Map. (Folded) $6.50	
United States Military Medical Facilities Map (Folded) $6.95	
COLLECTOR'S ITEM! Desert Shield Commemorative Maps. (Folded) $7.00 (2 unfolded wall maps in a hard tube) $16.00	
Assignment Washington: Military Road Atlas. Maps & Charts of Washington Area Military Installations. $8.95	
California State Military Road Map ALL NEW 1994! - (Folded) $4.95 **Florida State Military Road Map** ALL NEW 1994! - (Folded) $4.95 **Mid-Atlantic States Military Road Map** ALL NEW 1994! - (Folded) $4.95 **Texas State Military Road Map** ALL NEW 1994! - (Folded) $4.95	
Military Living Magazine, Camaraderie Washington. *Local Area magazine.* 1 year (12 issues) 1st Class Mailing $10.00	
Virginia Addresses add 4.5% sales tax (Books, Maps, & Atlases only) TOTAL $	

*If you are an R&R Space-A Report® subscriber, you may deduct $1.00 per book. (No discount on the R&R Report itself or on the maps or atlases.) For 1st Class Mail, add $1.00 per book or map. Mail Order Prices are for U.S. APO & FPO addresses. Please consult publisher for International Mail Price. Sorry, no billing.
GREAT FUND RAISERS! Please write for wholesale rates.
We're as close as your telephone...by using our Telephone Ordering Service. We honor VISA, MasterCard, and American Express. Call us at **703-237-0203 (Voice Mail after hours)** or Fax 703-237-2233 and order today! Sorry, no collect calls. Or...fill out and mail the order coupon below. Thank You!

NAME:_____
STREET:_____
CITY/STATE/ZIP:_____
PHONE:_____ SIGNATURE:_____
RANK (or rank of sponsor):____ Branch Of Service:_____
Active Duty:_Retired:_Widow/er:_100% Disabled Veteran:_Guard:_Reservist:_Other:_
Card #_____ Card Expiration Date:_____

Mail check/money order to Military Living Publications, P.O. Box 2347, Falls Church, VA 22042-0347 - Tel: **703-237-0203** - FAX: 703-237-2233.

Prices subject to change. Please check here if we may ship and bill difference.☐

AT TIMES LIKE THIS.........

At times like this, when major changes are being made in the Uniformed Services, information on Space-A air travel, Temporary Military Lodging and Military RV, Camping & Rec Areas can suddenly change.

If you want to be in the know before most everyone else, subscribe to *Military Living's R&R Space-A Report* ®! Breaking news will be carried in this six time yearly all ranks travel newsletter which is available by subscription only. To subscribe, see the coupons in this book or call **(703) 237-0203 for information or to order with VISA, MasterCard or American Express.**

CENTRAL ORDER COUPON
Military Living Publications
P.O. Box 2347, Falls Church VA 22042-0347
TEL: (703) 237-0203 • FAX: (703) 237-2233

Publications	QTY
R&R Space-A Report®. *The worldwide travel newsletter.* 6 issues per year. 5 yrs/$47.00 - 2 yrs/$22.00 - 3 yrs/$30.00 - 1 yr/$14.00	
Military Space-A Air Basic Training. $11.00	
Military Space-A Air Opportunities Air Route Map. (Folded) $10.00	
Military Space-A Air Opportunities Around the World. $15.95	
Temporary Military Lodging Around the World. $13.95	
Military RV, Camping & Rec Areas Around the World. $11.95	
U.S. Forces Travel and Transfer Guide, USA and Caribbean Areas. $11.95	
U.S. Military Museums, Historic Sites & Exhibits. (Soft Cover) $16.95 - (Hard Cover) $26.95	
United States Military Road Atlas $16.95	
U.S.Military Installation Road Map. (Folded) $6.50	
United States Military Medical Facilities Map (Folded) $6.95	
COLLECTOR'S ITEM! Desert Shield Commemorative Maps. (Folded) $7.00 (2 unfolded wall maps in a hard tube) $16.00	
Assignment Washington: Military Road Atlas. Maps & Charts of Washington Area Military Installations. $8.95	
California State Military Road Map ALL NEW 1994! - (Folded) $4.95 **Florida State Military Road Map** ALL NEW 1994! - (Folded) $4.95 **Mid-Atlantic States Military Road Map** ALL NEW 1994! - (Folded) $4.95 **Texas State Military Road Map** ALL NEW 1994! - (Folded) $4.95	
Military Living Magazine, Camaraderie Washington. *Local Area magazine.* 1 year (12 issues) 1st Class Mailing $10.00	
Virginia Addresses add 4.5% sales tax (Books, Maps, & Atlases only) TOTAL $	

*If you are an R&R Space-A Report® subscriber, you may deduct $1.00 per book. (No discount on the R&R Report itself or on the maps or atlases.) For 1st Class Mail, add $1.00 per book or map. Mail Order Prices are for U.S. APO & FPO addresses. Please consult publisher for International Mail Price. Sorry, no billing.
GREAT FUND RAISERS! Please write for wholesale rates.
We're as close as your telephone...by using our Telephone Ordering Service. We honor VISA, MasterCard, and American Express. Call us at **703-237-0203 (Voice Mail after hours)** or Fax 703-237-2233 and order today! Sorry, no collect calls. Or...fill out and mail the order coupon below. Thank You!

NAME:

STREET:

CITY/STATE/ZIP:

PHONE: SIGNATURE:

RANK (or rank of sponsor): Branch Of Service:

Active Duty:_Retired:_Widow/er:_100% Disabled Veteran:_Guard:_Reservist:_Other:__

Card # Card Expiration Date:

Mail check/money order to Military Living Publications, P.O. Box 2347, Falls Church, VA 22042-0347 - **Tel: 703-237-0203** - FAX: 703-237-2233.

Prices subject to change. Please check here if we may ship and bill difference.☐

TRAVEL ON LESS PER DAY... THE MILITARY WAY™

WITH MILITARY LIVING

"One Shot" Help

MOVING TO WASHINGTON, DC?
As a military family, one of our chief goals is to boost military family morale... so mail this coupon today and help will be on its way.
Hope to hear from you soon.
Ann & Roy Crawford, Publishers
Military Living Magazine

TO: Mrs. Ann Crawford, Publisher, Military Living
P.O. Box 2347, Falls Church, VA 22042-0347
Phone: (703) 237-0203

Our Family is:
□ Army   □ Coast Guard   □ Active Duty
□ Navy   □ P.H.S.   □ Retired
□ Air Force   □ NOAA   □ 100% DAV
□ Marine Corps □ Other

Military member's name/rank: _____

Spouse's name _____

Address: _____

City/State: _____ Zip Code _____

Telephone: _____

Area assigned to _____
We expect to arrive: _____

We would like info, if possible on the following:
□ Relocation Services
□ House □ Apt. □ Condo
□ Renting □ Buying
□ Car
□ Furniture

□ Major Appliances
□ Short-term Housing
□ Military Lodging
□ Hotel/Motel □ B & B
□ Short Term Apt.

Type of job _____

□ Banking/Checking Accounts
□ Employment Opportunities for Spouse
□ Real Estate Career Opportunities
□ Legal Services/Settlement Atty.

□ College Opportunities
□ Investment Opportunities
□ Travel in Nearby Areas
□ Back Issues of Military Living
□ Window Treatments
□ Dentist
□ Doctor

MOVING TO METRO WASHINGTON, DC COUPON

NOTES

IT'S SMART TO BE
S*M*A*R*T

S*M*A*R*T - the SPECIAL MILITARY ACTIVE {&} RETIRED
TRAVEL CLUB, Inc. is a nationwide RV travel club with membership
limited to Retired and Active Duty personnel from the seven
Uniformed Services (including ready Reserve and National Guard) who
have an avid interest in Recreational Vehicles (RV-ing) and widows or
widowers of individuals who would have been eligible for membership
if living. All former POW's, Medal of Honor Awardees, and 100%
Disabled Veterans are also eligible.

S*M*A*R*T is UNIQUE! Its special characteristic is the common
experience of long military service shared by all of our members.
Although we all share a military background, it is a social club, with
no concern about members military grade and achievements. We have
members in nearly every military enlisted and officer grade, from all
seven Services.

S*M*A*R*T now has 26 chapters throughout the country, and gaining
new members and new chapters everywhere! We hold a National
Muster, or "Rally", each spring, regional musters every fall, and local
chapter rallies several times each year, as often as each chapter wants.
It's a great way to meet new friends in a unique club!

If you fit the membership criteria, don't let another day go by without
exploring this great opportunity to join one of the best, most rewarding
and fun-filled RV groups in the United States! Complete the following
request for more information now, or call our National Headquarters
for a membership application today!

For more information, complete the following, cut on line, and mail.

Send To: S*M*A*R*T Inc.
      600 University Office Blvd. Suite 1-A
      Pensacola, FL 32504 Phone: (904) 478-1986
Status: Active ( ) Retired ( ) Widow ( ) POW ( ) MOH ( )
Please Print: Name_____
             Address_____
             City _____ State ____ Zip _____
Complete details and membership application will be forwarded ASAP!